# MATHEMATICS

## *Textbook for Class IX*

NCERT

राष्ट्रीय शैक्षिक अनुसंधान और प्रशिक्षण परिषद्
NATIONAL COUNCIL OF EDUCATIONAL RESEARCH AND TRAINING

ISBN 81-7450-489-3

**First Edition**
February 2006  Phalguna 1927

**Reprinted**
October 2006 Kartika 1928
October 2007 Kartika 1929
January 2009 Magha 1930
January 2010 Pausa 1931
January 2012 Magha 1933
November 2012 Kartika 1934
October 2013 Kartika 1935
December 2014 Pausa 1936
December 2015 Agrahayana 1937
December 2016 Pausa 1938

**PD 520T RPS**

© *National Council of Educational Research and Training, 2006*

₹ 135.00

*Printed on 80 GSM paper with NCERT watermark*

Published at the Publication Division by the Secretary, National Council of Educational Research and Training, Sri Aurobindo Marg, New Delhi 110 016 and printed at Pitambra Books Pvt. Ltd., B-95, Industrial Area, Bijoli, Jhansi, U.P. 284 001

**OFFICES OF THE PUBLICATION DIVISION, NCERT**

NCERT Campus
Sri Aurobindo Marg
New Delhi 110 016                     Phone : 011-26562708

108, 100 Feet Road
Hosdakere Halli Extension
Banashankari III Stage
Bangaluru 560 085                     Phone : 080-26725740

Navjivan Trust Building
P.O.Navjivan
Ahmedabad 380 014                     Phone : 079-27541446

CWC Campus
Opp. Dhankal Bus Stop
Panihati
Kolkata 700 114                       Phone : 033-25530454

CWC Complex
Maligaon
Guwahati 781 021                      Phone : 0361-2674869

**Publication Team**

| | |
|---|---|
| Head, Publication Division | : *M. Siraj Anwar* |
| Chief Editor | : *Shveta Uppal* |
| Chief Business Manager | : *Gautam Ganguly* |
| Chief Production Officer (In-charge) | : *Arun Chitkara* |
| Editor | : *Bijnan Sutar* |
| Production Assistant | : *Rajesh Pippal* |

**Cover and Illustrations**
Digital Expressions

# FOREWORD

The National Curriculum Framework (NCF), 2005, recommends that children's life at school must be linked to their life outside the school. This principle marks a departure from the legacy of bookish learning which continues to shape our system and causes a gap between the school, home and community. The syllabi and textbooks developed on the basis of NCF signify an attempt to implement this basic idea. They also attempt to discourage rote learning and the maintenance of sharp boundaries between different subject areas. We hope these measures will take us significantly further in the direction of a child-centred system of education outlined in the national Policy on Education (1986).

The success of this effort depends on the steps that school principals and teachers will take to encourage children to reflect on their own learning and to pursue imaginative activities and questions. We must recognize that, given space, time and freedom, children generate new knowledge by engaging with the information passed on to them by adults. Treating the prescribed textbook as the sole basis of examination is one of the key reasons why other resources and sites of learning are ignored. Inculcating creativity and initiative is possible if we perceive and treat children as participants in learning, not as receivers of a fixed body of knowledge.

This aims imply considerable change is school routines and mode of functioning. Flexibility in the daily time-table is as necessary as rigour in implementing the annual calendar so that the required number of teaching days are actually devoted to teaching. The methods used for teaching and evaluation will also determine how effective this textbook proves for making children's life at school a happy experience, rather then a source of stress or boredom. Syllabus designers have tried to address the problem of curricular burden by restructuring and reorienting knowledge at different stages with greater consideration for child psychology and the time available for teaching. The textbook attempts to enhance this endeavour by giving higher priority and space to opportunities for contemplation and wondering, discussion in small groups, and activities requiring hands-on experience.

The National Council of Educational Research and Training (NCERT) appreciates the hard work done by the textbook development committee responsible for this book. We wish to thank the Chairperson of the advisory group in science and mathematics, Professor J.V. Narlikar and the Chief Advisor for this book, Professor P. Sinclair of IGNOU, New Delhi for guiding the work of this committee. Several teachers contributed to the development of this textbook; we are grateful to their principals for making this possible. We are indebted to the institutions and organizations which have generously permitted us to draw upon their resources, material and personnel. We are especially grateful to the members of the National Monitoring Committee, appointed by the Department of Secondary and Higher Education, Ministry of Human Resource Development under the Chairpersonship of Professor Mrinal Miri and Professor G.P. Deshpande, for their valuable time and contribution. As an organisation committed to systemic reform and continuous improvement in the quality of its products, NCERT welcomes comments and suggestions which will enable us to undertake further revision and refinement.

*Director*
National Council of Educational
Research and Training

New Delhi
*20 December 2005*

# TEXTBOOK DEVELOPMENT COMMITTEE

**CHAIRPERSON, ADVISORY GROUP IN SCIENCE AND MATHEMATICS**

J.V. Narlikar, *Emeritus Professor, Chairman,* Advisory Committee, Inter University Centre for Astronomy & Astrophysics (IUCAA), Ganeshkhind, Pune University, Pune

**CHIEF ADVISOR**

P. Sinclair, Director, NCERT and *Professor of Mathematics* , IGNOU, New Delhi

**CHIEF COORDINATOR**

Hukum Singh, *Professor* (Retd.), DESM, NCERT

**MEMBERS**

A.K. Wazalwar, *Professor and Head,* DESM, NCERT

Anjali Lal, *PGT,* DAV Public School, Sector-14, Gurgaon

Anju Nirula, *PGT,* DAV Public School, Pushpanjali Enclave, Pitampura, Delhi

G.P. Dikshit, *Professor* (Retd.), Department of Mathematics & Astronomy, Lucknow University, Lucknow

K.A.S.S.V. Kameswara Rao, *Associate Professor,* Regional Institute of Education, Bhubaneswar

Mahendra R. Gajare, *TGT,* Atul Vidyalya, Atul, Dist. Valsad

Mahendra Shanker, *Lecturer* (S.G.) (Retd.), NCERT

Rama Balaji, *TGT,* K.V., MEG & Centre, ST. John's Road, Bangalore

Sanjay Mudgal, *Lecturer,* CIET, NCERT

Shashidhar Jagadeeshan, *Teacher and Member,* Governing Council, Centre for Learning, Bangalore

S. Venkataraman, *Lecturer,* School of Sciences, IGNOU, New Delhi

Uaday Singh, *Lecturer,* DESM, NCERT

Ved Dudeja, *Vice-Principal* (Retd.), Govt. Girls Sec. School, Sainik Vihar, Delhi

**MEMBER-COORDINATOR**

Ram Avtar, *Professor* (Retd.), DESM, NCERT (till December 2005)
R.P. Maurya, *Professor,* DESM, NCERT (Since January 2006)

# ACKNOWLEDGEMENTS

The Council gratefully acknowledges the valuable contributions of the following participants of the Textbook Review Workshop: A.K. Saxena, *Professor* (Retd.), Lucknow University, Lucknow; Sunil Bajaj, *HOD*, SCERT, Gurgaon; K.L. Arya, *Professor* (Retd.), DESM, NCERT; Vandita Kalra, *Lecturer,* Sarvodaya Kanya Vidyalya, Vikas Puri, District Centre, New Delhi; Jagdish Singh, *PGT,* Sainik School, Kapurthala; P.K. Bagga, *TGT,* S.B.V. Subhash Nagar, New Delhi; R.C. Mahana, *TGT,* Kendriya Vidyalya, Sambalpur; D.R. Khandave, *TGT,* JNV, Dudhnoi, Goalpara; S.S. Chattopadhyay, *Assistant Master,* Bidhan Nagar Government High School, Kolkata; V.A. Sujatha, *TGT,* K.V. Vasco No. 1, Goa; Akila Sahadevan, *TGT,* K.V., Meenambakkam, Chennai; S.C. Rauto, *TGT,* Central School for Tibetans, Mussoorie; Sunil P. Xavier, *TGT,* JNV, Neriyamangalam, Ernakulam; Amit Bajaj, *TGT,* CRPF Public School, Rohini, Delhi; R.K. Pande, *TGT,* D.M. School, RIE, Bhopal; V. Madhavi, *TGT,* Sanskriti School, Chanakyapuri, New Delhi; G. Sri Hari Babu, *TGT,* JNV, Sirpur Kagaznagar, Adilabad; and R.K. Mishra, *TGT*, A.E.C. School, Narora.

Special thanks are due to M. Chandra, *Professor* and *Head* (Retd.), DESM, NCERT for her support during the development of this book.

The Council acknowledges the efforts of *Computer Incharge,* Deepak Kapoor; *D.T.P. Operator,* Naresh Kumar; *Copy Editor,* Pragati Bhardwaj; and *Proof Reader,* Yogita Sharma.

Contribution of APC–Office, administration of DESM, Publication Department and Secretariat of NCERT is also duly acknowledged.

# CONTENTS

FOREWORD     *iii*

## 1. NUMBER SYSTEMS     **1**

1.1   Introduction     1
1.2   Irrational Numbers     5
1.3   Real Numbers and their Decimal Expansions     8
1.4   Representing Real Numbers on the Number Line     15
1.5   Operations on Real Numbers     18
1.6   Laws of Exponents for Real Numbers     24
1.7   Summary     27

## 2. POLYNOMIALS     **28**

2.1   Introduction     28
2.2   Polynomials in One Variable     28
2.3   Zeroes of a Polynomial     32
2.4   Remainder Theorem     35
2.5   Factorisation of Polynomials     40
2.6   Algebraic Identities     44
2.7   Summary     50

## 3. COORDINATE GEOMETRY     **51**

3.1   Introduction     51
3.2   Cartesian System     54
3.3   Plotting a Point in the Plane if its Coordinates are given     61
3.4   Summary     65

## 4. LINEAR EQUATIONS IN TWO VARIABLES     **66**

4.1   Introduction     66
4.2   Linear Equations     66
4.3   Solution of a Linear Equation     68
4.4   Graph of a Linear Equation in Two Variables     70
4.5   Equations of Lines Parallel to $x$-axis and $y$-axis     75
4.6   Summary     77

| | | | |
|---|---|---|---:|
| **5.** | **INTRODUCTION TO EUCLID'S GEOMETRY** | | **78** |
| | 5.1 | Introduction | 78 |
| | 5.2 | Euclid's Definitions, Axioms and Postulates | 80 |
| | 5.3 | Equivalent Versions of Euclid's Fifth Postulate | 86 |
| | 5.4 | Summary | 88 |
| **6.** | **LINES AND ANGLES** | | **89** |
| | 6.1 | Introduction | 89 |
| | 6.2 | Basic Terms and Definitions | 90 |
| | 6.3 | Intersecting Lines and Non-intersecting Lines | 92 |
| | 6.4 | Pairs of Angles | 92 |
| | 6.5 | Parallel Lines and a Transversal | 98 |
| | 6.6 | Lines Parallel to the same Line | 101 |
| | 6.7 | Angle Sum Property of a Triangle | 105 |
| | 6.8 | Summary | 108 |
| **7.** | **TRIANGLES** | | **108** |
| | 7.1 | Introduction | 109 |
| | 7.2 | Congruence of Triangles | 109 |
| | 7.3 | Criteria for Congruence of Triangles | 112 |
| | 7.4 | Some Properties of a Triangle | 120 |
| | 7.5 | Some More Criteria for Congruence of Triangles | 125 |
| | 7.6 | Inequalities in a Triangle | 129 |
| | 7.7 | Summary | 134 |
| **8.** | **QUADRILATERALS** | | **135** |
| | 8.1 | Introduction | 135 |
| | 8.2 | Angle Sum Property of a Quadrilateral | 136 |
| | 8.3 | Types of Quadrilaterals | 137 |
| | 8.4 | Properties of a Parallelogram | 139 |
| | 8.5 | Another Condition for a Quadrilteral to be a Parallelogram | 145 |
| | 8.6 | The Mid-point Theorem | 148 |
| | 8.7 | Summary | 151 |
| **9.** | **AREAS OF PARALLELOGRAMS AND TRIANGLES** | | **152** |
| | 9.1 | Introduction | 152 |
| | 9.2 | Figures on the same Base and Between the same Parallels | 154 |

| | 9.3 | Parallelograms on the same Base and between the same Parallels | 156 |
| | 9.4 | Triangles on the same Base and between the same Parallels | 160 |
| | 9.5 | Summary | 167 |
| **10.** | **CIRCLES** | | **168** |
| | 10.1 | Introduction | 168 |
| | 10.2 | Circles and its Related Terms : A Review | 169 |
| | 10.3 | Angle Subtended by a Chord at a Point | 171 |
| | 10.4 | Perpendicular from the Centre to a Chord | 173 |
| | 10.5 | Circle through Three Points | 174 |
| | 10.6 | Equal Chords and their Distances from the Centre | 176 |
| | 10.7 | Angle Subtended by an Arc of a Circle | 179 |
| | 10.8 | Cyclic Quadrilaterals | 182 |
| | 10.9 | Summary | 187 |
| **11.** | **CONSTRUCTIONS** | | **187** |
| | 11.1 | Introduction | 188 |
| | 11.2 | Basic Constructions | 189 |
| | 11.3 | Some Constructions of Triangles | 191 |
| | 11.4 | Summary | 196 |
| **12.** | **HERON'S FORMULA** | | **197** |
| | 12.1 | Introduction | 197 |
| | 12.2 | Area of a Triangle – by Heron's Formula | 199 |
| | 12.3 | Application of Heron's Formula in finding Areas of Quadrilaterals | 203 |
| | 12.4 | Summary | 207 |
| **13.** | **SURFACE AREAS AND VOLUMES** | | **208** |
| | 13.1 | Introduction | 208 |
| | 13.2 | Surface Area of a Cuboid and a Cube | 208 |
| | 13.3 | Surface Area of a Right Circular Cylinder | 214 |
| | 13.4 | Surface Area of a Right Circular Cone | 217 |
| | 13.5 | Surface Area of a Sphere | 222 |
| | 13.6 | Volume of a Cuboid | 226 |
| | 13.7 | Volume of a Cylinder | 228 |

13.8   Volume of a Right Circular Cone — 231

13.9   Volume of a Sphere — 234

10.10  Summary — 237

**14. STATISTICS — 238**

14.1   Introduction — 238

14.2   Collection of Data — 239

14.3   Presentation of Data — 240

14.4   Graphical Representation of Data — 247

14.5   Measures of Central Tendency — 261

14.6   Summary — 270

**15. PROBABILITY — 271**

15.1   Introduction — 271

15.2   Probability – an Experimental Approach — 272

15.3   Summary — 285

**APPENDIX – 1   PROOFS IN MATHEMATICS — 286**

A1.1   Introduction — 286

A1.2   Mathematically Acceptable Statements — 287

A1.3   Deductive Reasoning — 290

A1.4   Theorems, Conjectures and Axioms — 293

A1.5   What is a Mathematical Proof? — 298

A1.6   Summary — 305

**APPENDIX – 2   INTRODUCTION TO MATHEMATICAL MODELLING — 306**

A2.1   Introduction — 306

A2.2   Review of Word Problems — 307

A2.3   Some Mathematical Models — 311

A2.4   The Process of Modelling, its Advantages and Limitations — 319

A2.5   Summary — 322

**ANSWERS/HINTS — 325-350**

# CHAPTER 1

# NUMBER SYSTEMS

## 1.1 Introduction

In your earlier classes, you have learnt about the number line and how to represent various types of numbers on it (see Fig. 1.1).

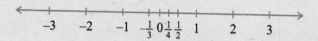

Fig. 1.1 : **The number line**

Just imagine you start from zero and go on walking along this number line in the positive direction. As far as your eyes can see, there are numbers, numbers and numbers!

Fig. 1.2

Now suppose you start walking along the number line, and collecting some of the numbers. Get a bag ready to store them!

You might begin with picking up only natural numbers like 1, 2, 3, and so on. You know that this list goes on for ever. (Why is this true?) So, now your bag contains infinitely many natural numbers! Recall that we denote this collection by the symbol **N**.

Now turn and walk all the way back, pick up zero and put it into the bag. You now have the collection of *whole numbers* which is denoted by the symbol **W**.

Now, stretching in front of you are many, many negative integers. Put all the negative integers into your bag. What is your new collection? Recall that it is the collection of all *integers*, and it is denoted by the symbol **Z**.

Why **Z** ?

**Z** comes from the German word "zahlen", which means "to count".

Are there some numbers still left on the line? Of course! There are numbers like $\frac{1}{2}, \frac{3}{4}$, or even $\frac{-2005}{2006}$. If you put all such numbers also into the bag, it will now be the

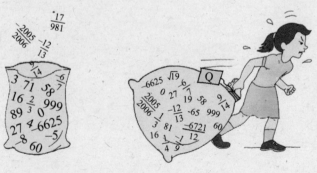

collection of *rational numbers*. The collection of rational numbers is denoted by **Q**. 'Rational' comes from the word 'ratio', and Q comes from the word 'quotient'.

You may recall the definition of rational numbers:

A number '*r*' is called a *rational number*, if it can be written in the form $\frac{p}{q}$, where *p* and *q* are integers and $q \neq 0$. (Why do we insist that $q \neq 0$?)

Notice that all the numbers now in the bag can be written in the form $\frac{p}{q}$, where *p* and *q* are integers and $q \neq 0$. For example, $-25$ can be written as $\frac{-25}{1}$; here $p = -25$ and $q = 1$. Therefore, the rational numbers also include the natural numbers, whole numbers and integers.

You also know that the rational numbers do not have a unique representation in the form $\frac{p}{q}$, where *p* and *q* are integers and $q \neq 0$. For example, $\frac{1}{2} = \frac{2}{4} = \frac{10}{20} = \frac{25}{50} = \frac{47}{94}$, and so on. These are *equivalent rational numbers (or fractions)*. However, when we say that $\frac{p}{q}$ is a rational number, or when we represent $\frac{p}{q}$ on the number line, we assume that $q \neq 0$ and that *p* and *q* have no common factors other than 1 (that is, *p* and *q* are *co-prime*). So, on the number line, among the infinitely many fractions equivalent to $\frac{1}{2}$, we will choose $\frac{1}{2}$ to represent all of them.

Now, let us solve some examples about the different types of numbers, which you have studied in earlier classes.

**Example 1 :** Are the following statements true or false? Give reasons for your answers.

(i) Every whole number is a natural number.

(ii) Every integer is a rational number.

(iii) Every rational number is an integer.

**Solution :** (i) False, because zero is a whole number but not a natural number.

(ii) True, because every integer *m* can be expressed in the form $\frac{m}{1}$, and so it is a rational number.

(iii) False, because $\dfrac{3}{5}$ is not an integer.

Example 2 : Find five rational numbers between 1 and 2.

We can approach this problem in at least two ways.

Solution 1 : Recall that to find a rational number between $r$ and $s$, you can add $r$ and $s$ and divide the sum by 2, that is $\dfrac{r+s}{2}$ lies between $r$ and $s$. So, $\dfrac{3}{2}$ is a number between 1 and 2. You can proceed in this manner to find four more rational numbers between 1 and 2. These four numbers are $\dfrac{5}{4}, \dfrac{11}{8}, \dfrac{13}{8}$ and $\dfrac{7}{4}$.

Solution 2 : The other option is to find all the five rational numbers in one step. Since we want five numbers, we write 1 and 2 as rational numbers with denominator $5 + 1$, i.e., $1 = \dfrac{6}{6}$ and $2 = \dfrac{12}{6}$. Then you can check that $\dfrac{7}{6}, \dfrac{8}{6}, \dfrac{9}{6}, \dfrac{10}{6}$ and $\dfrac{11}{6}$ are all rational numbers between 1 and 2. So, the five numbers are $\dfrac{7}{6}, \dfrac{4}{3}, \dfrac{3}{2}, \dfrac{5}{3}$ and $\dfrac{11}{6}$.

Remark : Notice that in Example 2, you were asked to find five rational numbers between 1 and 2. But, you must have realised that in fact there are infinitely many rational numbers between 1 and 2. In general, **there are infinitely many rational numbers between any two given rational numbers**.

Let us take a look at the number line again. Have you picked up all the numbers? Not, yet. The fact is that there are infinitely many more numbers left on the number line! There are gaps in between the places of the numbers you picked up, and not just one or two but infinitely many. The amazing thing is that there are infinitely many numbers lying between any two of these gaps too!

So we are left with the following questions:

1. What are the numbers, that are left on the number line, called?

2. How do we recognise them? That is, how do we distinguish them from the rationals (rational numbers)?

These questions will be answered in the next section.

## EXERCISE 1.1

1. Is zero a rational number? Can you write it in the form $\frac{p}{q}$, where $p$ and $q$ are integers and $q \neq 0$?

2. Find six rational numbers between 3 and 4.

3. Find five rational numbers between $\frac{3}{5}$ and $\frac{4}{5}$.

4. State whether the following statements are true or false. Give reasons for your answers.
   (i) Every natural number is a whole number.
   (ii) Every integer is a whole number.
   (iii) Every rational number is a whole number.

## 1.2 Irrational Numbers

We saw, in the previous section, that there may be numbers on the number line that are not rationals. In this section, we are going to investigate these numbers. So far, all the numbers you have come across, are of the form $\frac{p}{q}$, where $p$ and $q$ are integers and $q \neq 0$. So, you may ask: are there numbers which are not of this form? There are indeed such numbers.

The Pythagoreans in Greece, followers of the famous mathematician and philosopher Pythagoras, were the first to discover the numbers which were not rationals, around 400 BC. These numbers are called *irrational numbers* (*irrationals*), because they cannot be written in the form of a ratio of integers. There are many myths surrounding the discovery of irrational numbers by the Pythagorean, Hippacus of Croton. In all the myths, Hippacus has an unfortunate end, either for discovering that $\sqrt{2}$ is irrational or for disclosing the secret about $\sqrt{2}$ to people outside the secret Pythagorean sect!

**Pythagoras**
**(569 BCE – 479 BCE)**
Fig. 1.3

Let us formally define these numbers.

A number 's' is called *irrational*, if it cannot be written in the form $\frac{p}{q}$, where $p$ and $q$ are integers and $q \neq 0$.

You already know that there are infinitely many rationals. It turns out that there are infinitely many irrational numbers too. Some examples are:

$$\sqrt{2}, \sqrt{3}, \sqrt{15}, \pi, 0.10110111011110...$$

**Remark :** Recall that when we use the symbol $\sqrt{\phantom{x}}$, we assume that it is the positive square root of the number. So $\sqrt{4} = 2$, though both 2 and –2 are square roots of 4.

Some of the irrational numbers listed above are familiar to you. For example, you have already come across many of the square roots listed above and the number $\pi$.

The Pythagoreans proved that $\sqrt{2}$ is irrational. Later in approximately 425 BC, Theodorus of Cyrene showed that $\sqrt{3}, \sqrt{5}, \sqrt{6}, \sqrt{7}, \sqrt{10}, \sqrt{11}, \sqrt{12}, \sqrt{13}, \sqrt{14}, \sqrt{15}$ and $\sqrt{17}$ are also irrationals. Proofs of irrationality of $\sqrt{2}$, $\sqrt{3}$, $\sqrt{5}$, etc., shall be discussed in Class X. As to $\pi$, it was known to various cultures for thousands of years, it was proved to be irrational by Lambert and Legendre only in the late 1700s. In the next section, we will discuss why 0.10110111011110... and $\pi$ are irrational.

Let us return to the questions raised at the end of the previous section. Remember the bag of rational numbers. If we now put all irrational numbers into the bag, will there be any number left on the number line? The answer is no! It turns out that the collection of all rational numbers and irrational numbers together make up what we call the collection of *real numbers*,  which is denoted by **R**. Therefore, a real number is either rational or irrational. So, we can say that **every real number is represented by a unique point on the number line. Also, every point on the number line represents a unique real number**. This is why we call the number line, the *real number line*.

In the 1870s two German mathematicians, Cantor and Dedekind, showed that : Corresponding to every real number, there is a point on the real number line, and corresponding to every point on the number line, there exists a unique real number.

**R. Dedekind (1831-1916)**
Fig. 1.4

**G. Cantor (1845-1918)**
Fig. 1.5

Let us see how we can locate some of the irrational numbers on the number line.

**Example 3 :** Locate $\sqrt{2}$ on the number line.

**Solution :** It is easy to see how the Greeks might have discovered $\sqrt{2}$. Consider a unit square OABC, with each side 1 unit in length (see Fig. 1.6). Then you can see by the Pythagoras theorem that

Fig. 1.6

$OB = \sqrt{1^2 + 1^2} = \sqrt{2}$. How do we represent $\sqrt{2}$ on the number line?

This is easy. Transfer Fig. 1.6 onto the number line making sure that the vertex O coincides with zero (see Fig. 1.7).

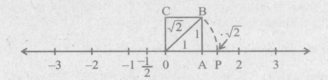

Fig. 1.7

We have just seen that OB = $\sqrt{2}$. Using a compass with centre O and radius OB, draw an arc intersecting the number line at the point P. Then P corresponds to $\sqrt{2}$ on the number line.

**Example 4 :** Locate $\sqrt{3}$ on the number line.

**Solution :** Let us return to Fig. 1.7.

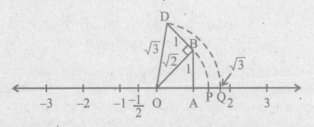

Fig. 1.8

Construct BD of unit length perpendicular to OB (as in Fig. 1.8). Then using the Pythagoras theorem, we see that OD = $\sqrt{\left(\sqrt{2}\right)^2 + 1^2} = \sqrt{3}$. Using a compass, with centre O and radius OD, draw an arc which intersects the number line at the point Q. Then Q corresponds to $\sqrt{3}$.

In the same way, you can locate $\sqrt{n}$ for any positive integer $n$, after $\sqrt{n-1}$ has been located.

## EXERCISE 1.2

1.  State whether the following statements are true or false. Justify your answers.

    (i)   Every irrational number is a real number.

    (ii)  Every point on the number line is of the form $\sqrt{m}$, where $m$ is a natural number.

    (iii) Every real number is an irrational number.

2.  Are the square roots of all positive integers irrational? If not, give an example of the square root of a number that is a rational number.

3.  Show how $\sqrt{5}$ can be represented on the number line.

4.  **Classroom activity (Constructing the 'square root spiral') :** Take a large sheet of paper and construct the 'square root spiral' in the following fashion. Start with a point O and draw a line segment $OP_1$ of unit length. Draw a line segment $P_1P_2$ perpendicular to $OP_1$ of unit length (see Fig. 1.9). Now draw a line segment $P_2P_3$ perpendicular to $OP_2$. Then draw a line segment $P_3P_4$ perpendicular to $OP_3$. Continuing in this manner, you can get the line segment $P_{n-1}P_n$ by drawing a line segment of unit length perpendicular to $OP_{n-1}$. In this manner, you will have created the points $P_2, P_3,...., P_n,....$, and joined them to create a beautiful spiral depicting $\sqrt{2}, \sqrt{3}, \sqrt{4}, ...$

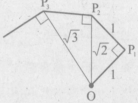

Fig. 1.9 : Constructing square root spiral

## 1.3 Real Numbers and their Decimal Expansions

In this section, we are going to study rational and irrational numbers from a different point of view. We will look at the decimal expansions of real numbers and see if we can use the expansions to distinguish between rationals and irrationals. We will also explain how to visualise the representation of real numbers on the number line using their decimal expansions. Since rationals are more familiar to us, let us start with them. Let us take three examples : $\dfrac{10}{3}, \dfrac{7}{8}, \dfrac{1}{7}$.

Pay special attention to the remainders and see if you can find any pattern.

**Example 5 :** Find the decimal expansions of $\frac{10}{3}$, $\frac{7}{8}$ and $\frac{1}{7}$.

**Solution :**

$$
\begin{array}{r|l}
 & 3.333... \\
\hline
3 & 10 \\
 & 9 \\
\hline
 & 10 \\
 & 9 \\
\hline
 & 10 \\
 & 9 \\
\hline
 & 10 \\
 & 9 \\
\hline
 & 1 \\
\end{array}
\qquad
\begin{array}{r|l}
 & 0.875 \\
\hline
8 & 7.0 \\
 & 64 \\
\hline
 & 60 \\
 & 56 \\
\hline
 & 40 \\
 & 40 \\
\hline
 & 0 \\
\end{array}
\qquad
\begin{array}{r|l}
 & 0.142857... \\
\hline
7 & 1.0 \\
 & 7 \\
\hline
 & 30 \\
 & 28 \\
\hline
 & 20 \\
 & 14 \\
\hline
 & 60 \\
 & 56 \\
\hline
 & 40 \\
 & 35 \\
\hline
 & 50 \\
 & 49 \\
\hline
 & 1 \\
\end{array}
$$

Remainders : 1, 1, 1, 1, 1...    Remainders : 6, 4, 0    Remainders : 3, 2, 6, 4, 5, 1,
Divisor : 3    Divisor : 8    3, 2, 6, 4, 5, 1,...

Divisor : 7

What have you noticed? You should have noticed at least three things:

(i)  The remainders either become 0 after a certain stage, or start repeating themselves.

(ii)  The number of entries in the repeating string of remainders is less than the divisor

(in $\frac{1}{3}$ one number repeats itself and the divisor is 3, in $\frac{1}{7}$ there are six entries

326451 in the repeating string of remainders and 7 is the divisor).

(iii)  If the remainders repeat, then we get a repeating block of digits in the quotient

(for $\frac{1}{3}$, 3 repeats in the quotient and for $\frac{1}{7}$, we get the repeating block 142857 in

the quotient).

Although we have noticed this pattern using only the examples above, it is true for all

rationals of the form $\frac{p}{q}$ ($q \neq 0$). On division of $p$ by $q$, two main things happen – either

the remainder becomes zero or never becomes zero and we get a repeating string of
remainders. Let us look at each case separately.

## Case (i) : The remainder becomes zero

In the example of $\frac{7}{8}$, we found that the remainder becomes zero after some steps and

the decimal expansion of $\frac{7}{8}$ = 0.875. Other examples are $\frac{1}{2}$ = 0.5, $\frac{639}{250}$ = 2.556. In all

these cases, the decimal expansion terminates or ends after a finite number of steps.
We call the decimal expansion of such numbers *terminating*.

## Case (ii) : The remainder never becomes zero

In the examples of $\frac{1}{3}$ and $\frac{1}{7}$, we notice that the remainders repeat after a certain

stage forcing the decimal expansion to go on for ever. In other words, we have a
repeating block of digits in the quotient. We say that this expansion is non-terminating

recurring. For example, $\frac{1}{3}$ = 0.3333... and $\frac{1}{7}$ = 0.142857142857142857...

The usual way of showing that 3 repeats in the quotient of $\frac{1}{3}$ is to write it as $0.\overline{3}$.

Similarly, since the block of digits 142857 repeats in the quotient of $\frac{1}{7}$, we write $\frac{1}{7}$ as

$0.\overline{142857}$, where the bar above the digits indicates the block of digits that repeats.
Also 3.57272... can be written as $3.5\overline{72}$. So, all these examples give us *non-terminating recurring (repeating)* decimal expansions.

Thus, we see that the decimal expansion of rational numbers have only two choices:
either they are terminating or non-terminating recurring.

Now suppose, on the other hand, on your walk on the number line, you come across a
number like 3.142678 whose decimal expansion is terminating or a number like
1.272727... that is, $1.\overline{27}$, whose decimal expansion is non-terminating recurring, can
you conclude that it is a rational number? The answer is yes!

We will not prove it but illustrate this fact with a few examples. The terminating cases are easy.

Example 6 : Show that 3.142678 is a rational number. In other words, express 3.142678 in the form $\frac{p}{q}$, where $p$ and $q$ are integers and $q \neq 0$.

Solution : We have $3.142678 = \frac{3142678}{1000000}$, and hence is a rational number.

Now, let us consider the case when the decimal expansion is non-terminating recurring.

Example 7 : Show that $0.3333... = 0.\overline{3}$ can be expressed in the form $\frac{p}{q}$, where $p$ and $q$ are integers and $q \neq 0$.

Solution : Since we do not know what $0.\overline{3}$ is , let us call it '$x$' and so

$$x = 0.3333...$$

Now here is where the trick comes in. Look at

$$10\, x = 10 \times (0.333...) = 3.333...$$

Now, $\qquad\qquad 3.3333... = 3 + x$, since $x = 0.3333...$

Therefore, $\qquad\qquad 10\, x = 3 + x$

Solving for $x$, we get

$$9x = 3,\ \text{i.e.,}\ x = \frac{1}{3}$$

Example 8 : Show that $1.272727... = 1.\overline{27}$ can be expressed in the form $\frac{p}{q}$, where $p$ and $q$ are integers and $q \neq 0$.

Solution : Let $x = 1.272727...$ Since two digits are repeating, we multiply $x$ by 100 to get

$$100\, x = 127.2727...$$

So, $\qquad\qquad 100\, x = 126 + 1.272727... = 126 + x$

Therefore, $\qquad\qquad 100\, x - x = 126,\ \text{i.e.,}\ 99\, x = 126$

i.e.,
$$x = \frac{126}{99} = \frac{14}{11}$$

You can check the reverse that $\frac{14}{11} = 1.\overline{27}$.

**Example 9 :** Show that $0.2353535... = 0.2\overline{35}$ can be expressed in the form $\frac{p}{q}$,
where $p$ and $q$ are integers and $q \neq 0$.

**Solution :** Let $x = 0.2\overline{35}$. Over here, note that 2 does not repeat, but the block 35 repeats. Since two digits are repeating, we multiply $x$ by 100 to get

$$100\,x = 23.53535...$$

So, $\quad\quad\quad\quad\quad 100\,x = 23.3 + 0.23535... = 23.3 + x$

Therefore, $\quad\quad\quad 99\,x = 23.3$

i.e., $\quad\quad\quad\quad\quad 99\,x = \frac{233}{10}$, which gives $x = \frac{233}{990}$

You can also check the reverse that $\frac{233}{990} = 0.2\overline{35}$.

So, every number with a non-terminating recurring decimal expansion can be expressed in the form $\frac{p}{q}$ $(q \neq 0)$, where $p$ and $q$ are integers. Let us summarise our results in the following form :

*The decimal expansion of a rational number is either terminating or non-terminating recurring. Moreover, a number whose decimal expansion is terminating or non-terminating recurring is rational.*

So, now we know what the decimal expansion of a rational number can be. What about the decimal expansion of irrational numbers? Because of the property above, we can conclude that their decimal expansions are *non-terminating non-recurring*.

So, the property for irrational numbers, similar to the property stated above for rational numbers, is

*The decimal expansion of an irrational number is non-terminating non-recurring. Moreover, a number whose decimal expansion is non-terminating non-recurring is irrational.*

Recall $s$ = 0.10110111011110... from the previous section. Notice that it is non-terminating and non-recurring. Therefore, from the property above, it is irrational. Moreover, notice that you can generate infinitely many irrationals similar to $s$.

What about the famous irrationals $\sqrt{2}$ and $\pi$? Here are their decimal expansions up to a certain stage.

$$\sqrt{2} = 1.4142135623730950488016887242096...$$

$$\pi = 3.14159265358979323846264338327950...$$

(Note that, we often take $\frac{22}{7}$ as an approximate value for $\pi$, but $\pi \neq \frac{22}{7}$.)

Over the years, mathematicians have developed various techniques to produce more and more digits in the decimal expansions of irrational numbers. For example, you might have learnt to find digits in the decimal expansion of $\sqrt{2}$ by the division method. Interestingly, in the Sulbasutras (rules of chord), a mathematical treatise of the Vedic period (800 BC - 500 BC), you find an approximation of $\sqrt{2}$ as follows:

$$\sqrt{2} = 1 + \frac{1}{3} + \left(\frac{1}{4} \times \frac{1}{3}\right) - \left(\frac{1}{34} \times \frac{1}{4} \times \frac{1}{3}\right) = 1.4142156$$

Notice that it is the same as the one given above for the first five decimal places. The history of the hunt for digits in the decimal expansion of $\pi$ is very interesting.

The Greek genius Archimedes was the first to compute digits in the decimal expansion of $\pi$. He showed 3.140845 < $\pi$ < 3.142857. Aryabhatta (476 – 550 C.E.), the great Indian mathematician and astronomer, found the value of $\pi$ correct to four decimal places (3.1416). Using high speed computers and advanced algorithms, $\pi$ has been computed to over 1.24 trillion decimal places!

**Archimedes (287 BCE – 212 BCE)**
Fig. 1.10

Now, let us see how to obtain irrational numbers.

**Example 10 :** Find an irrational number between $\frac{1}{7}$ and $\frac{2}{7}$.

**Solution :** We saw that $\frac{1}{7} = 0.\overline{142857}$. So, you can easily calculate $\frac{2}{7} = 0.\overline{285714}$.

To find an irrational number between $\frac{1}{7}$ and $\frac{2}{7}$, we find a number which is non-terminating non-recurring lying between them. Of course, you can find infinitely many such numbers.

An example of such a number is 0.150150015000150000...

## EXERCISE 1.3

1. Write the following in decimal form and say what kind of decimal expansion each has :

   (i) $\dfrac{36}{100}$

   (ii) $\dfrac{1}{11}$

   (iii) $4\dfrac{1}{8}$

   (iv) $\dfrac{3}{13}$

   (v) $\dfrac{2}{11}$

   (vi) $\dfrac{329}{400}$

2. You know that $\dfrac{1}{7} = 0.\overline{142857}$. Can you predict what the decimal expansions of $\dfrac{2}{7}, \dfrac{3}{7}, \dfrac{4}{7}, \dfrac{5}{7}, \dfrac{6}{7}$ are, without actually doing the long division? If so, how?

   [**Hint** : Study the remainders while finding the value of $\dfrac{1}{7}$ carefully.]

3. Express the following in the form $\dfrac{p}{q}$, where $p$ and $q$ are integers and $q \neq 0$.

   (i) $0.\overline{6}$

   (ii) $0.4\overline{7}$

   (iii) $0.\overline{001}$

4. Express 0.99999 .... in the form $\dfrac{p}{q}$. Are you surprised by your answer? With your teacher and classmates discuss why the answer makes sense.

5. What can the maximum number of digits be in the repeating block of digits in the decimal expansion of $\dfrac{1}{17}$? Perform the division to check your answer.

6. Look at several examples of rational numbers in the form $\dfrac{p}{q}$ $(q \neq 0)$, where $p$ and $q$ are integers with no common factors other than 1 and having terminating decimal representations (expansions). Can you guess what property $q$ must satisfy?

7. Write three numbers whose decimal expansions are non-terminating non-recurring.

8. Find three different irrational numbers between the rational numbers $\dfrac{5}{7}$ and $\dfrac{9}{11}$.

9. Classify the following numbers as rational or irrational :

   (i) $\sqrt{23}$

   (ii) $\sqrt{225}$

   (iii) 0.3796

   (iv) 7.478478...

   (v) 1.101001000100001...

## 1.4 Representing Real Numbers on the Number Line

In the previous section, you have seen that any real number has a decimal expansion. This helps us to represent it on the number line. Let us see how.

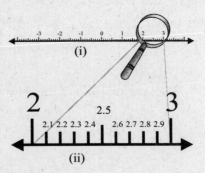

Suppose we want to locate 2.665 on the number line. We know that this lies between 2 and 3.

So, let us look closely at the portion of the number line between 2 and 3. Suppose we divide this into 10 equal parts and mark each point of division as in Fig. 1.11 (i). Then the first mark to

**Fig. 1.11**

the right of 2 will represent 2.1, the second 2.2, and so on. You might be finding some difficulty in observing these points of division between 2 and 3 in Fig. 1.11 (i). To have a clear view of the same, you may take a magnifying glass and look at the portion between 2 and 3. It will look like what you see in Fig. 1.11 (ii). Now, 2.665 lies between 2.6 and 2.7. So, let us focus on the portion between 2.6 and 2.7 [See Fig. 1.12(i)]. We imagine to divide this again into ten equal parts. The first mark will represent 2.61, the next 2.62, and so on. To see this clearly, we magnify this as shown in Fig. 1.12 (ii).

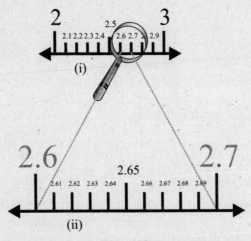

**Fig. 1.12**

Again, 2.665 lies between 2.66 and 2.67. So, let us focus on this portion of the number line [see Fig. 1.13(i)] and imagine to divide it again into ten equal parts. We magnify it to see it better, as in Fig. 1.13 (ii). The first mark represents 2.661, the next one represents 2.662, and so on. So, 2.665 is the 5th mark in these subdivisions.

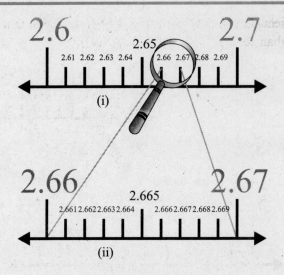

**Fig. 1.13**

We call this process of visualisation of representation of numbers on the number line, through a magnifying glass, as the **process of successive magnification**.

So, we have seen that it is possible by sufficient successive magnifications to visualise the position (or representation) of a real number with a terminating decimal expansion on the number line.

Let us now try and visualise the position (or representation) of a real number with a non-terminating recurring decimal expansion on the number line. We can look at appropriate intervals through a magnifying glass and by successive magnifications visualise the position of the number on the number line.

**Example 11** : Visualize the representation of $5.3\overline{7}$ on the number line upto 5 decimal places, that is, up to 5.37777.

**Solution** : Once again we proceed by successive magnification, and successively decrease the lengths of the portions of the number line in which $5.3\overline{7}$ is located. First, we see that $5.3\overline{7}$ is located between 5 and 6. In the next step, we locate $5.3\overline{7}$ between 5.3 and 5.4. To get a more accurate visualization of the representation, we divide this portion of the number line into 10 equal parts and use a magnifying glass to visualize that $5.3\overline{7}$ lies between 5.37 and 5.38. To visualize $5.3\overline{7}$ more accurately, we again divide the portion between 5.37 and 5.38 into ten equal parts and use a magnifying glass to visualize that $5.3\overline{7}$ lies between 5.377 and 5.378. Now to visualize $5.3\overline{7}$ still more accurately, we divide the portion between 5.377 an 5.378 into 10 equal parts, and visualize the representation of $5.3\overline{7}$ as in Fig. 1.14 (iv). Notice that $5.3\overline{7}$ is located closer to 5.3778 than to 5.3777 [see Fig 1.14 (iv)].

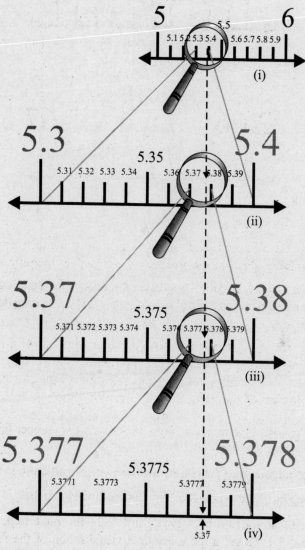

Fig. 1.14

**Remark** : We can proceed endlessly in this manner, successively viewing through a magnifying glass and simultaneously imagining the decrease in the length of the portion of the number line in which $5.3\overline{7}$ is located. The size of the portion of the line we specify depends on the degree of accuracy we would like for the visualisation of the position of the number on the number line.

You might have realised by now that the same procedure can be used to visualise a real number with a non-terminating non-recurring decimal expansion on the number line.

In the light of the discussions above and visualisations, we can again say that *every real number is represented by a unique point on the number line. Further, every point on the number line represents one and only one real number.*

### EXERCISE 1.4

1. Visualise 3.765 on the number line, using successive magnification.

2. Visualise $4.\overline{26}$ on the number line, up to 4 decimal places.

## 1.5 Operations on Real Numbers

You have learnt, in earlier classes, that rational numbers satisfy the commutative, associative and distributive laws for addition and multiplication. Moreover, if we add, subtract, multiply or divide (except by zero) two rational numbers, we still get a rational number (that is, rational numbers are 'closed' with respect to addition, subtraction, multiplication and division). It turns out that irrational numbers also satisfy the commutative, associative and distributive laws for addition and multiplication. However, the sum, difference, quotients and products of irrational numbers are not *always* irrational. For example, $\left(\sqrt{6}\right)+\left(-\sqrt{6}\right), \left(\sqrt{2}\right)-\left(\sqrt{2}\right), \left(\sqrt{3}\right)\cdot\left(\sqrt{3}\right)$ and $\dfrac{\sqrt{17}}{\sqrt{17}}$ are rationals.

Let us look at what happens when we add and multiply a rational number with an irrational number. For example, $\sqrt{3}$ is irrational. What about $2+\sqrt{3}$ and $2\sqrt{3}$ ? Since $\sqrt{3}$ has a non-terminating non-recurring decimal expansion, the same is true for $2+\sqrt{3}$ and $2\sqrt{3}$. Therefore, both $2+\sqrt{3}$ and $2\sqrt{3}$ are also irrational numbers.

**Example 12 :** Check whether $7\sqrt{5}$, $\dfrac{7}{\sqrt{5}}$, $\sqrt{2}+21$, $\pi-2$ are irrational numbers or not.

**Solution :** $\sqrt{5} = 2.236...$ , $\sqrt{2} = 1.4142...$, $\pi = 3.1415...$

Then $7\sqrt{5} = 15.652...$, $\dfrac{7}{\sqrt{5}} = \dfrac{7\sqrt{5}}{\sqrt{5}\sqrt{5}} = \dfrac{7\sqrt{5}}{5} = 3.1304...$

$\sqrt{2} + 21 = 22.4142...$, $\pi - 2 = 1.1415...$

All these are non-terminating non-recurring decimals. So, all these are irrational numbers.

Now, let us see what generally happens if we add, subtract, multiply, divide, take square roots and even $n$th roots of these irrational numbers, where $n$ is any natural number. Let us look at some examples.

**Example 13 :** Add $2\sqrt{2} + 5\sqrt{3}$ and $\sqrt{2} - 3\sqrt{3}$.

**Solution :** $\left(2\sqrt{2} + 5\sqrt{3}\right) + \left(\sqrt{2} - 3\sqrt{3}\right) = \left(2\sqrt{2} + \sqrt{2}\right) + \left(5\sqrt{3} - 3\sqrt{3}\right)$

$$= (2+1)\sqrt{2} + (5-3)\sqrt{3} = 3\sqrt{2} + 2\sqrt{3}$$

**Example 14 :** Multiply $6\sqrt{5}$ by $2\sqrt{5}$.

**Solution :** $6\sqrt{5} \times 2\sqrt{5} = 6 \times 2 \times \sqrt{5} \times \sqrt{5} = 12 \times 5 = 60$

**Example 15 :** Divide $8\sqrt{15}$ by $2\sqrt{3}$.

**Solution :** $8\sqrt{15} \div 2\sqrt{3} = \dfrac{8\sqrt{3} \cdot \times \sqrt{5}}{2\sqrt{3}} = 4\sqrt{5}$

These examples may lead you to expect the following facts, **which are true**:

(i)   The sum or difference of a rational number and an irrational number is irrational.

(ii)  The product or quotient of a non-zero rational number with an irrational number is irrational.

(iii) If we add, subtract, multiply or divide two irrationals, the result may be rational or irrational.

We now turn our attention to the operation of taking square roots of real numbers. Recall that, if $a$ is a natural number, then $\sqrt{a} = b$ means $b^2 = a$ and $b > 0$. The same definition can be extended for positive real numbers.

Let $a > 0$ be a real number. Then $\sqrt{a} = b$ means $b^2 = a$ and $b > 0$.

In Section 1.2, we saw how to represent $\sqrt{n}$ for any positive integer $n$ on the number line. We now show how to find $\sqrt{x}$ for any given positive real number $x$ geometrically.

For example, let us find it for $x = 3.5$, i.e., we find $\sqrt{3.5}$ geometrically.

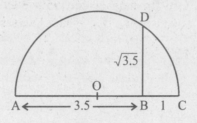

Fig. 1.15

Mark the distance 3.5 units from a fixed point A on a given line to obtain a point B such that AB = 3.5 units (see Fig. 1.15). From B, mark a distance of 1 unit and mark the new point as C. Find the mid-point of AC and mark that point as O. Draw a semicircle with centre O and radius OC. Draw a line perpendicular to AC passing through B and intersecting the semicircle at D. Then, BD = $\sqrt{3.5}$.

More generally, to find $\sqrt{x}$, for any positive real number $x$, we mark B so that AB = $x$ units, and, as in Fig. 1.16, mark C so that BC = 1 unit. Then, as we have done for the case $x = 3.5$, we find BD = $\sqrt{x}$ (see Fig. 1.16). We can prove this result using the Pythagoras Theorem.

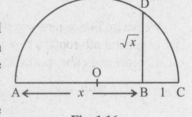

Fig. 1.16

Notice that, in Fig. 1.16, $\Delta$ OBD is a right-angled triangle. Also, the radius of the circle is $\dfrac{x+1}{2}$ units.

Therefore, OC = OD = OA = $\dfrac{x+1}{2}$ units.

Now, OB = $x - \left(\dfrac{x+1}{2}\right) = \dfrac{x-1}{2}$.

So, by the Pythagoras Theorem, we have

$$BD^2 = OD^2 - OB^2 = \left(\frac{x+1}{2}\right)^2 - \left(\frac{x-1}{2}\right)^2 = \frac{4x}{4} = x.$$

This shows that BD = $\sqrt{x}$.

This construction gives us a visual, and geometric way of showing that $\sqrt{x}$ exists for all real numbers $x > 0$. If you want to know the position of $\sqrt{x}$ on the number line, then let us treat the line BC as the number line, with B as zero, C as 1, and so on. Draw an arc with centre B and radius BD, which intersects the number line in E (see Fig. 1.17). Then, E represents $\sqrt{x}$.

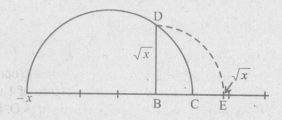

Fig. 1.17

We would like to now extend the idea of square roots to cube roots, fourth roots, and in general $n$th roots, where $n$ is a positive integer. Recall your understanding of square roots and cube roots from earlier classes.

What is $\sqrt[3]{8}$ ? Well, we know it has to be some positive number whose cube is 8, and you must have guessed $\sqrt[3]{8} = 2$. Let us try $\sqrt[5]{243}$. Do you know some number $b$ such that $b^5 = 243$? The answer is 3. Therefore, $\sqrt[5]{243} = 3$.

From these examples, can you define $\sqrt[n]{a}$ for a real number $a > 0$ and a positive integer $n$?

Let $a > 0$ be a real number and $n$ be a positive integer. Then $\sqrt[n]{a} = b$, if $b^n = a$ and $b > 0$. Note that the symbol ' $\sqrt{\phantom{x}}$ ' used in $\sqrt{2}, \sqrt[3]{8}, \sqrt[n]{a}$ , etc. is called the *radical sign*.

We now list some identities relating to square roots, which are useful in various ways. You are already familiar with some of these from your earlier classes. The remaining ones follow from the distributive law of multiplication over addition of real numbers, and from the identity $(x + y)(x - y) = x^2 - y^2$, for any real numbers $x$ and $y$. Let $a$ and $b$ be positive real numbers. Then

(i)   $\sqrt{ab} = \sqrt{a}\sqrt{b}$

(ii)   $\sqrt{\dfrac{a}{b}} = \dfrac{\sqrt{a}}{\sqrt{b}}$

(iii) $\left(\sqrt{a}+\sqrt{b}\right)\left(\sqrt{a}-\sqrt{b}\right)=a-b$ · (iv) $\left(a+\sqrt{b}\right)\left(a-\sqrt{b}\right)=a^2-b$

(v) $\left(\sqrt{a}+\sqrt{b}\right)\left(\sqrt{c}+\sqrt{d}\right)=\sqrt{ac}+\sqrt{ad}+\sqrt{bc}+\sqrt{bd}$

(vi) $\left(\sqrt{a}+\sqrt{b}\right)^2=a+2\sqrt{ab}+b$

Let us look at some particular cases of these identities.

**Example 16 :** Simplify the following expressions:

(i) $\left(5+\sqrt{7}\right)\left(2+\sqrt{5}\right)$                     (ii) $\left(5+\sqrt{5}\right)\left(5-\sqrt{5}\right)$

(iii) $\left(\sqrt{3}+\sqrt{7}\right)^2$                     (iv) $\left(\sqrt{11}-\sqrt{7}\right)\left(\sqrt{11}+\sqrt{7}\right)$

**Solution :** (i) $\left(5+\sqrt{7}\right)\left(2+\sqrt{5}\right)=10+5\sqrt{5}+2\sqrt{7}+\sqrt{35}$

(ii) $\left(5+\sqrt{5}\right)\left(5-\sqrt{5}\right)=5^2-\left(\sqrt{5}\right)^2=25-5=20$

(iii) $\left(\sqrt{3}+\sqrt{7}\right)^2=\left(\sqrt{3}\right)^2+2\sqrt{3}\sqrt{7}+\left(\sqrt{7}\right)^2=3+2\sqrt{21}+7=10+2\sqrt{21}$

(iv) $\left(\sqrt{11}-\sqrt{7}\right)\left(\sqrt{11}+\sqrt{7}\right)=\left(\sqrt{11}\right)^2-\left(\sqrt{7}\right)^2=11-7=4$

**Remark :** Note that 'simplify' in the example above has been used to mean that the expression should be written as the sum of a rational and an irrational number.

We end this section by considering the following problem. Look at $\dfrac{1}{\sqrt{2}}$· Can you tell where it shows up on the number line? You know that it is irrational. May be it is easier to handle if the denominator is a rational number. Let us see, if we can 'rationalise' the denominator, that is, to make the denominator into a rational number. To do so, we need the identities involving square roots. Let us see how.

**Example 17 :** Rationalise the denominator of $\dfrac{1}{\sqrt{2}}$.

**Solution :** We want to write $\dfrac{1}{\sqrt{2}}$ as an equivalent expression in which the denominator is a rational number. We know that $\sqrt{2}\cdot\sqrt{2}$ is rational. We also know that multiplying

$\dfrac{1}{\sqrt{2}}$ by $\dfrac{\sqrt{2}}{\sqrt{2}}$ will give us an equivalent expression, since $\dfrac{\sqrt{2}}{\sqrt{2}} = 1$. So, we put these two

facts together to get

$$\frac{1}{\sqrt{2}} = \frac{1}{\sqrt{2}} \times \frac{\sqrt{2}}{\sqrt{2}} = \frac{\sqrt{2}}{2}.$$

In this form, it is easy to locate $\dfrac{1}{\sqrt{2}}$ on the number line. It is half way between 0 and

$\sqrt{2}$ !

**Example 18 :** Rationalise the denominator of $\dfrac{1}{2 + \sqrt{3}}$.

**Solution :** We use the Identity (iv) given earlier. Multiply and divide $\dfrac{1}{2 + \sqrt{3}}$ by

$2 - \sqrt{3}$ to get $\dfrac{1}{2 + \sqrt{3}} \times \dfrac{2 - \sqrt{3}}{2 - \sqrt{3}} = \dfrac{2 - \sqrt{3}}{4 - 3} = 2 - \sqrt{3}$.

**Example 19 :** Rationalise the denominator of $\dfrac{5}{\sqrt{3} - \sqrt{5}}$.

**Solution :** Here we use the Identity (iii) given earlier.

So, $\dfrac{5}{\sqrt{3} - \sqrt{5}} = \dfrac{5}{\sqrt{3} - \sqrt{5}} \times \dfrac{\sqrt{3} + \sqrt{5}}{\sqrt{3} + \sqrt{5}} = \dfrac{5(\sqrt{3} + \sqrt{5})}{3 - 5} = \left(\dfrac{-5}{2}\right)(\sqrt{3} + \sqrt{5})$

**Example 20 :** Rationalise the denominator of $\dfrac{1}{7 + 3\sqrt{2}}$.

**Solution :** $\dfrac{1}{7 + 3\sqrt{2}} = \dfrac{1}{7 + 3\sqrt{2}} \times \left(\dfrac{7 - 3\sqrt{2}}{7 - 3\sqrt{2}}\right) = \dfrac{7 - 3\sqrt{2}}{49 - 18} = \dfrac{7 - 3\sqrt{2}}{31}$

So, when the denominator of an expression contains a term with a square root (or a number under a radical sign), the process of converting it to an equivalent expression whose denominator is a rational number is called *rationalising the denominator*.

## EXERCISE 1.5

1. Classify the following numbers as rational or irrational:

   (i)  $2 - \sqrt{5}$          (ii) $\left(3 + \sqrt{23}\right) - \sqrt{23}$  (iii) $\dfrac{2\sqrt{7}}{7\sqrt{7}}$

   (iv) $\dfrac{1}{\sqrt{2}}$                        (v) $2\pi$

2. Simplify each of the following expressions:

   (i)  $\left(3 + \sqrt{3}\right)\left(2 + \sqrt{2}\right)$          (ii) $\left(3 + \sqrt{3}\right)\left(3 - \sqrt{3}\right)$

   (iii) $\left(\sqrt{5} + \sqrt{2}\right)^2$                  (iv) $\left(\sqrt{5} - \sqrt{2}\right)\left(\sqrt{5} + \sqrt{2}\right)$

3. Recall, $\pi$ is defined as the ratio of the circumference (say $c$) of a circle to its diameter

   (say $d$). That is, $\pi = \dfrac{c}{d}$. This seems to contradict the fact that $\pi$ is irrational. How will

   you resolve this contradiction?

4. Represent $\sqrt{9.3}$ on the number line.

5. Rationalise the denominators of the following:

   (i)  $\dfrac{1}{\sqrt{7}}$                          (ii) $\dfrac{1}{\sqrt{7} - \sqrt{6}}$

   (iii) $\dfrac{1}{\sqrt{5} + \sqrt{2}}$                        (iv) $\dfrac{1}{\sqrt{7} - 2}$

## 1.6 Laws of Exponents for Real Numbers

Do you remember how to simplify the following?

   (i)  $17^2 \cdot 17^5 =$                    (ii) $(5^2)^7 =$

   (iii) $\dfrac{23^{10}}{23^7} =$                      (iv) $7^3 \cdot 9^3 =$

Did you get these answers? They are as follows:

   (i)  $17^2 \cdot 17^5 = 17^7$                  (ii) $(5^2)^7 = 5^{14}$

   (iii) $\dfrac{23^{10}}{23^7} = 23^3$                  (iv) $7^3 \cdot 9^3 = 63^3$

To get these answers, you would have used the following laws of exponents, which you have learnt in your earlier classes. (Here $a$, $n$ and $m$ are natural numbers. Remember, $a$ is called the base and $m$ and $n$ are the exponents.)

(i) $a^m \cdot a^n = a^{m+n}$

(ii) $(a^m)^n = a^{mn}$

(iii) $\dfrac{a^m}{a^n} = a^{m-n}$, $m > n$

(iv) $a^m b^m = (ab)^m$

What is $(a)^0$? Yes, it is 1! So you have learnt that $(a)^0 = 1$. So, using (iii), we can get $\dfrac{1}{a^n} = a^{-n}$. We can now extend the laws to negative exponents too.

So, for example :

(i) $17^2 \cdot 17^{-5} = 17^{-3} = \dfrac{1}{17^3}$

(ii) $(5^2)^{-7} = 5^{-14}$

(iii) $\dfrac{23^{-10}}{23^7} = 23^{-17}$

(iv) $(7)^{-3} \cdot (9)^{-3} = (63)^{-3}$

Suppose we want to do the following computations:

(i) $2^{\frac{2}{3}} \cdot 2^{\frac{1}{3}}$

(ii) $\left(3^{\frac{1}{5}}\right)^4$

(iii) $\dfrac{7^{\frac{1}{5}}}{7^{\frac{1}{3}}}$

(iv) $13^{\frac{1}{5}} \cdot 17^{\frac{1}{5}}$

How would we go about it? It turns out that we can extend the laws of exponents that we have studied earlier, even when the base is a positive real number and the exponents are rational numbers. (Later you will study that it can further to be extended when the exponents are real numbers.) But before we state these laws, and to even make sense of these laws, we need to first understand what, for example $4^{\frac{3}{2}}$ is. So, we have some work to do!

In Section 1.4, we defined $\sqrt[n]{a}$ for a real number $a > 0$ as follows:

Let $a > 0$ be a real number and $n$ a positive integer. Then $\sqrt[n]{a} = b$, if $b^n = a$ and $b > 0$.

In the language of exponents, we define $\sqrt[n]{a} = a^{\frac{1}{n}}$. So, in particular, $\sqrt[3]{2} = 2^{\frac{1}{3}}$.

There are now two ways to look at $4^{\frac{3}{2}}$.

$$4^{\frac{3}{2}} = \left(4^{\frac{1}{2}}\right)^3 = 2^3 = 8$$

$$4^{\frac{3}{2}} = \left(4^3\right)^{\frac{1}{2}} = (64)^{\frac{1}{2}} = 8$$

Therefore, we have the following definition:

Let $a > 0$ be a real number. Let $m$ and $n$ be integers such that $m$ and $n$ have no common factors other than 1, and $n > 0$. Then,

$$a^{\frac{m}{n}} = \left(\sqrt[n]{a}\right)^m = \sqrt[n]{a^m}$$

We now have the following extended laws of exponents:

Let $a > 0$ be a real number and $p$ and $q$ be rational numbers. Then, we have

(i) $a^p \cdot a^q = a^{p+q}$

(ii) $(a^p)^q = a^{pq}$

(iii) $\dfrac{a^p}{a^q} = a^{p-q}$

(iv) $a^p b^p = (ab)^p$

You can now use these laws to answer the questions asked earlier.

**Example 21 :** Simplify (i) $2^{\frac{2}{3}} \cdot 2^{\frac{1}{3}}$ 

(ii) $\left(3^{\frac{1}{5}}\right)^4$

(iii) $\dfrac{7^{\frac{1}{5}}}{7^{\frac{1}{3}}}$

(iv) $13^{\frac{1}{5}} \cdot 17^{\frac{1}{5}}$

**Solution :**

(i) $2^{\frac{2}{3}} \cdot 2^{\frac{1}{3}} = 2^{\left(\frac{2}{3} + \frac{1}{3}\right)} = 2^{\frac{3}{3}} = 2^1 = 2$

(ii) $\left(3^{\frac{1}{5}}\right)^4 = 3^{\frac{4}{5}}$

(iii) $\dfrac{7^{\frac{1}{5}}}{7^{\frac{1}{3}}} = 7^{\left(\frac{1}{5} - \frac{1}{3}\right)} = 7^{\frac{3-5}{15}} = 7^{\frac{-2}{15}}$

(iv) $13^{\frac{1}{5}} \cdot 17^{\frac{1}{5}} = (13 \times 17)^{\frac{1}{5}} = 221^{\frac{1}{5}}$

## EXERCISE 1.6

1. Find :    (i) $64^{\frac{1}{2}}$      (ii) $32^{\frac{1}{5}}$      (iii) $125^{\frac{1}{3}}$

2. Find :    (i) $9^{\frac{3}{2}}$      (ii) $32^{\frac{2}{5}}$      (iii) $16^{\frac{3}{4}}$      (iv) $125^{\frac{-1}{3}}$

3. Simplify :    (i) $2^{\frac{2}{3}} \cdot 2^{\frac{1}{5}}$      (ii) $\left(\dfrac{1}{3^3}\right)^7$      (iii) $\dfrac{11^{\frac{1}{2}}}{11^{\frac{1}{4}}}$      (iv) $7^{\frac{1}{2}} \cdot 8^{\frac{1}{2}}$

## 1.7 Summary

In this chapter, you have studied the following points:

1. A number $r$ is called a rational number, if it can be written in the form $\frac{p}{q}$, where $p$ and $q$ are integers and $q \neq 0$.

2. A number $s$ is called a irrational number, if it cannot be written in the form $\frac{p}{q}$, where $p$ and $q$ are integers and $q \neq 0$.

3. The decimal expansion of a rational number is either terminating or non-terminating recurring. Moreover, a number whose decimal expansion is terminating or non-terminating recurring is rational.

4. The decimal expansion of an irrational number is non-terminating non-recurring. Moreover, a number whose decimal expansion is non-terminating non-recurring is irrational.

5. All the rational and irrational numbers make up the collection of real numbers.

6. There is a unique real number corresponding to every point on the number line. Also, corresponding to each real number, there is a unique point on the number line.

7. If $r$ is rational and $s$ is irrational, then $r + s$ and $r - s$ are irrational numbers, and $rs$ and $\frac{r}{s}$ are irrational numbers, $r \neq 0$.

8. For positive real numbers $a$ and $b$, the following identities hold:

   (i) $\sqrt{ab} = \sqrt{a}\sqrt{b}$        (ii) $\sqrt{\dfrac{a}{b}} = \dfrac{\sqrt{a}}{\sqrt{b}}$

   (iii) $\left(\sqrt{a} + \sqrt{b}\right)\left(\sqrt{a} - \sqrt{b}\right) = a - b$    (iv) $\left(a + \sqrt{b}\right)\left(a - \sqrt{b}\right) = a^2 - b$

   (v) $\left(\sqrt{a} + \sqrt{b}\right)^2 = a + 2\sqrt{ab} + b$

9. To rationalise the denominator of $\dfrac{1}{\sqrt{a} + b}$, we multiply this by $\dfrac{\sqrt{a} - b}{\sqrt{a} - b}$, where $a$ and $b$ are integers.

10. Let $a > 0$ be a real number and $p$ and $q$ be rational numbers. Then

   (i) $a^p \cdot a^q = a^{p+q}$        (ii) $(a^p)^q = a^{pq}$

   (iii) $\dfrac{a^p}{a^q} = a^{p-q}$        (iv) $a^p b^p = (ab)^p$

# CHAPTER 2

# POLYNOMIALS

## 2.1 Introduction

You have studied algebraic expressions, their addition, subtraction, multiplication and division in earlier classes. You also have studied how to factorise some algebraic expressions. You may recall the algebraic identities :

$$(x + y)^2 = x^2 + 2xy + y^2$$
$$(x - y)^2 = x^2 - 2xy + y^2$$
and
$$x^2 - y^2 = (x + y)(x - y)$$

and their use in factorisation. In this chapter, we shall start our study with a particular type of algebraic expression, called *polynomial,* and the terminology related to it. We shall also study the *Remainder Theorem* and *Factor Theorem* and their use in the factorisation of polynomials. In addition to the above, we shall study some more algebraic identities and their use in factorisation and in evaluating some given expressions.

## 2.2 Polynomials in One Variable

Let us begin by recalling that a variable is denoted by a symbol that can take any real value. We use the letters $x$, $y$, $z$, etc. to denote variables. Notice that $2x$, $3x$, $-x$, $-\dfrac{1}{2}x$ are algebraic expressions. All these expressions are of the form (a constant) $\times x$. Now suppose we want to write an expression which is (a constant) $\times$ (a variable) and we do not know what the constant is. In such cases, we write the constant as $a$, $b$, $c$, etc. So the expression will be $ax$, say.

However, there is a difference between a letter denoting a constant and a letter denoting a variable. The values of the constants remain the same throughout a particular situation, that is, the values of the constants do not change in a given problem, but the value of a variable can keep changing.

Now, consider a square of side 3 units (see Fig. 2.1). What is its perimeter? You know that the perimeter of a square is the sum of the lengths of its four sides. Here, each side is 3 units. So, its perimeter is $4 \times 3$, i.e., 12 units. What will be the perimeter if each side of the square is 10 units? The perimeter is $4 \times 10$, i.e., 40 units. In case the length of each side is $x$ units (see Fig. 2.2), the perimeter is given by $4x$ units. So, as the length of the side varies, the perimeter varies.

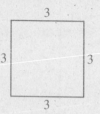

Fig. 2.1

Can you find the area of the square PQRS? It is $x \times x = x^2$ square units. $x^2$ is an algebraic expression. You are also familiar with other algebraic expressions like $2x$, $x^2 + 2x$, $x^3 - x^2 + 4x + 7$. Note that, all the algebraic expressions we have considered so far have only whole numbers as the exponents of the variable. Expressions of this form are called *polynomials in one variable*. In the examples above, the variable is $x$. For instance, $x^3 - x^2 + 4x + 7$ is a polynomial in $x$. Similarly, $3y^2 + 5y$ is a polynomial in the variable $y$ and $t^2 + 4$ is a polynomial in the variable $t$.

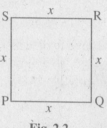

Fig. 2.2

In the polynomial $x^2 + 2x$, the expressions $x^2$ and $2x$ are called the **terms** of the polynomial. Similarly, the polynomial $3y^2 + 5y + 7$ has three terms, namely, $3y^2$, $5y$ and 7. Can you write the terms of the polynomial $-x^3 + 4x^2 + 7x - 2$ ? This polynomial has 4 terms, namely, $-x^3$, $4x^2$, $7x$ and $-2$.

Each term of a polynomial has a **coefficient**. So, in $-x^3 + 4x^2 + 7x - 2$, the coefficient of $x^3$ is $-1$, the coefficient of $x^2$ is 4, the coefficient of $x$ is 7 and $-2$ is the coefficient of $x^0$ (Remember, $x^0 = 1$). Do you know the coefficient of $x$ in $x^2 - x + 7$? It is $-1$.

2 is also a polynomial. In fact, 2, $-5$, 7, etc. are examples of *constant polynomials*. The constant polynomial 0 is called the **zero polynomial**. This plays a very important role in the collection of all polynomials, as you will see in the higher classes.

Now, consider algebraic expressions such as $x + \dfrac{1}{x}$, $\sqrt{x} + 3$ and $\sqrt[3]{y} + y^2$. Do you know that you can write $x + \dfrac{1}{x} = x + x^{-1}$? Here, the exponent of the second term, i.e., $x^{-1}$ is $-1$, which is not a whole number. So, this algebraic expression is not a polynomial.

Again, $\sqrt{x} + 3$ can be written as $x^{\frac{1}{2}} + 3$. Here the exponent of $x$ is $\dfrac{1}{2}$, which is not a whole number. So, is $\sqrt{x} + 3$ a polynomial? No, it is not. What about $\sqrt[3]{y} + y^2$? It is also not a polynomial (Why?).

If the variable in a polynomial is $x$, we may denote the polynomial by $p(x)$, or $q(x)$, or $r(x)$, etc. So, for example, we may write :

$$p(x) = 2x^2 + 5x - 3$$
$$q(x) = x^3 - 1$$
$$r(y) = y^3 + y + 1$$
$$s(u) = 2 - u - u^2 + 6u^5$$

A polynomial can have any (finite) number of terms. For instance, $x^{150} + x^{149} + \ldots + x^2 + x + 1$ is a polynomial with 151 terms.

Consider the polynomials $2x$, $2$, $5x^3$, $-5x^2$, $y$ and $u^4$. Do you see that each of these polynomials has only one term? Polynomials having only one term are called *monomials* ('mono' means 'one').

Now observe each of the following polynomials:

$$p(x) = x + 1, \qquad q(x) = x^2 - x, \qquad r(y) = y^{30} + 1, \qquad t(u) = u^{43} - u^2$$

How many terms are there in each of these? Each of these polynomials has only two terms. Polynomials having only two terms are called *binomials* ('bi' means 'two').

Similarly, polynomials having only three terms are called *trinomials* ('tri' means 'three'). Some examples of trinomials are

$$p(x) = x + x^2 + \pi, \qquad\qquad q(x) = \sqrt{2} + x - x^2,$$
$$r(u) = u + u^2 - 2, \qquad\qquad t(y) = y^4 + y + 5.$$

Now, look at the polynomial $p(x) = 3x^7 - 4x^6 + x + 9$. What is the term with the highest power of $x$ ? It is $3x^7$. The exponent of $x$ in this term is 7. Similarly, in the polynomial $q(y) = 5y^6 - 4y^2 - 6$, the term with the highest power of $y$ is $5y^6$ and the exponent of $y$ in this term is 6. We call the highest power of the variable in a polynomial as the *degree of the polynomial*. So, the degree of the polynomial $3x^7 - 4x^6 + x + 9$ is 7 and the degree of the polynomial $5y^6 - 4y^2 - 6$ is 6. **The degree of a non-zero constant polynomial is zero**.

**Example 1 :** Find the degree of each of the polynomials given below:

(i) $x^5 - x^4 + 3$ \qquad\qquad (ii) $2 - y^2 - y^3 + 2y^8$ \qquad\qquad (iii) 2

**Solution :** (i) The highest power of the variable is 5. So, the degree of the polynomial is 5.

(ii) The highest power of the variable is 8. So, the degree of the polynomial is 8.

(iii) The only term here is 2 which can be written as $2x^0$. So the exponent of $x$ is 0. Therefore, the degree of the polynomial is 0.

Now observe the polynomials $p(x) = 4x + 5$, $q(y) = 2y$, $r(t) = t + \sqrt{2}$ and $s(u) = 3 - u$. Do you see anything common among all of them? The degree of each of these polynomials is one. A polynomial of degree one is called a *linear polynomial*. Some more linear polynomials in one variable are $2x - 1$, $\sqrt{2}\, y + 1$, $2 - u$. Now, try and find a linear polynomial in $x$ with 3 terms? You would not be able to find it because a linear polynomial in $x$ can have at most two terms. So, any linear polynomial in $x$ will be of the form $ax + b$, where $a$ and $b$ are constants and $a \neq 0$ (why?). Similarly, $ay + b$ is a linear polynomial in $y$.

Now consider the polynomials :

$$2x^2 + 5, \;\; 5x^2 + 3x + \pi, \;\; x^2 \text{ and } x^2 + \frac{2}{5}x$$

Do you agree that they are all of degree two? A polynomial of degree two is called a *quadratic polynomial*. Some examples of a quadratic polynomial are $5 - y^2$, $4y + 5y^2$ and $6 - y - y^2$. Can you write a quadratic polynomial in one variable with four different terms? You will find that a quadratic polynomial in one variable will have at most 3 terms. If you list a few more quadratic polynomials, you will find that any quadratic polynomial in $x$ is of the form $ax^2 + bx + c$, where $a \neq 0$ and $a$, $b$, $c$ are constants. Similarly, quadratic polynomial in $y$ will be of the form $ay^2 + by + c$, provided $a \neq 0$ and $a$, $b$, $c$ are constants.

We call a polynomial of degree three a *cubic polynomial*. Some examples of a cubic polynomial in $x$ are $4x^3$, $2x^3 + 1$, $5x^3 + x^2$, $6x^3 - x$, $6 - x^3$, $2x^3 + 4x^2 + 6x + 7$. How many terms do you think a cubic polynomial in one variable can have? It can have at most 4 terms. These may be written in the form $ax^3 + bx^2 + cx + d$, where $a \neq 0$ and $a$, $b$, $c$ and $d$ are constants.

Now, that you have seen what a polynomial of degree 1, degree 2, or degree 3 looks like, can you write down a polynomial in one variable of degree $n$ for any natural number $n$? A polynomial in one variable $x$ of degree $n$ is an expression of the form

$$a_n x^n + a_{n-1} x^{n-1} + \ldots + a_1 x + a_0$$

where $a_0$, $a_1$, $a_2$, $\ldots$, $a_n$ are constants and $a_n \neq 0$.

In particular, if $a_0 = a_1 = a_2 = a_3 = \ldots = a_n = 0$ (all the constants are zero), we get the **zero polynomial**, which is denoted by 0. What is the degree of the zero polynomial? The degree of the zero polynomial is *not defined*.

So far we have dealt with polynomials in one variable only. We can also have polynomials in more than one variable. For example, $x^2 + y^2 + xyz$ (where variables are $x$, $y$ and $z$) is a polynomial in three variables. Similarly $p^2 + q^{10} + r$ (where the variables are $p$, $q$ and $r$), $u^3 + v^2$ (where the variables are $u$ and $v$) are polynomials in three and two variables, respectively. You will be studying such polynomials in detail later.

## EXERCISE 2.1

1. Which of the following expressions are polynomials in one variable and which are not? State reasons for your answer.

   (i) $4x^2 - 3x + 7$     (ii) $y^2 + \sqrt{2}$          (iii) $3\sqrt{t} + t\sqrt{2}$        (iv) $y + \dfrac{2}{y}$

   (v) $x^{10} + y^3 + t^{50}$

2. Write the coefficients of $x^2$ in each of the following:

   (i) $2 + x^2 + x$       (ii) $2 - x^2 + x^3$       (iii) $\dfrac{\pi}{2} x^2 + x$          (iv) $\sqrt{2}\, x - 1$

3. Give one example each of a binomial of degree 35, and of a monomial of degree 100.

4. Write the degree of each of the following polynomials:

   (i) $5x^3 + 4x^2 + 7x$                          (ii) $4 - y^2$

   (iii) $5t - \sqrt{7}$                               (iv) 3

5. Classify the following as linear, quadratic and cubic polynomials:

   (i) $x^2 + x$            (ii) $x - x^3$           (iii) $y + y^2 + 4$        (iv) $1 + x$

   (v) $3t$                 (vi) $r^2$               (vii) $7x^3$

## 2.3 Zeroes of a Polynomial

Consider the polynomial   $p(x) = 5x^3 - 2x^2 + 3x - 2$.

If we replace $x$ by 1 everywhere in $p(x)$, we get

$$p(1) = 5 \times (1)^3 - 2 \times (1)^2 + 3 \times (1) - 2$$
$$= 5 - 2 + 3 - 2$$
$$= 4$$

So, we say that the value of $p(x)$ at $x = 1$ is 4.

Similarly,          $p(0) = 5(0)^3 - 2(0)^2 + 3(0) - 2$
$$= -2$$

Can you find $p(-1)$?

**Example 2 :** Find the value of each of the following polynomials at the indicated value of variables:

   (i) $p(x) = 5x^2 - 3x + 7$ at $x = 1$.

   (ii) $q(y) = 3y^3 - 4y + \sqrt{11}$ at $y = 2$.

   (iii) $p(t) = 4t^4 + 5t^3 - t^2 + 6$ at $t = a$.

**Solution :** (i) $p(x) = 5x^2 - 3x + 7$

The value of the polynomial $p(x)$ at $x = 1$ is given by

$$p(1) = 5(1)^2 - 3(1) + 7$$
$$= 5 - 3 + 7 = 9$$

(ii) $q(y) = 3y^3 - 4y + \sqrt{11}$

The value of the polynomial $q(y)$ at $y = 2$ is given by

$$q(2) = 3(2)^3 - 4(2) + \sqrt{11} = 24 - 8 + \sqrt{11} = 16 + \sqrt{11}$$

(iii) $p(t) = 4t^4 + 5t^3 - t^2 + 6$

The value of the polynomial $p(t)$ at $t = a$ is given by

$$p(a) = 4a^4 + 5a^3 - a^2 + 6$$

Now, consider the polynomial $p(x) = x - 1$.

What is $p(1)$? Note that : $p(1) = 1 - 1 = 0$.

As $p(1) = 0$, we say that 1 is a *zero* of the polynomial $p(x)$.

Similarly, you can check that 2 is a *zero* of $q(x)$, where $q(x) = x - 2$.

In general, we say that a *zero* of a polynomial $p(x)$ is a number $c$ such that $p(c) = 0$.

You must have observed that the zero of the polynomial $x - 1$ is obtained by equating it to 0, i.e., $x - 1 = 0$, which gives $x = 1$. We say $p(x) = 0$ is a polynomial equation and 1 is the *root of the polynomial* equation $p(x) = 0$. So we say 1 is the zero of the polynomial $x - 1$, or a *root* of the polynomial equation $x - 1 = 0$.

Now, consider the constant polynomial 5. Can you tell what its zero is? It has no zero because replacing $x$ by any number in $5x^0$ still gives us 5. In fact, *a non-zero constant polynomial has no zero*. What about the zeroes of the zero polynomial? By convention, *every real number is a zero of the zero polynomial*.

**Example 3 :** Check whether –2 and 2 are zeroes of the polynomial $x + 2$.

**Solution :** Let $p(x) = x + 2$.

Then $p(2) = 2 + 2 = 4$, $p(-2) = -2 + 2 = 0$

Therefore, –2 is a zero of the polynomial $x + 2$, but 2 is not.

**Example 4 :** Find a zero of the polynomial $p(x) = 2x + 1$.

**Solution :** Finding a zero of $p(x)$, is the same as solving the equation

$$p(x) = 0$$

Now, $\qquad 2x + 1 = 0$ gives us $x = -\dfrac{1}{2}$

So, $-\dfrac{1}{2}$ is a zero of the polynomial $2x + 1$.

Now, if $p(x) = ax + b$, $a \neq 0$, is a linear polynomial, how can we find a zero of $p(x)$? Example 4 may have given you some idea. Finding a zero of the polynomial $p(x)$, amounts to solving the polynomial equation $p(x) = 0$.

Now, $p(x) = 0$ means $\qquad ax + b = 0$, $a \neq 0$

So, $\qquad\qquad\qquad ax = -b$

i.e., $\qquad\qquad\qquad x = -\dfrac{b}{a}$ .

So, $x = -\dfrac{b}{a}$ is the only zero of $p(x)$, i.e., a *linear polynomial has one and only one zero*.

Now we can say that 1 is *the* zero of $x - 1$, and $-2$ is *the* zero of $x + 2$.

**Example 5 :** Verify whether 2 and 0 are zeroes of the polynomial $x^2 - 2x$.

**Solution : Let** $\qquad\qquad p(x) = x^2 - 2x$

Then $\qquad\qquad p(2) = 2^2 - 4 = 4 - 4 = 0$

and $\qquad\qquad p(0) = 0 - 0 = 0$

Hence, 2 and 0 are both zeroes of the polynomial $x^2 - 2x$.

Let us now list our observations:

(i) A zero of a polynomial need not be 0.

(ii) 0 may be a zero of a polynomial.

(iii) Every linear polynomial has one and only one zero.

(iv) A polynomial can have more than one zero.

## EXERCISE 2.2

1. Find the value of the polynomial $5x - 4x^2 + 3$ at

 (i) $x = 0$ $\qquad\qquad$ (ii) $x = -1$ $\qquad\qquad$ (iii) $x = 2$

2. Find $p(0), p(1)$ and $p(2)$ for each of the following polynomials:

 (i) $p(y) = y^2 - y + 1$ $\qquad$ (ii) $p(t) = 2 + t + 2t^2 - t^3$

 (iii) $p(x) = x^3$ $\qquad\qquad\qquad$ (iv) $p(x) = (x - 1)(x + 1)$

3. Verify whether the following are zeroes of the polynomial, indicated against them.

(i) $p(x) = 3x + 1$, $x = -\dfrac{1}{3}$

(ii) $p(x) = 5x - \pi$, $x = \dfrac{4}{5}$

(iii) $p(x) = x^2 - 1$, $x = 1, -1$

(iv) $p(x) = (x + 1)(x - 2)$, $x = -1, 2$

(v) $p(x) = x^2$, $x = 0$

(vi) $p(x) = lx + m$, $x = -\dfrac{m}{l}$

(vii) $p(x) = 3x^2 - 1$, $x = -\dfrac{1}{\sqrt{3}}, \dfrac{2}{\sqrt{3}}$

(viii) $p(x) = 2x + 1$, $x = \dfrac{1}{2}$

4. Find the zero of the polynomial in each of the following cases:

(i) $p(x) = x + 5$

(ii) $p(x) = x - 5$

(iii) $p(x) = 2x + 5$

(iv) $p(x) = 3x - 2$

(v) $p(x) = 3x$

(vi) $p(x) = ax, a \neq 0$

(vii) $p(x) = cx + d, c \neq 0, c, d$ are real numbers.

## 2.4 Remainder Theorem

Let us consider two numbers 15 and 6. You know that when we divide 15 by 6, we get the quotient 2 and remainder 3. Do you remember how this fact is expressed? We write 15 as

$$15 = (6 \times 2) + 3$$

We observe that the *remainder* 3 is less than the *divisor* 6. Similarly, if we divide 12 by 6, we get

$$12 = (6 \times 2) + 0$$

What is the remainder here? Here the remainder is 0, and we say that 6 is a *factor* of 12 or 12 is a *multiple* of 6.

Now, the question is: can we divide one polynomial by another? To start with, let us try and do this when the divisor is a monomial. So, let us divide the polynomial $2x^3 + x^2 + x$ by the monomial $x$.

We have $(2x^3 + x^2 + x) \div x = \dfrac{2x^3}{x} + \dfrac{x^2}{x} + \dfrac{x}{x}$

$$= 2x^2 + x + 1$$

In fact, you may have noticed that $x$ is common to each term of $2x^3 + x^2 + x$. So we can write $2x^3 + x^2 + x$ as $x(2x^2 + x + 1)$.

We say that $x$ and $2x^2 + x + 1$ are *factors* of $2x^3 + x^2 + x$, and $2x^3 + x^2 + x$ is a *multiple* of $x$ as well as a multiple of $2x^2 + x + 1$.

Consider another pair of polynomials $3x^2 + x + 1$ and $x$.

Here,                    $(3x^2 + x + 1) \div x = (3x^2 \div x) + (x \div x) + (1 \div x)$.

We see that we cannot divide 1 by $x$ to get a polynomial term. So in this case we stop here, and note that 1 is the remainder. Therefore, we have

$$3x^2 + x + 1 = \{x \times (3x + 1)\} + 1$$

In this case, $3x + 1$ is the quotient and 1 is the remainder. Do you think that $x$ is a factor of $3x^2 + x + 1$? Since the remainder is not zero, it is not a factor.

Now let us consider an example to see how we can divide a polynomial by any non-zero polynomial.

**Example 6 :** Divide $p(x)$ by $g(x)$, where $p(x) = x + 3x^2 - 1$ and $g(x) = 1 + x$.

**Solution :** We carry out the process of division by means of the following steps:

**Step 1 :** We write the dividend $x + 3x^2 - 1$ and the divisor $1 + x$ in the standard form, i.e., after arranging the terms in the descending order of their degrees. So, the dividend is $3x^2 + x - 1$ and divisor is $x + 1$.

**Step 2 :** We divide the first term of the dividend by the first term of the divisor, i.e., we divide $3x^2$ by $x$, and get $3x$. This gives us the first term of the quotient.

$$\frac{3x^2}{x} = 3x = \text{first term of quotient}$$

**Step 3 :** We multiply the divisor by the first term of the quotient, and subtract this product from the dividend, i.e., we multiply $x + 1$ by $3x$ and subtract the product $3x^2 + 3x$ from the dividend $3x^2 + x - 1$. This gives us the remainder as $-2x - 1$.

$$x + 1 \overline{\smash{\big)}\ 3x^2 + x - 1} $$
$$\underline{3x^2 + 3x} $$
$$-2x - 1$$

with quotient term $3x$.

**Step 4 :** We treat the remainder $-2x - 1$ as the new dividend. The divisor remains the same. We repeat Step 2 to get the next term of the quotient, i.e., we divide the first term $-2x$ of the (new) dividend by the first term $x$ of the divisor and obtain $-2$. Thus, $-2$ is the second term in the quotient.

$$\frac{-2x}{x} = -2$$
$$= \text{second term of quotient}$$

New Quotient
$= 3x - 2$

**Step 5 :** We multiply the divisor by the second term of the quotient and subtract the product from the dividend. That is, we multiply $x + 1$ by $- 2$ and subtract the product $- 2x - 2$ from the dividend $- 2x - 1$. This gives us 1 as the remainder.

$$
\begin{array}{r}
(x + 1)(-2) \\
= -2x - 2
\end{array}
\left|
\begin{array}{l}
-2x - 1 \\
-2x - 2 \\
\underline{+ \quad +} \\
\quad + 1
\end{array}
\right.
$$

This process continues till the remainder is 0 or the degree of the new dividend is less than the degree of the divisor. At this stage, this new dividend becomes the remainder and the sum of the quotients gives us the whole quotient.

**Step 6 :** Thus, the quotient in full is $3x - 2$ and the remainder is 1.

Let us look at what we have done in the process above as a whole:

$$
\begin{array}{r}
3x - 2 \\
x + 1 \overline{\smash{\big)}\; 3x^2 + x - 1} \\
\underline{3x^2 + 3x} \\
\underline{\phantom{-}-\phantom{--}-} \\
- 2x - 1 \\
- 2x - 2 \\
\underline{+ \quad +} \\
1
\end{array}
$$

Notice that $3x^2 + x - 1 = (x + 1)(3x - 2) + 1$

i.e., **Dividend = (Divisor × Quotient) + Remainder**

In general, if $p(x)$ and $g(x)$ are two polynomials such that degree of $p(x) \geq$ degree of $g(x)$ and $g(x) \neq 0$, then we can find polynomials $q(x)$ and $r(x)$ such that:

$$p(x) = g(x)q(x) + r(x),$$

where $r(x) = 0$ or degree of $r(x) <$ degree of $g(x)$. Here we say that $p(x)$ divided by $g(x)$, gives $q(x)$ as quotient and $r(x)$ as remainder.

In the example above, the divisor was a linear polynomial. In such a situation, let us see if there is any link between the remainder and certain values of the dividend.

In $p(x) = 3x^2 + x - 1$, if we replace $x$ by $-1$, we have

$p(-1) = 3(-1)^2 + (-1) -1 = 1$

So, the remainder obtained on dividing $p(x) = 3x^2 + x - 1$ by $x + 1$ is the same as the value of the polynomial $p(x)$ at the zero of the polynomial $x + 1$, i.e., $-1$.

Let us consider some more examples.

**Example 7** : Divide the polynomial $3x^4 - 4x^3 - 3x - 1$ by $x - 1$.

**Solution** : By long division, we have:

$$
\begin{array}{r}
3x^3 - x^2 - x - 4 \\
x - 1\overline{\smash{)}\ 3x^4 - 4x^3 - 3x - 1} \\
\underline{3x^4 - 3x^3} \\
-x^3 \quad\ - 3x - 1 \\
\underline{x^3 + x^2} \\
-x^2 - 3x - 1 \\
\underline{-x^2 + x} \\
-4x - 1 \\
\underline{-4x + 4} \\
-5
\end{array}
$$

Here, the remainder is $-5$. Now, the zero of $x - 1$ is $1$. So, putting $x = 1$ in $p(x)$, we see that

$$
\begin{aligned}
p(1) &= 3(1)^4 - 4(1)^3 - 3(1) - 1 \\
&= 3 - 4 - 3 - 1 \\
&= -5, \text{ which is the remainder.}
\end{aligned}
$$

**Example 8** : Find the remainder obtained on dividing $p(x) = x^3 + 1$ by $x + 1$.

**Solution** : By long division,

$$
\begin{array}{r}
x^2 - x + 1 \\
x + 1\overline{\smash{)}\ x^3 + 1} \\
\underline{x^3 + x^2} \\
-x^2 \quad\ + 1 \\
\underline{-x^2 - x} \\
x + 1 \\
\underline{x + 1} \\
0
\end{array}
$$

So, we find that the remainder is 0.

Here $p(x) = x^3 + 1$, and the root of $x + 1 = 0$ is $x = -1$. We see that

$$p(-1) = (-1)^3 + 1$$
$$= -1 + 1$$
$$= 0,$$

which is equal to the remainder obtained by actual division.

Is it not a simple way to find the remainder obtained on dividing a polynomial by a *linear polynomial*? We shall now generalise this fact in the form of the following theorem. We shall also show you why the theorem is true, by giving you a proof of the theorem.

**Remainder Theorem** : *Let $p(x)$ be any polynomial of degree greater than or equal to one and let a be any real number. If $p(x)$ is divided by the linear polynomial $x - a$, then the remainder is $p(a)$.*

**Proof** : Let $p(x)$ be any polynomial with degree greater than or equal to 1. Suppose that when $p(x)$ is divided by $x - a$, the quotient is $q(x)$ and the remainder is $r(x)$, i.e.,

$$p(x) = (x - a) \, q(x) + r(x)$$

Since the degree of $x - a$ is 1 and the degree of $r(x)$ is less than the degree of $x - a$, the degree of $r(x) = 0$. This means that $r(x)$ is a constant, say $r$.

So, for every value of $x$, $r(x) = r$.
Therefore, $$p(x) = (x - a) \, q(x) + r$$

In particular, if $x = a$, this equation gives us

$$p(a) = (a - a) \, q(a) + r$$
$$= r,$$

which proves the theorem.

Let us use this result in another example.

**Example 9** : Find the remainder when $x^4 + x^3 - 2x^2 + x + 1$ is divided by $x - 1$.

**Solution** : Here, $p(x) = x^4 + x^3 - 2x^2 + x + 1$, and the zero of $x - 1$ is 1.

So, $$p(1) = (1)^4 + (1)^3 - 2(1)^2 + 1 + 1$$
$$= 2$$

So, by the Remainder Theorem, 2 is the remainder when $x^4 + x^3 - 2x^2 + x + 1$ is divided by $x - 1$.

**Example 10** : Check whether the polynomial $q(t) = 4t^3 + 4t^2 - t - 1$ is a multiple of $2t + 1$.

**Solution :** As you know, $q(t)$ will be a multiple of $2t + 1$ only, if $2t + 1$ divides $q(t)$ leaving remainder zero. Now, taking $2t + 1 = 0$, we have $t = -\dfrac{1}{2}$.

Also,   $q\left(-\dfrac{1}{2}\right) = 4\left(-\dfrac{1}{2}\right)^3 + 4\left(-\dfrac{1}{2}\right)^2 - \left(-\dfrac{1}{2}\right) - 1 = -\dfrac{1}{2} + 1 + \dfrac{1}{2} - 1 = 0$

So the remainder obtained on dividing $q(t)$ by $2t + 1$ is 0.

So, $2t + 1$ is a factor of the given polynomial $q(t)$, that is $q(t)$ is a multiple of $2t + 1$.

## EXERCISE 2.3

1.  Find the remainder when $x^3 + 3x^2 + 3x + 1$ is divided by

    (i) $x + 1$         (ii) $x - \dfrac{1}{2}$         (iii) $x$         (iv) $x + \pi$         (v) $5 + 2x$

2.  Find the remainder when $x^3 - ax^2 + 6x - a$ is divided by $x - a$.

3.  Check whether $7 + 3x$ is a factor of $3x^3 + 7x$.

## 2.5 Factorisation of Polynomials

Let us now look at the situation of Example 10 above more closely. It tells us that since

the remainder, $q\left(-\dfrac{1}{2}\right) = 0$, $(2t + 1)$ is a factor of $q(t)$, i.e., $q(t) = (2t + 1)\, g(t)$

for some polynomial $g(t)$. This is a particular case of the following theorem.

**Factor Theorem :** If $p(x)$ is a polynomial of degree $n \geq 1$ and $a$ is any real number, then (i) $x - a$ is a factor of $p(x)$, if $p(a) = 0$, and (ii) $p(a) = 0$, if $x - a$ is a factor of $p(x)$.

Proof: By the Remainder Theorem, $p(x) = (x - a)\, q(x) + p(a)$.

    (i)  If $p(a) = 0$, then $p(x) = (x - a)\, q(x)$, which shows that $x - a$ is a factor of $p(x)$.

    (ii) Since $x - a$ is a factor of $p(x)$, $p(x) = (x - a)\, g(x)$ for same polynomial $g(x)$.
         In this case, $p(a) = (a - a)\, g(a) = 0$.

**Example 11 :** Examine whether $x + 2$ is a factor of $x^3 + 3x^2 + 5x + 6$ and of $2x + 4$.

**Solution :** The zero of $x + 2$ is $-2$. Let $p(x) = x^3 + 3x^2 + 5x + 6$ and $s(x) = 2x + 4$

Then,           $p(-2) = (-2)^3 + 3(-2)^2 + 5(-2) + 6$

$$= -8 + 12 - 10 + 6$$

$$= 0$$

So, by the Factor Theorem, $x + 2$ is a factor of $x^3 + 3x^2 + 5x + 6$.

Again, $\qquad\qquad s(-2) = 2(-2) + 4 = 0$

So, $x + 2$ is a factor of $2x + 4$. In fact, you can check this without applying the Factor Theorem, since $2x + 4 = 2(x + 2)$.

**Example 12 :** Find the value of $k$, if $x - 1$ is a factor of $4x^3 + 3x^2 - 4x + k$.

**Solution :** As $x - 1$ is a factor of $p(x) = 4x^3 + 3x^2 - 4x + k$, $p(1) = 0$

Now, $\qquad\qquad p(1) = 4(1)^3 + 3(1)^2 - 4(1) + k$

So, $\qquad\qquad 4 + 3 - 4 + k = 0$

i.e., $\qquad\qquad k = -3$

We will now use the Factor Theorem to factorise some polynomials of degree 2 and 3. You are already familiar with the factorisation of a quadratic polynomial like $x^2 + lx + m$. You had factorised it by splitting the middle term $lx$ as $ax + bx$ so that $ab = m$. Then $x^2 + lx + m = (x + a)(x + b)$. We shall now try to factorise quadratic polynomials of the type $ax^2 + bx + c$, where $a \neq 0$ and $a, b, c$ are constants.

Factorisation of the polynomial $ax^2 + bx + c$ **by splitting the middle term** is as follows:

Let its factors be $(px + q)$ and $(rx + s)$. Then

$$ax^2 + bx + c = (px + q)(rx + s) = pr\, x^2 + (ps + qr)\, x + qs$$

Comparing the coefficients of $x^2$, we get $a = pr$.

Similarly, comparing the coefficients of $x$, we get $b = ps + qr$.

And, on comparing the constant terms, we get $c = qs$.

This shows us that $b$ is the sum of two numbers $ps$ and $qr$, whose product is $(ps)(qr) = (pr)(qs) = ac$.

Therefore, to factorise $ax^2 + bx + c$, we have to write $b$ as the sum of two numbers whose product is $ac$. This will be clear from Example 13.

**Example 13 :** Factorise $6x^2 + 17x + 5$ by splitting the middle term, and by using the Factor Theorem.

**Solution 1 :** (By splitting method) : If we can find two numbers $p$ and $q$ such that $p + q = 17$ and $pq = 6 \times 5 = 30$, then we can get the factors.

So, let us look for the pairs of factors of 30. Some are 1 and 30, 2 and 15, 3 and 10, 5 and 6. Of these pairs, 2 and 15 will give us $p + q = 17$.

So, $6x^2 + 17x + 5 = 6x^2 + (2 + 15)x + 5$

$$= 6x^2 + 2x + 15x + 5$$

$$= 2x(3x + 1) + 5(3x + 1)$$

$$= (3x + 1)(2x + 5)$$

**Solution 2** : (Using the Factor Theorem)

$6x^2 + 17x + 5 = 6\left(x^2 + \dfrac{17}{6}x + \dfrac{5}{6}\right) = 6\,p(x)$, say. If $a$ and $b$ are the zeroes of $p(x)$, then

$6x^2 + 17x + 5 = 6(x - a)(x - b)$. So, $ab = \dfrac{5}{6}$. Let us look at some possibilities for $a$ and

$b$. They could be $\pm\dfrac{1}{2}, \pm\dfrac{1}{3}, \pm\dfrac{5}{3}, \pm\dfrac{5}{2}, \pm 1$. Now, $p\left(\dfrac{1}{2}\right) = \dfrac{1}{4} + \dfrac{17}{6}\left(\dfrac{1}{2}\right) + \dfrac{5}{6} \neq 0$. But

$p\left(\dfrac{-1}{3}\right) = 0$. So, $\left(x + \dfrac{1}{3}\right)$ is a factor of $p(x)$. Similarly, by trial, you can find that

$\left(x + \dfrac{5}{2}\right)$ is a factor of $p(x)$.

Therefore,    $6x^2 + 17x + 5 = 6\left(x + \dfrac{1}{3}\right)\left(x + \dfrac{5}{2}\right)$

$$= 6\left(\dfrac{3x + 1}{3}\right)\left(\dfrac{2x + 5}{2}\right)$$

$$= (3x + 1)(2x + 5)$$

For the example above, the use of the splitting method appears more efficient. However, let us consider another example.

**Example 14** : Factorise $y^2 - 5y + 6$ by using the Factor Theorem.

**Solution** : Let $p(y) = y^2 - 5y + 6$. Now, if $p(y) = (y - a)(y - b)$, you know that the constant term will be $ab$. So, $ab = 6$. So, to look for the factors of $p(y)$, we look at the factors of 6.

The factors of 6 are 1, 2 and 3.

Now,  $p(2) = 2^2 - (5 \times 2) + 6 = 0$

So, $y - 2$ is a factor of $p(y)$.

Also, $p(3) = 3^2 - (5 \times 3) + 6 = 0$

So, $y - 3$ is also a factor of $y^2 - 5y + 6$.

Therefore, $y^2 - 5y + 6 = (y - 2)(y - 3)$

Note that $y^2 - 5y + 6$ can also be factorised by splitting the middle term $-5y$.

Now, let us consider factorising cubic polynomials. Here, the splitting method will not be appropriate to start with. We need to find at least one factor first, as you will see in the following example.

Example 15 : Factorise $x^3 - 23x^2 + 142x - 120$.

Solution : Let $p(x) = x^3 - 23x^2 + 142x - 120$

We shall now look for all the factors of $-120$. Some of these are $\pm 1, \pm 2, \pm 3,$

$\pm 4, \pm 5, \pm 6, \pm 8, \pm 10, \pm 12, \pm 15, \pm 20, \pm 24, \pm 30, \pm 60.$

By trial, we find that $p(1) = 0$. So $x - 1$ is a factor of $p(x)$.

Now we see that $x^3 - 23x^2 + 142x - 120 = x^3 - x^2 - 22x^2 + 22x + 120x - 120$

$$= x^2(x - 1) - 22x(x - 1) + 120(x - 1) \quad \text{(Why?)}$$

$$= (x - 1)(x^2 - 22x + 120) \quad \text{[Taking } (x - 1) \text{ common]}$$

We could have also got this by dividing $p(x)$ by $x - 1$.

Now $x^2 - 22x + 120$ can be factorised either by splitting the middle term or by using the Factor theorem. By splitting the middle term, we have:

$$x^2 - 22x + 120 = x^2 - 12x - 10x + 120$$

$$= x(x - 12) - 10(x - 12)$$

$$= (x - 12)(x - 10)$$

So,            $x^3 - 23x^2 - 142x - 120 = (x - 1)(x - 10)(x - 12)$

## EXERCISE 2.4

1. Determine which of the following polynomials has $(x + 1)$ a factor :

   (i) $x^3 + x^2 + x + 1$                    (ii) $x^4 + x^3 + x^2 + x + 1$

   (iii) $x^4 + 3x^3 + 3x^2 + x + 1$          (iv) $x^3 - x^2 - \left(2 + \sqrt{2}\right)x + \sqrt{2}$

2. Use the Factor Theorem to determine whether $g(x)$ is a factor of $p(x)$ in each of the following cases:

(i) $p(x) = 2x^3 + x^2 - 2x - 1, g(x) = x + 1$

(ii) $p(x) = x^3 + 3x^2 + 3x + 1, g(x) = x + 2$

(iii) $p(x) = x^3 - 4x^2 + x + 6, g(x) = x - 3$

**3.** Find the value of $k$, if $x - 1$ is a factor of $p(x)$ in each of the following cases:

(i)  $p(x) = x^2 + x + k$                     (ii)  $p(x) = 2x^2 + kx + \sqrt{2}$

(iii) $p(x) = kx^2 - \sqrt{2}\,x + 1$            (iv) $p(x) = kx^2 - 3x + k$

**4.** Factorise :

(i)  $12x^2 - 7x + 1$                          (ii) $2x^2 + 7x + 3$

(iii) $6x^2 + 5x - 6$                          (iv) $3x^2 - x - 4$

**5.** Factorise :

(i)  $x^3 - 2x^2 - x + 2$                       (ii) $x^3 - 3x^2 - 9x - 5$

(iii) $x^3 + 13x^2 + 32x + 20$                  (iv) $2y^3 + y^2 - 2y - 1$

## 2.6 Algebraic Identities

From your earlier classes, you may recall that an algebraic identity is an algebraic equation that is true for all values of the variables occurring in it. You have studied the following algebraic identities in earlier classes:

**Identity I**   : $(x + y)^2 = x^2 + 2xy + y^2$

**Identity II**  : $(x - y)^2 = x^2 - 2xy + y^2$

**Identity III** : $x^2 - y^2 = (x + y)(x - y)$

**Identity IV**  : $(x + a)(x + b) = x^2 + (a + b)x + ab$

You must have also used some of these algebraic identities to factorise the algebraic expressions. You can also see their utility in computations.

**Example 16 :** Find the following products using appropriate identities:

(i) $(x + 3)(x + 3)$        (ii) $(x - 3)(x + 5)$

**Solution :** (i) Here we can use Identity I : $(x + y)^2 = x^2 + 2xy + y^2$. Putting $y = 3$ in it, we get

$$(x + 3)(x + 3) = (x + 3)^2 = x^2 + 2(x)(3) + (3)^2$$
$$= x^2 + 6x + 9$$

(ii) Using Identity IV above, i.e., $(x + a)(x + b) = x^2 + (a + b)x + ab$, we have

$$(x - 3)(x + 5) = x^2 + (-3 + 5)x + (-3)(5)$$
$$= x^2 + 2x - 15$$

**Example 17 :** Evaluate $105 \times 106$ without multiplying directly.

**Solution :**    $105 \times 106 = (100 + 5) \times (100 + 6)$

$$= (100)^2 + (5 + 6)(100) + (5 \times 6), \text{ using Identity IV}$$

$$= 10000 + 1100 + 30$$

$$= 11130$$

You have seen some uses of the identities listed above in finding the product of some given expressions. These identities are useful in factorisation of algebraic expressions also, as you can see in the following examples.

**Example 18 :** Factorise:

(i) $49a^2 + 70ab + 25b^2$     (ii) $\dfrac{25}{4}x^2 - \dfrac{y^2}{9}$

**Solution :** (i) Here you can see that

$$49a^2 = (7a)^2, \ 25b^2 = (5b)^2, \ 70ab = 2(7a)(5b)$$

Comparing the given expression with $x^2 + 2xy + y^2$, we observe that $x = 7a$ and $y = 5b$.

Using Identity I, we get

$$49a^2 + 70ab + 25b^2 = (7a + 5b)^2 = (7a + 5b)(7a + 5b)$$

(ii) We have $\dfrac{25}{4}x^2 - \dfrac{y^2}{9} = \left(\dfrac{5}{2}x\right)^2 - \left(\dfrac{y}{3}\right)^2$

Now comparing it with Identity III, we get

$$\frac{25}{4}x^2 - \frac{y^2}{9} = \left(\frac{5}{2}x\right)^2 - \left(\frac{y}{3}\right)^2$$

$$= \left(\frac{5}{2}x + \frac{y}{3}\right)\left(\frac{5}{2}x - \frac{y}{3}\right)$$

So far, all our identities involved products of binomials. Let us now extend the Identity I to a trinomial $x + y + z$. We shall compute $(x + y + z)^2$ by using Identity I.

Let $x + y = t$. Then,

$$(x + y + z)^2 = (t + z)^2$$

$$= t^2 + 2tz + t^2 \qquad\qquad \text{(Using Identity I)}$$

$$= (x + y)^2 + 2(x + y)z + z^2 \qquad \text{(Substituting the value of } t)$$

$$= x^2 + 2xy + y^2 + 2xz + 2yz + z^2 \qquad \text{(Using Identity I)}$$
$$= x^2 + y^2 + z^2 + 2xy + 2yz + 2zx \quad \text{(Rearranging the terms)}$$

So, we get the following identity:

**Identity V : $(x + y + z)^2 = x^2 + y^2 + z^2 + 2xy + 2yz + 2zx$**

**Remark :** We call the right hand side expression **the expanded form** of the left hand side expression. Note that the expansion of $(x + y + z)^2$ consists of three square terms and three product terms.

**Example 19 :** Write $(3a + 4b + 5c)^2$ in expanded form.

**Solution :** Comparing the given expression with $(x + y + z)^2$, we find that
$$x = 3a, \ y = 4b \text{ and } z = 5c.$$

Therefore, using Identity V, we have
$$(3a + 4b + 5c)^2 = (3a)^2 + (4b)^2 + (5c)^2 + 2(3a)(4b) + 2(4b)(5c) + 2(5c)(3a)$$
$$= 9a^2 + 16b^2 + 25c^2 + 24ab + 40bc + 30ac$$

**Example 20 :** Expand $(4a - 2b - 3c)^2$.

**Solution :** Using Identity V, we have
$$(4a - 2b - 3c)^2 = [4a + (-2b) + (-3c)]^2$$
$$= (4a)^2 + (-2b)^2 + (-3c)^2 + 2(4a)(-2b) + 2(-2b)(-3c) + 2(-3c)(4a)$$
$$= 16a^2 + 4b^2 + 9c^2 - 16ab + 12bc - 24ac$$

**Example 21 :** Factorise $4x^2 + y^2 + z^2 - 4xy - 2yz + 4xz$.

**Solution :** We have $4x^2 + y^2 + z^2 - 4xy - 2yz + 4xz = (2x)^2 + (-y)^2 + (z)^2 + 2(2x)(-y)$
$$+ 2(-y)(z) + 2(2x)(z)$$
$$= [2x + (-y) + z]^2 \qquad \text{(Using Identity V)}$$
$$= (2x - y + z)^2 = (2x - y + z)(2x - y + z)$$

So far, we have dealt with identities involving second degree terms. Now let us extend Identity I to compute $(x + y)^3$. We have:
$$(x + y)^3 = (x + y)(x + y)^2$$
$$= (x + y)(x^2 + 2xy + y^2)$$
$$= x(x^2 + 2xy + y^2) + y(x^2 + 2xy + y^2)$$
$$= x^3 + 2x^2y + xy^2 + x^2y + 2xy^2 + y^3$$
$$= x^3 + 3x^2y + 3xy^2 + y^3$$
$$= x^3 + y^3 + 3xy(x + y)$$

So, we get the following identity:

**Identity VI :** $(x + y)^3 = x^3 + y^3 + 3xy(x + y)$

Also, by replacing $y$ by $-y$ in the Identity VI, we get

**Identity VII :** $(x - y)^3 = x^3 - y^3 - 3xy(x - y)$
$$= x^3 - 3x^2y + 3xy^2 - y^3$$

**Example 22 :** Write the following cubes in the expanded form:

$\qquad$ (i) $(3a + 4b)^3$ $\qquad$ (ii) $(5p - 3q)^3$

**Solution :** (i) Comparing the given expression with $(x + y)^3$, we find that
$$x = 3a \text{ and } y = 4b.$$

So, using Identity VI, we have:
$$(3a + 4b)^3 = (3a)^3 + (4b)^3 + 3(3a)(4b)(3a + 4b)$$
$$= 27a^3 + 64b^3 + 108a^2b + 144ab^2$$

(ii) Comparing the given expression with $(x - y)^3$, we find that
$$x = 5p, y = 3q.$$

So, using Identity VII, we have:
$$(5p - 3q)^3 = (5p)^3 - (3q)^3 - 3(5p)(3q)(5p - 3q)$$
$$= 125p^3 - 27q^3 - 225p^2q + 135pq^2$$

**Example 23 :** Evaluate each of the following using suitable identities:

$\qquad$ (i) $(104)^3$ $\qquad$ (ii) $(999)^3$

**Solution :** (i) We have
$$(104)^3 = (100 + 4)^3$$
$$= (100)^3 + (4)^3 + 3(100)(4)(100 + 4)$$
$$\text{(Using Identity VI)}$$
$$= 1000000 + 64 + 124800$$
$$= 1124864$$

(ii) We have
$$(999)^3 = (1000 - 1)^3$$
$$= (1000)^3 - (1)^3 - 3(1000)(1)(1000 - 1)$$
$$\text{(Using Identity VII)}$$
$$= 1000000000 - 1 - 2997000$$
$$= 997002999$$

**Example 24 :** Factorise $8x^3 + 27y^3 + 36x^2y + 54xy^2$

**Solution :** The given expression can be written as

$$(2x)^3 + (3y)^3 + 3(4x^2)(3y) + 3(2x)(9y^2)$$
$$= (2x)^3 + (3y)^3 + 3(2x)^2(3y) + 3(2x)(3y)^2$$
$$= (2x + 3y)^3 \qquad \text{(Using Identity VI)}$$
$$= (2x + 3y)(2x + 3y)(2x + 3y)$$

Now consider $(x + y + z)(x^2 + y^2 + z^2 - xy - yz - zx)$

On expanding, we get the product as

$$x(x^2 + y^2 + z^2 - xy - yz - zx) + y(x^2 + y^2 + z^2 - xy - yz - zx)$$
$$+ z(x^2 + y^2 + z^2 - xy - yz - zx) = x^3 + xy^2 + xz^2 - x^2y - xyz - zx^2 + x^2y$$
$$+ y^3 + yz^2 - xy^2 - y^2z - xyz + x^2z + y^2z + z^3 - xyz - yz^2 - xz^2$$
$$= x^3 + y^3 + z^3 - 3xyz \qquad \text{(On simplification)}$$

So, we obtain the following identity:

**Identity VIII : $x^3 + y^3 + z^3 - 3xyz = (x + y + z)(x^2 + y^2 + z^2 - xy - yz - zx)$**

**Example 25 :** Factorise : $8x^3 + y^3 + 27z^3 - 18xyz$

**Solution :** Here, we have

$$8x^3 + y^3 + 27z^3 - 18xyz$$
$$= (2x)^3 + y^3 + (3z)^3 - 3(2x)(y)(3z)$$
$$= (2x + y + 3z)[(2x)^2 + y^2 + (3z)^2 - (2x)(y) - (y)(3z) - (2x)(3z)]$$
$$= (2x + y + 3z)(4x^2 + y^2 + 9z^2 - 2xy - 3yz - 6xz)$$

## EXERCISE 2.5

1.  Use suitable identities to find the following products:

    (i)  $(x + 4)(x + 10)$ 　　　　(ii) $(x + 8)(x - 10)$ 　　　(iii) $(3x + 4)(3x - 5)$

    (iv) $(y^2 + \dfrac{3}{2})(y^2 - \dfrac{3}{2})$ 　　　　(v) $(3 - 2x)(3 + 2x)$

2.  Evaluate the following products without multiplying directly:

    (i)  $103 \times 107$ 　　　　(ii) $95 \times 96$ 　　　(iii) $104 \times 96$

3.  Factorise the following using appropriate identities:

    (i)  $9x^2 + 6xy + y^2$ 　　　　(ii) $4y^2 - 4y + 1$ 　　　(iii) $x^2 - \dfrac{y^2}{100}$

POLYNOMIALS

4. Expand each of the following, using suitable identities:

   (i) $(x + 2y + 4z)^2$      (ii) $(2x - y + z)^2$      (iii) $(-2x + 3y + 2z)^2$

   (iv) $(3a - 7b - c)^2$      (v) $(-2x + 5y - 3z)^2$      (vi) $\left[\dfrac{1}{4}a - \dfrac{1}{2}b + 1\right]^2$

5. Factorise:

   (i) $4x^2 + 9y^2 + 16z^2 + 12xy - 24yz - 16xz$

   (ii) $2x^2 + y^2 + 8z^2 - 2\sqrt{2}\,xy + 4\sqrt{2}\,yz - 8xz$

6. Write the following cubes in expanded form:

   (i) $(2x + 1)^3$      (ii) $(2a - 3b)^3$      (iii) $\left[\dfrac{3}{2}x + 1\right]^3$      (iv) $\left[x - \dfrac{2}{3}y\right]^3$

7. Evaluate the following using suitable identities:

   (i) $(99)^3$      (ii) $(102)^3$      (iii) $(998)^3$

8. Factorise each of the following:

   (i) $8a^3 + b^3 + 12a^2b + 6ab^2$      (ii) $8a^3 - b^3 - 12a^2b + 6ab^2$

   (iii) $27 - 125a^3 - 135a + 225a^2$      (iv) $64a^3 - 27b^3 - 144a^2b + 108ab^2$

   (v) $27p^3 - \dfrac{1}{216} - \dfrac{9}{2}p^2 + \dfrac{1}{4}p$

9. Verify : (i) $x^3 + y^3 = (x + y)(x^2 - xy + y^2)$      (ii) $x^3 - y^3 = (x - y)(x^2 + xy + y^2)$

10. Factorise each of the following:

    (i) $27y^3 + 125z^3$      (ii) $64m^3 - 343n^3$

    [**Hint :** See Question 9.]

11. Factorise : $27x^3 + y^3 + z^3 - 9xyz$

12. Verify that $x^3 + y^3 + z^3 - 3xyz = \dfrac{1}{2}(x + y + z)\left[(x - y)^2 + (y - z)^2 + (z - x)^2\right]$

13. If $x + y + z = 0$, show that $x^3 + y^3 + z^3 = 3xyz$.

14. Without actually calculating the cubes, find the value of each of the following:

    (i) $(-12)^3 + (7)^3 + (5)^3$

    (ii) $(28)^3 + (-15)^3 + (-13)^3$

15. Give possible expressions for the length and breadth of each of the following rectangles, in which their areas are given:

   | Area : $25a^2 - 35a + 12$ | Area : $35y^2 + 13y - 12$ |
   |---|---|
   | (i) | (ii) |

**16.** What are the possible expressions for the dimensions of the cuboids whose volumes are given below?

| | |
|---|---|
| Volume : $3x^2 - 12x$. | Volume : $12ky^2 + 8ky - 20k$ |
| (i) | (ii) |

## 2.7 Summary

In this chapter, you have studied the following points:

1. A *polynomial p(x)* in one variable $x$ is an algebraic expression in $x$ of the form

$$p(x) = a_n x^n + a_{n-1} x^{n-1} + \ldots + a_2 x^2 + a_1 x + a_0,$$

where $a_0, a_1, a_2, \ldots, a_n$ are constants and $a_n \neq 0$.

$a_0, a_1, a_2, \ldots, a_n$ are respectively the *coefficients* of $x^0, x, x^2, \ldots, x^n$, and $n$ is called the *degree of the polynomial*. Each of $a_n x^n, a_{n-1} x^{n-1}, \ldots, a_0$, with $a_n \neq 0$, is called a *term* of the polynomial $p(x)$.

2. A polynomial of one term is called a monomial.

3. A polynomial of two terms is called a binomial.

4. A polynomial of three terms is called a trinomial.

5. A polynomial of degree one is called a linear polynomial.

6. A polynomial of degree two is called a quadratic polynomial.

7. A polynomial of degree three is called a cubic polynomial.

8. A real number '$a$' is a *zero* of a polynomial $p(x)$ if $p(a) = 0$. In this case, $a$ is also called a *root* of the equation $p(x) = 0$.

9. Every linear polynomial in one variable has a unique zero, a non-zero constant polynomial has no zero, and every real number is a zero of the zero polynomial.

10. Remainder Theorem : If $p(x)$ is any polynomial of degree greater than or equal to 1 and $p(x)$ is divided by the linear polynomial $x - a$, then the remainder is $p(a)$.

11. Factor Theorem : $x - a$ is a factor of the polynomial $p(x)$, if $p(a) = 0$. Also, if $x - a$ is a factor of $p(x)$, then $p(a) = 0$.

12. $(x + y + z)^2 = x^2 + y^2 + z^2 + 2xy + 2yz + 2zx$

13. $(x + y)^3 = x^3 + y^3 + 3xy(x + y)$

14. $(x - y)^3 = x^3 - y^3 - 3xy(x - y)$

15. $x^3 + y^3 + z^3 - 3xyz = (x + y + z)(x^2 + y^2 + z^2 - xy - yz - zx)$

# CHAPTER 3

# COORDINATE GEOMETRY

What's the good of Mercator's North Poles and Equators, Tropics, Zones and Meridian Lines?' So the Bellman would cry; and crew would reply ' They are merely conventional signs!'

LEWIS CARROLL, *The Hunting of the Snark*

## 3.1 Introduction

You have already studied how to locate a point on a number line. You also know how to describe the position of a point on the line. There are many other situations, in which to find a point we are required to describe its position with reference to more than one line. For example, consider the following situations:

**I.** In Fig. 3.1, there is a main road running in the East-West direction and streets with numbering from West to East. Also, on each street, house numbers are marked. To look for a friend's house here, is it enough to know only one reference point? For instance, if we only know that she lives on Street 2, will we be able to find her house easily? Not as easily as when we know two pieces of information about it, namely, the number of the street on which it is situated, and the house number. If we want to reach the house which is situated in the 2nd street and has the number 5, first of all we would identify the 2nd street and then the house numbered 5 on it. In Fig. 3.1, H shows the location of the house. Similarly, P shows the location of the house corresponding to Street number 7 and House number 4.

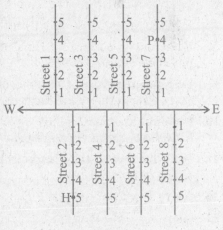

Fig. 3.1

**II.** Suppose you put a dot on a sheet of paper [Fig.3.2 (a)]. If we ask you to tell us the position of the dot on the paper, how will you do this? Perhaps you will try in some such manner: "The dot is in the upper half of the paper", or "It is near the left edge of the paper", or "It is very near the left hand upper corner of the sheet". Do any of these statements fix the position of the dot precisely? No! But, if you say " The dot is nearly 5 cm away from the left edge of the paper", it helps to give some idea but still does not fix the position of the dot. A little thought might enable you to say that the dot is also at a distance of 9 cm above the bottom line. We now know exactly where the dot is!

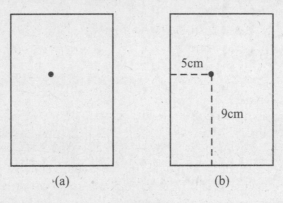

(a)                                                        (b)

**Fig. 3.2**

For this purpose, we fixed the position of the dot by specifying its distances from two fixed lines, the left edge of the paper and the bottom line of the paper [Fig.3.2 (b)]. In other words, we need **two** independent informations for finding the position of the dot.

Now, perform the following classroom activity known as 'Seating Plan'.

**Activity 1 (Seating Plan) :** Draw a plan of the seating in your classroom, pushing all the desks together. Represent each desk by a square. In each square, write the name of the student occupying the desk, which the square represents. Position of each student in the classroom is described precisely by using two independent informations:

(i)   the column in which she or he sits,

(ii)  the row in which she or he sits.

If you are sitting on the desk lying in the 5th column and 3rd row (represented by the shaded square in Fig. 3.3), your position could be written as (5, 3), first writing the column number, and then the row number. Is this the same as (3, 5)? Write down the names and positions of other students in your class. For example, if Sonia is sitting in the 4th column and 1st row, write S(4,1). The teacher's desk is not part of your seating plan. We are treating the teacher just as an observer.

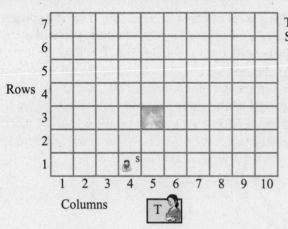

T shows teacher's desk
S shows Sonia's desk

**Fig. 3.3**

In the discussion above, you observe that position of any object lying in a plane can be represented with the help of two perpendicular lines. In case of 'dot', we require distance of the dot from bottom line as well as from left edge of the paper. In case of seating plan, we require the number of the column and that of the row. This simple idea has far reaching consequences, and has given rise to a very important branch of Mathematics known as *Coordinate Geometry*. In this chapter, we aim to introduce some basic concepts of coordinate geometry. You will study more about these in your higher classes. This study was initially developed by the French philosopher and mathematician *René Déscartes*.

René Déscartes, the great French mathematician of the seventeenth century, liked to lie in bed and think! One day, when resting in bed, he solved the problem of describing the position of a point in a plane. His method was a development of the older idea of latitude and longitude. In honour of Déscartes, the system used for describing the position of a point in a plane is also known as the *Cartesian system*.

René Déscartes (1596 -1650)
Fig. 3.4

## EXERCISE 3.1

1. How will you describe the position of a table lamp on your study table to another person?

2. **(Street Plan)** : A city has two main roads which cross each other at the centre of the city. These two roads are along the North-South direction and East-West direction.

All the other streets of the city run parallel to these roads and are 200 m apart. There are 5 streets in each direction. Using 1cm = 200 m, draw a model of the city on your notebook. Represent the roads/streets by single lines.

There are many cross- streets in your model. A particular cross-street is made by two streets, one running in the North - South direction and another in the East - West direction. Each cross street is referred to in the following manner : If the $2^{nd}$ street running in the North - South direction and $5^{th}$ in the East - West direction meet at some crossing, then we will call this cross-street (2, 5). Using this convention, find:

(i)   how many cross - streets can be referred to as (4, 3).

(ii)  how many cross - streets can be referred to as (3, 4).

## 3.2 Cartesian System

You have studied the *number line* in the chapter on 'Number System'. On the number line, distances from a fixed point are marked in equal units positively in one direction and negatively in the other. The point from which the distances are marked is called the *origin*. We use the number line to represent the numbers by marking points on a line at equal distances. If one unit distance represents the number '1', then 3 units distance represents the number '3', '0' being at the origin. The point in the positive direction at a distance $r$ from the origin represents the number $r$. The point in the negative direction at a distance $r$ from the origin represents the number $-r$. Locations of different numbers on the number line are shown in Fig. 3.5.

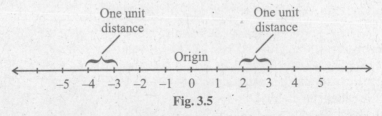

Fig. 3.5

Descartes invented the idea of placing two such lines perpendicular to each other on a plane, and locating points on the plane by referring them to these lines. The perpendicular lines may be in any direction such as in Fig.3.6. But, when we choose

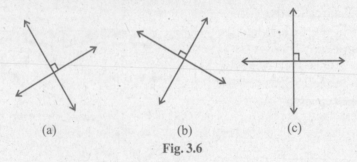

(a)                    (b)                    (c)

Fig. 3.6

these two lines to locate a point in a plane *in this chapter*, one line will be horizontal and the other will be vertical, as in Fig. 3.6(c).

These lines are actually obtained as follows : Take two number lines, calling them X′X and Y′Y. Place X′X horizontal [as in Fig. 3.7(a)] and write the numbers on it just as written on the number line. We do the same thing with Y′Y except that Y′Y is vertical, not horizontal [Fig. 3.7(b)].

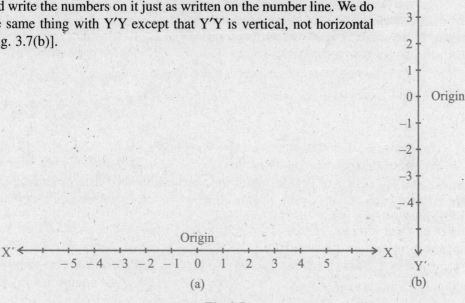

Fig. 3.7

Combine both the lines in such a way that the two lines cross each other at their zeroes, or origins (Fig. 3.8). The horizontal line X′X is called the *x* - axis and the vertical line Y′Y is called the *y* - axis. The point where X′X and Y′Y cross is called the **origin**, and is denoted by O. Since the positive numbers lie on the directions OX and OY, OX and OY are called the **positive directions** of the *x* - axis and the *y* - axis, respectively. Similarly, OX′ and OY′ are called the **negative directions** of the *x* - axis and the *y* - axis, respectively.

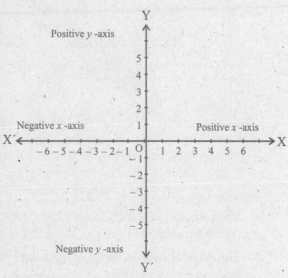

Fig. 3.8

You observe that the axes (plural of the word 'axis') divide the plane into four parts. These four parts are called the *quadrants* (one fourth part), numbered I, II, III and IV anticlockwise from OX (see Fig.3.9). So, the plane consists of the axes and these quadrants. We call the plane, the *Cartesian plane*, or the *coordinate plane*, or the *xy-plane*. The axes are called the *coordinate axes*.

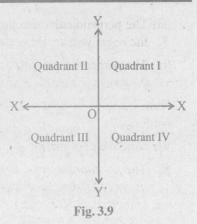

Fig. 3.9

Now, let us see why this system is so basic to mathematics, and how it is useful. Consider the following diagram where the axes are drawn on graph paper. Let us see the distances of the points P and Q from the axes. For this, we draw perpendiculars PM on the *x* - axis and PN on the *y* - axis. Similarly, we draw perpendiculars QR and QS as shown in Fig. 3.10.

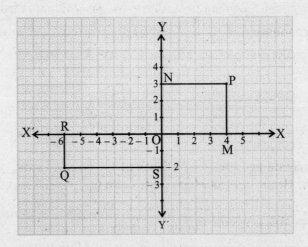

Fig.3.10

You find that

(i) The perpendicular distance of the point P from the *y* - axis measured along the positive direction of the *x* - axis is PN = OM = 4 units.

(ii) The perpendicular distance of the point P from the *x* - axis measured along the positive direction of the *y* - axis is PM = ON = 3 units.

(iii) The perpendicular distance of the point Q from the $y$ - axis measured along the negative direction of the $x$ - axis is OR = SQ = 6 units.

(iv) The perpendicular distance of the point Q from the $x$ - axis measured along the negative direction of the $y$ - axis is OS = RQ = 2 units.

Now, using these distances, how can we describe the points so that there is no confusion?

We write the coordinates of a point, using the following conventions:

(i) The $x$ - *coordinate* of a point is its perpendicular distance from the $y$ - axis measured along the $x$ -axis (positive along the positive direction of the $x$ - axis and negative along the negative direction of the $x$ - axis). For the point P, it is + 4 and for Q, it is – 6. The $x$ - coordinate is also called the *abscissa*.

(ii) The $y$ - *coordinate* of a point is its perpendicular distance from the $x$ - axis measured along the $y$ - axis (positive along the positive direction of the $y$ - axis and negative along the negative direction of the $y$ - axis). For the point P, it is + 3 and for Q, it is –2. The $y$ - coordinate is also called the *ordinate*.

(iii) In stating the coordinates of a point in the coordinate plane, the $x$ - coordinate comes first, and then the $y$ - coordinate. We place the coordinates in brackets.

Hence, the coordinates of P are (4, 3) and the coordinates of Q are (– 6, – 2).

Note that the coordinates describe a point in the plane *uniquely*. (3, 4) is not the same as (4, 3).

**Example 1 :** See Fig. 3.11 and complete the following statements:

(i)  The abscissa and the ordinate of the point B are _ _ _ and _ _ _, respectively. Hence, the coordinates of B are (_ _, _ _).

(ii)  The $x$-coordinate and the $y$-coordinate of the point M are _ _ _ and _ _ _, respectively. Hence, the coordinates of M are (_ _, _ _).

(iii)  The $x$-coordinate and the $y$-coordinate of the point L are _ _ _ and _ _ _, respectively. Hence, the coordinates of L are (_ _, _ _).

(iv)  The $x$-coordinate and the $y$-coordinate of the point S are _ _ _ and _ _ _, respectively. Hence, the coordinates of S are (_ _, _ _).

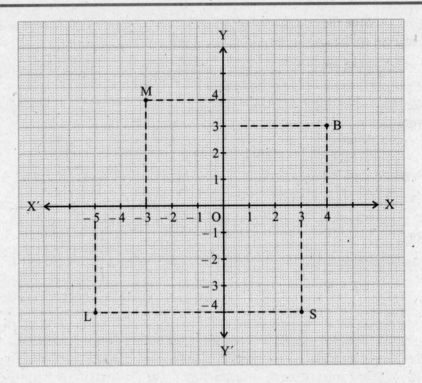

Fig. 3.11

**Solution :** (i) Since the distance of the point B from the $y$ - axis is 4 units, the $x$ - coordinate or abscissa of the point B is 4. The distance of the point B from the $x$ - axis is 3 units; therefore, the $y$ - coordinate, i.e., the ordinate, of the point B is 3. Hence, the coordinates of the point B are (4, 3).

As in (i) above :

(ii) The $x$ - coordinate and the $y$ - coordinate of the point M are –3 and 4, respectively. Hence, the coordinates of the point M are (–3, 4).

(iii) The $x$ - coordinate and the $y$ - coordinate of the point L are –5 and – 4, respectively. Hence, the coordinates of the point L are (–5, – 4).

(iv) The $x$ - coordinate and the $y$- coordinate of the point S are 3 and – 4, respectively. Hence, the coordinates of the point S are (3, – 4).

**Example 2 :** Write the coordinates of the points marked on the axes in Fig. 3.12.

**Solution :** You can see that :

(i) The point A is at a distance of + 4 units from the y - axis and at a distance zero from the x - axis. Therefore, the x - coordinate of A is 4 and the y - coordinate is 0. Hence, the coordinates of A are (4, 0).

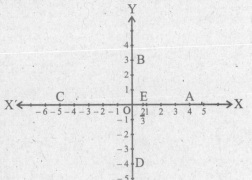

Fig. 3.12

(ii) The coordinates of B are (0, 3). Why?

(iii) The coordinates of C are (– 5, 0). Why?

(iv) The coordinates of D are (0, – 4). Why?

(v) The coordinates of E are $\left(\dfrac{2}{3}, 0\right)$. Why?

Since every point on the x - axis has no distance (zero distance) from the x - axis, therefore, the y - coordinate of every point lying on the x - axis is always zero. Thus, the coordinates of any point on the x - axis are of the form (x, 0), where x is the distance of the point from the y - axis. Similarly, the coordinates of any point on the y - axis are of the form (0, y), where y is the distance of the point from the x - axis. Why? ·

What are the coordinates of the **origin O**? *It has zero distance from both the axes so that its abscissa and ordinate are both zero. Therefore, the coordinates of the origin are* **(0, 0)**.

In the examples above, you may have observed the following relationship between the signs of the coordinates of a point and the quadrant of a point in which it lies.

(i)    If a point is in the 1st quadrant, then the point will be in the form (+, +), since the 1st quadrant is enclosed by the positive x - axis and the positive y - axis.

(ii)   If a point is in the 2nd quadrant, then the point will be in the form (–, +), since the 2nd quadrant is enclosed by the negative x - axis and the positive y - axis.

(iii)  If a point is in the 3rd quadrant, then the point will be in the form (–, –), since the 3rd quadrant is enclosed by the negative x - axis and the negative y - axis.

(iv)  If a point is in the 4th quadrant, then the point will be in the form (+, –), since the 4th quadrant is enclosed by the positive x - axis and the negative y - axis (see Fig. 3.13).

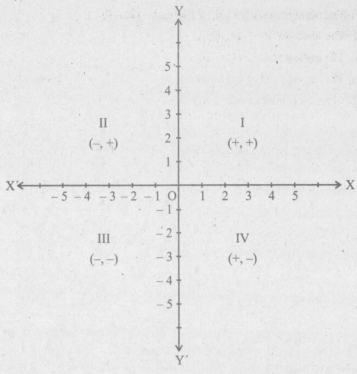

Fig. 3.13

**Remark :** The system we have discussed above for describing a point in a plane is only a convention, which is accepted all over the world. The system could also have been, for example, the ordinate first, and the abscissa second. However, the whole world sticks to the system we have described to avoid any confusion.

## EXERCISE 3.2

1.  Write the answer of each of the following questions:

    (i)   What is the name of horizontal and the vertical lines drawn to determine the position of any point in the Cartesian plane?

    (ii)  What is the name of each part of the plane formed by these two lines?

    (iii) Write the name of the point where these two lines intersect.

2.  See Fig.3.14, and write the following:

    (i)   The coordinates of B.

    (ii)  The coordinates of C.

    (iii) The point identified by the coordinates (–3, –5).

(iv)  The point identified by the coordinates (2, – 4).

(v)   The abscissa of the point D.

(vi)  The ordinate of the point H.

(vii) The coordinates of the point L.

(viii) The coordinates of the point M.

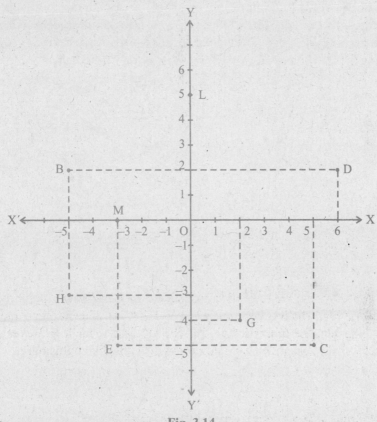

Fig. 3.14

## 3.3 Plotting a Point in the Plane if its Coordinates are Given

Uptil now we have drawn the points for you, and asked you to give their coordinates. Now we will show you how we place these points in the plane if we know its coordinates. We call this process "plotting the point".

Let the coordinates of a point be (3, 5). We want to plot this point in the coordinate plane. We draw the coordinate axes, and choose our units such that one centimetre represents one unit on both the axes. The coordinates of the point (3, 5) tell us that the distance of this point from the $y$ - axis along the positive $x$ - axis is 3 units and the distance of the point from the $x$ - axis along the positive $y$ - axis is 5 units. Starting from the origin O, we count 3 units on the positive $x$ - axis and mark the corresponding point as A. Now, starting from A, we move in the positive direction of the $y$ - axis and count 5 units and mark the corresponding point as P (see Fig.3.15). You see that the distance of P from the $y$ - axis is 3 units and from the $x$ - axis is 5 units. Hence, P is the position of the point. Note that P lies in the 1st quadrant, since both the coordinates of P are positive. Similarly, you can plot the point Q $(5, -4)$ in the coordinate plane. The distance of Q from the $x$ - axis is 4 units along the negative $y$ - axis, so that its $y$ - coordinate is $-4$ (see Fig.3.15). The point Q lies in the 4th quadrant. Why?

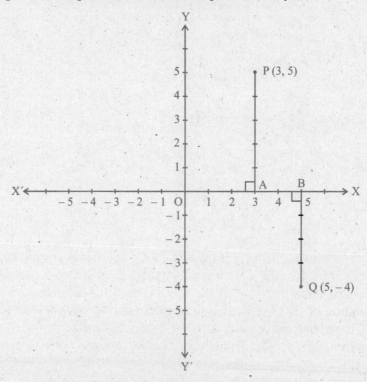

Fig. 3.15

**Example 3 :** Locate the points $(5, 0)$, $(0, 5)$, $(2, 5)$, $(5, 2)$, $(-3, 5)$, $(-3, -5)$, $(5, -3)$ and $(6, 1)$ in the Cartesian plane.

**Solution :** Taking 1cm = 1unit, we draw the $x$ - axis and the $y$ - axis. The positions of the points are shown by dots in Fig.3.16.

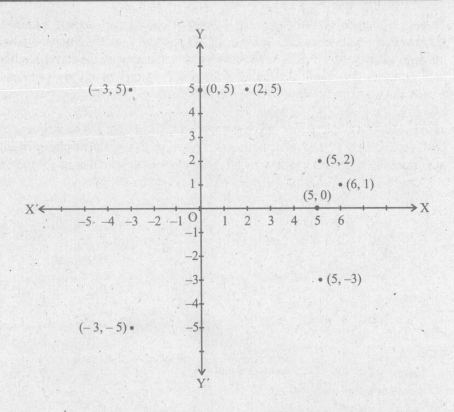

**Fig. 3.16**

**Note :** In the example above, you see that (5, 0) and (0, 5) are not at the same position. Similarly, (5, 2) and (2, 5) are at different positions. Also, (–3, 5) and (5, –3) are at different positions. By taking several such examples, you will find that, if *x ≠ y*, **then the position of (x, y) in the Cartesian plane is different from the position of (y, x).** So, if we interchange the coordinates *x* and *y*, the position of (*y*, *x*) will differ from the position of (*x*, *y*). This means that the order of *x* and *y* is important in (*x*, *y*). Therefore, (*x*, *y*) is called an ordered pair. The ordered pair (*x*, *y*) ≠ ordered pair (*y*, *x*), if *x ≠ y*. Also (*x*, *y*) = (*y*, *x*), if *x* = *y*.

**Example 4 :** Plot the following ordered pairs (*x*, *y*) of numbers as points in the Cartesian plane. Use the scale 1cm = 1 unit on the axes.

| *x* | – 3 | 0 | – 1 | 4 | 2 |
|---|---|---|---|---|---|
| *y* | 7 | –3.5 | – 3 | 4 | – 3 |

**Solution :** The pairs of numbers given in the table can be represented by the points $(-3, 7)$, $(0, -3.5)$, $(-1, -3)$, $(4, 4)$ and $(2, -3)$. The locations of the points are shown by dots in Fig.3.17.

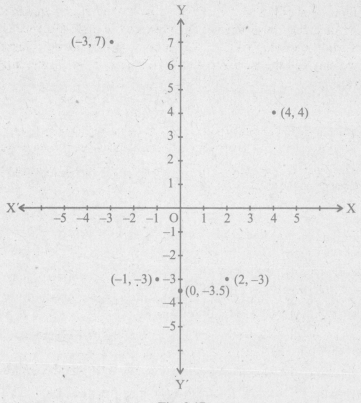

Fig. 3.17

**Activity 2 :** *A game for two persons* (Requirements: two counters or coins, graph paper, two dice of different colours, say red and green):

Place each counter at $(0, 0)$. Each player throws two dice simultaneously. When the first player does so, suppose the red die shows 3 and the green one shows 1. So, she moves her counter to $(3, 1)$. Similarly, if the second player throws 2 on the red and 4 on the green, she moves her counter to $(2, 4)$. On the second throw, if the first player throws 1 on the red and 4 on the green, she moves her counter from $(3, 1)$ to $(3 + 1, 1 + 4)$, that is, adding 1 to the $x$ - coordinate and 4 to the $y$ - coordinate of $(3, 1)$.

The purpose of the game is to arrive first at $(10, 10)$ without overshooting, i.e., neither the abscissa nor the ordinate can be greater than 10. Also, a counter should not coincide with the position held by another counter. For example, if the first player's counter moves on to a point already occupied by the counter of the second player, then the second player's counter goes to (0, 0). If a move is not possible without overshooting, the player misses that turn. You can extend this game to play with more friends.

**Remark :** Plotting of points in the Cartesian plane can be compared to some extent with drawing of graphs in different situations such as Time-Distance Graph, Side-Perimeter Graph, etc which you have come across in earlier classes. In such situations, we may call the axes, $t$-axis, $d$-axis, $s$-axis or $p$-axis, etc. in place of the $x$ and $y$ axes.

## EXERCISE 3.3

1. In which quadrant or on which axis do each of the points $(-2, 4)$, $(3, -1)$, $(-1, 0)$, $(1, 2)$ and $(-3, -5)$ lie? Verify your answer by locating them on the Cartesian plane.

2. Plot the points $(x, y)$ given in the following table on the plane, choosing suitable units of distance on the axes.

| x | − 2 | −1 | 0 | 1 | 3 |
|---|-----|-----|-----|-----|-----|
| y | 8 | 7 | − 1.25 | 3 | − 1 |

## 3.4 Summary

In this chapter, you have studied the following points :

1. To locate the position of an object or a point in a plane, we require two perpendicular lines. One of them is horizontal, and the other is vertical.

2. The plane is called the Cartesian, or coordinate plane and the lines are called the coordinate axes.

3. The horizontal line is called the $x$-axis, and the vertical line is called the $y$-axis.

4. The coordinate axes divide the plane into four parts called quadrants.

5. The point of intersection of the axes is called the origin.

6. The distance of a point from the $y$-axis is called its $x$-coordinate, or abscissa, and the distance of the point from the $x$-axis is called its $y$-coordinate, or ordinate.

7. If the abscissa of a point is $x$ and the ordinate is $y$, then $(x, y)$ are called the coordinates of the point.

8. The coordinates of a point on the $x$-axis are of the form $(x, 0)$ and that of the point on the $y$-axis are $(0, y)$.

9. The coordinates of the origin are $(0, 0)$.

10. The coordinates of a point are of the form $(+, +)$ in the first quadrant, $(-, +)$ in the second quadrant, $(-, -)$ in the third quadrant and $(+, -)$ in the fourth quadrant, where + denotes a positive real number and − denotes a negative real number.

11. If $x \neq y$, then $(x, y) \neq (y, x)$, and $(x, y) = (y, x)$, if $x = y$.

# CHAPTER 4

# LINEAR EQUATIONS IN TWO VARIABLES

*The principal use of the Analytic Art is to bring Mathematical Problems to Equations and to exhibit those Equations in the most simple terms that can be.*

—*Edmund Halley*

## 4.1 Introduction

In earlier classes, you have studied linear equations in one variable. Can you write down a linear equation in one variable? You may say that $x + 1 = 0$, $x + \sqrt{2} = 0$ and $\sqrt{2}\,y + \sqrt{3} = 0$ are examples of linear equations in one variable. You also know that such equations have a unique (i.e., one and only one) solution. You may also remember how to represent the solution on a number line. In this chapter, the knowledge of linear equations in one variable shall be recalled and extended to that of two variables. You will be considering questions like: Does a linear equation in two variables have a solution? If yes, is it unique? What does the solution look like on the Cartesian plane? You shall also use the concepts you studied in Chapter 3 to answer these questions.

## 4.2 Linear Equations

Let us first recall what you have studied so far. Consider the following equation:

$$2x + 5 = 0$$

Its solution, i.e., the root of the equation, is $-\dfrac{5}{2}$. This can be represented on the number line as shown below:

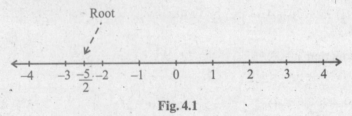

Fig. 4.1

While solving an equation, you must always keep the following points in mind:

The solution of a linear equation is not affected when:

(i) the same number is added to (or subtracted from) both the sides of the equation.

(ii) you multiply or divide both the sides of the equation by the same non-zero number.

Let us now consider the following situation:

In a One-day International Cricket match between India and Sri Lanka played in Nagpur, two Indian batsmen together scored 176 runs. Express this information in the form of an equation.

Here, you can see that the score of neither of them is known, i.e., there are two unknown quantities. Let us use $x$ and $y$ to denote them. So, the number of runs scored by one of the batsmen is $x$, and the number of runs scored by the other is $y$. We know that

$$x + y = 176,$$

which is the required equation.

This is an example of a linear equation in two variables. It is customary to denote the variables in such equations by $x$ and $y$, but other letters may also be used. Some examples of linear equations in two variables are:

$$1.2s + 3t = 5,\ p + 4q = 7,\ \pi u + 5v = 9 \text{ and } 3 = \sqrt{2}\,x - 7y.$$

Note that you can put these equations in the form $1.2s + 3t - 5 = 0$, $p + 4q - 7 = 0$, $\pi u + 5v - 9 = 0$ and $\sqrt{2}\,x - 7y - 3 = 0$, respectively.

So, any equation which can be put in the form $ax + by + c = 0$, where $a$, $b$ and $c$ are real numbers, and $a$ and $b$ are not both zero, is called a *linear equation in two variables*. This means that you can think of many many such equations.

**Example 1 :** Write each of the following equations in the form $ax + by + c = 0$ and indicate the values of $a$, $b$ and $c$ in each case:

(i) $2x + 3y = 4.37$    (ii) $x - 4 = \sqrt{3}\,y$    (iii) $4 = 5x - 3y$    (iv) $2x = y$

**Solution :** (i) $2x + 3y = 4.37$ can be written as $2x + 3y - 4.37 = 0$. Here $a = 2$, $b = 3$ and $c = -4.37$.

(ii) The equation $x - 4 = \sqrt{3}\,y$ can be written as $x - \sqrt{3}\,y - 4 = 0$. Here $a = 1$, $b = -\sqrt{3}$ and $c = -4$.

(iii) The equation $4 = 5x - 3y$ can be written as $5x - 3y - 4 = 0$. Here $a = 5$, $b = -3$ and $c = -4$. Do you agree that it can also be written as $-5x + 3y + 4 = 0$ ? In this case $a = -5$, $b = 3$ and $c = 4$.

(iv) The equation $2x = y$ can be written as $2x - y + 0 = 0$. Here $a = 2$, $b = -1$ and $c = 0$.

Equations of the type $ax + b = 0$ are also examples of linear equations in two variables because they can be expressed as

$$ax + 0.y + b = 0$$

For example, $4 - 3x = 0$ can be written as $-3x + 0.y + 4 = 0$.

**Example 2 :** Write each of the following as an equation in two variables:

(i) $x = -5$      (ii) $y = 2$      (iii) $2x = 3$      (iv) $5y = 2$

**Solution :** (i) $x = -5$ can be written as $1.x + 0.y = -5$, or $1.x + 0.y + 5 = 0$.

(ii) $y = 2$ can be written as $0.x + 1.y = 2$, or $0.x + 1.y - 2 = 0$.

(iii) $2x = 3$ can be written as $2x + 0.y - 3 = 0$.

(iv) $5y = 2$ can be written as $0.x + 5y - 2 = 0$.

## EXERCISE 4.1

1. The cost of a notebook is twice the cost of a pen. Write a linear equation in two variables to represent this statement.

   (Take the cost of a notebook to be ₹ $x$ and that of a pen to be ₹ $y$).

2. Express the following linear equations in the form $ax + by + c = 0$ and indicate the values of $a$, $b$ and $c$ in each case:

   (i) $2x + 3y = 9.3\overline{5}$    (ii) $x - \dfrac{y}{5} - 10 = 0$    (iii) $-2x + 3y = 6$    (iv) $x = 3y$

   (v) $2x = -5y$    (vi) $3x + 2 = 0$    (vii) $y - 2 = 0$    (viii) $5 = 2x$

### 4.3 Solution of a Linear Equation

You have seen that every linear equation in one variable has a unique solution. What can you say about the solution of a linear equation involving two variables? As there are two variables in the equation, a solution means a pair of values, one for $x$ and one for $y$ which satisfy the given equation. Let us consider the equation $2x + 3y = 12$. Here, $x = 3$ and $y = 2$ is a solution because when you substitute $x = 3$ and $y = 2$ in the equation above, you find that

$$2x + 3y = (2 \times 3) + (3 \times 2) = 12$$

This solution is written as an ordered pair $(3, 2)$, first writing the value for $x$ and then the value for $y$. Similarly, $(0, 4)$ is also a solution for the equation above.

On the other hand, (1, 4) is not a solution of $2x + 3y = 12$, because on putting $x = 1$ and $y = 4$ we get $2x + 3y = 14$, which is not 12. Note that (0, 4) is a solution but not (4, 0).

You have seen at least two solutions for $2x + 3y = 12$, i.e., (3, 2) and (0, 4). Can you find any other solution? Do you agree that (6, 0) is another solution? Verify the same. In fact, we can get many many solutions in the following way. Pick a value of your choice for $x$ (say $x = 2$) in $2x + 3y = 12$. Then the equation reduces to $4 + 3y = 12$, which is a linear equation in one variable. On solving this, you get $y = \dfrac{8}{3}$. So $\left(2, \dfrac{8}{3}\right)$ is another solution of $2x + 3y = 12$. Similarly, choosing $x = -5$, you find that the equation becomes $-10 + 3y = 12$. This gives $y = \dfrac{22}{3}$. So, $\left(-5, \dfrac{22}{3}\right)$ is another solution of $2x + 3y = 12$. So there is no end to different solutions of a linear equation in two variables. That is, *a linear equation in two variables has infinitely many solutions.*

**Example 3 :** Find four different solutions of the equation $x + 2y = 6$.

**Solution :** By inspection, $x = 2$, $y = 2$ is a solution because for $x = 2$, $y = 2$

$$x + 2y = 2 + 4 = 6$$

Now, let us choose $x = 0$. With this value of $x$, the given equation reduces to $2y = 6$ which has the unique solution $y = 3$. So $x = 0$, $y = 3$ is also a solution of $x + 2y = 6$. Similarly, taking $y = 0$, the given equation reduces to $x = 6$. So, $x = 6$, $y = 0$ is a solution of $x + 2y = 6$ as well. Finally, let us take $y = 1$. The given equation now reduces to $x + 2 = 6$, whose solution is given by $x = 4$. Therefore, (4, 1) is also a solution of the given equation. So four of the infinitely many solutions of the given equation are:

$$(2, 2), (0, 3), (6, 0) \text{ and } (4, 1).$$

**Remark :** Note that an easy way of getting a solution is to take $x = 0$ and get the corresponding value of $y$. Similarly, we can put $y = 0$ and obtain the corresponding value of $x$.

**Example 4 :** Find two solutions for each of the following equations:

(i)   $4x + 3y = 12$

(ii)  $2x + 5y = 0$

(iii) $3y + 4 = 0$

**Solution :** (i) Taking $x = 0$, we get $3y = 12$, i.e., $y = 4$. So, (0, 4) is a solution of the given equation. Similarly, by taking $y = 0$, we get $x = 3$. Thus, (3, 0) is also a solution.
(ii) Taking $x = 0$, we get $5y = 0$, i.e., $y = 0$. So (0, 0) is a solution of the given equation.

Now, if you take $y = 0$, you again get $(0, 0)$ as a solution, which is the same as the earlier one. To get another solution, take $x = 1$, say. Then you can check that the corresponding value of $y$ is $-\dfrac{2}{5}$. So $\left(1, -\dfrac{2}{5}\right)$ is another solution of $2x + 5y = 0$.

(iii) Writing the equation $3y + 4 = 0$ as $0.x + 3y + 4 = 0$, you will find that $y = -\dfrac{4}{3}$ for any value of $x$. Thus, two solutions can be given as $\left(0, -\dfrac{4}{3}\right)$ and $\left(1, -\dfrac{4}{3}\right)$.

## EXERCISE 4.2

1.  Which one of the following options is true, and why?

    $y = 3x + 5$ has

    (i) a unique solution,     (ii) only two solutions,     (iii) infinitely many solutions

2.  Write four solutions for each of the following equations:

    (i)   $2x + y = 7$        (ii) $\pi x + y = 9$        (iii) $x = 4y$

3.  Check which of the following are solutions of the equation $x - 2y = 4$ and which are not:

    (i)   $(0, 2)$         (ii) $(2, 0)$         (iii) $(4, 0)$

    (iv) $\left(\sqrt{2}, 4\sqrt{2}\right)$     (v) $(1, 1)$

4.  Find the value of $k$, if $x = 2$, $y = 1$ is a solution of the equation $2x + 3y = k$.

## 4.4 Graph of a Linear Equation in Two Variables

So far, you have obtained the solutions of a linear equation in two variables algebraically. Now, let us look at their geometric representation. You know that each such equation has infinitely many solutions. How can we show them in the coordinate plane? You may have got some indication in which we write the solution as pairs of values. The solutions of the linear equation in Example 3, namely,

$$x + 2y = 6 \qquad\qquad (1)$$

can be expressed in the form of a table as follows by writing the values of $y$ below the corresponding values of $x$ :

### Table 1

| x | 0 | 2 | 4 | 6 | . . . |
|---|---|---|---|---|-------|
| y | 3 | 2 | 1 | 0 | . . . |

In the previous chapter, you studied how to plot the points on a graph paper. Let us plot the points (0, 3), (2, 2), (4, 1) and (6, 0) on a graph paper. Now join any two of these points and obtain a line. Let us call this as line AB (see Fig. 4.2).

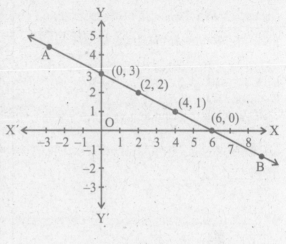

Fig. 4.2

Do you see that the other two points also lie on the line AB? Now, pick another point on this line, say (8, –1). Is this a solution? In fact, 8 + 2(–1) = 6. So, (8, –1) is a solution. Pick any other point on this line AB and verify whether its coordinates satisfy the equation or not. Now, take any point not lying on the line AB, say (2, 0). Do its coordinates satisfy the equation? Check, and see that they do not.

Let us list our observations:

1. Every point whose coordinates satisfy Equation (1) lies on the line AB.

2. Every point (a, b) on the line AB gives a solution $x = a$, $y = b$ of Equation (1).

3. Any point, which does not lie on the line AB, is not a solution of Equation (1).

So, you can conclude that every point on the line satisfies the equation of the line and every solution of the equation is a point on the line. In fact, a linear equation in two variables is represented geometrically by a line whose points make up the collection of solutions of the equation. This is called the *graph* of the linear equation. So, to obtain the graph of a linear equation in two variables, it is enough to plot two points corresponding to two solutions and join them by a line. However, it is advisable to plot more than two such points so that you can immediately check the correctness of the graph.

Remark : The reason that a, degree one, polynomial equation $ax + by + c = 0$ is called a *linear* equation is that its geometrical representation is a straight line.

Example 5 : Given the point (1, 2), find the equation of a line on which it lies. How many such equations are there?

Solution : Here (1, 2) is a solution of a linear equation you are looking for. So, you are looking for any line passing through the point (1, 2). One example of such a linear equation is $x + y = 3$. Others are $y – x = 1$, $y = 2x$, since they are also satisfied by the coordinates of the point (1, 2). In fact, there are infinitely many linear equations which are satisfied by the coordinates of the point (1, 2). Can you see this pictorially?

**Example 6 :** Draw the graph of $x + y = 7$.

**Solution :** To draw the graph, we need at least two solutions of the equation. You can check that $x = 0$, $y = 7$, and $x = 7$, $y = 0$ are solutions of the given equation. So, you can use the following table to draw the graph:

Table 2

| $x$ | 0 | 7 |
|-----|---|---|
| $y$ | 7 | 0 |

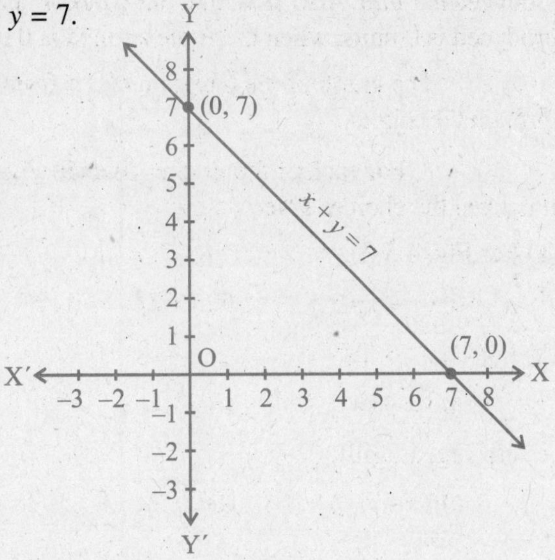

Draw the graph by plotting the two points from Table 2 and then by joining the same by a line (see Fig. 4.3).

Fig. 4.3

**Example 7 :** You know that the force applied on a body is directly proportional to the acceleration produced in the body. Write an equation to express this situation and plot the graph of the equation.

**Solution :** Here the variables involved are force and acceleration. Let the force applied be $y$ units and the acceleration produced be $x$ units. From ratio and proportion, you can express this fact as $y = kx$, where $k$ is a constant. (From your study of science, you know that $k$ is actually the mass of the body.)

Now, since we do not know what $k$ is, we cannot draw the precise graph of $y = kx$. However, if we give a certain value to $k$, then we can draw the graph. Let us take $k = 3$, i.e., we draw the line representing $y = 3x$.

For this we find two of its solutions, say $(0, 0)$ and $(2, 6)$ (see Fig. 4.4).

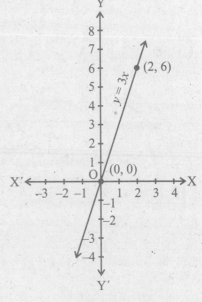

Fig. 4.4

From the graph, you can see that when the force applied is 3 units, the acceleration produced is 1 unit. Also, note that (0, 0) lies on the graph which means the acceleration produced is 0 units, when the force applied is 0 units.

**Remark :** The graph of the equation of the form $y = kx$ is a line which always passes through the origin.

**Example 8 :** For each of the graphs given in Fig. 4.5 select the equation whose graph it is from the choices given below:

(a) For Fig. 4.5 (i),

     (i)   $x + y = 0$         (ii) $y = 2x$         (iii) $y = x$         (iv) $y = 2x + 1$

(b) For Fig. 4.5 (ii),

     (i)   $x + y = 0$         (ii) $y = 2x$         (iii) $y = 2x + 4$         (iv) $y = x - 4$

(c) For Fig. 4.5 (iii),

     (i)   $x + y = 0$         (ii) $y = 2x$         (iii) $y = 2x + 1$         (iv) $y = 2x - 4$

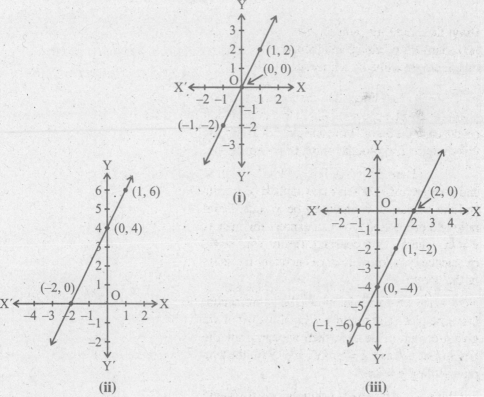

Fig. 4.5

**Solution :** (a) In Fig. 4.5 (i), the points on the line are $(-1, -2)$, $(0, 0)$, $(1, 2)$. By inspection, $y = 2x$ is the equation corresponding to this graph. You can find that the $y$-coordinate in each case is double that of the $x$-coordinate.

(b) In Fig. 4.5 (ii), the points on the line are $(-2, 0)$, $(0, 4)$, $(1, 6)$. You know that the coordinates of the points of the graph (line) satisfy the equation $y = 2x + 4$. So, $y = 2x + 4$ is the equation corresponding to the graph in Fig. 4.5 (ii).

(c) In Fig. 4.5 (iii), the points on the line are $(-1, -6)$, $(0, -4)$, $(1, -2)$, $(2, 0)$. By inspection, you can see that $y = 2x - 4$ is the equation corresponding to the given graph (line).

## EXERCISE 4.3

1. Draw the graph of each of the following linear equations in two variables:

   (i)  $x + y = 4$      (ii) $x - y = 2$      (iii) $y = 3x$      (iv) $3 = 2x + y$

2. Give the equations of two lines passing through $(2, 14)$. How many more such lines are there, and why?

3. If the point $(3, 4)$ lies on the graph of the equation $3y = ax + 7$, find the value of $a$.

4. The taxi fare in a city is as follows: For the first kilometre, the fare is ₹ 8 and for the subsequent distance it is ₹ 5 per km. Taking the distance covered as $x$ km and total fare as Rs $y$, write a linear equation for this information, and draw its graph.

5. From the choices given below, choose the equation whose graphs are given in Fig. 4.6 and Fig. 4.7.

   **For Fig. 4. 6**

   (i)  $y = x$

   (ii)  $x + y = 0$

   (iii)  $y = 2x$

   (iv)  $2 + 3y = 7x$

   **For Fig. 4.7**

   (i)  $y = x + 2$

   (ii)  $y = x - 2$

   (iii)  $y = -x + 2$

   (iv)  $x + 2y = 6$

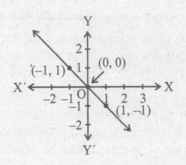

Fig. 4.6

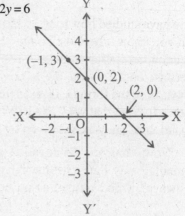

Fig. 4.7

6. If the work done by a body on application of a constant force is directly proportional to the distance travelled by the body, express this in the form of an equation in two variables and draw the graph of the same by taking the constant force as 5 units. Also read from the graph the work done when the distance travelled by the body is

      (i) 2 units          (ii) 0 unit

7. Yamini and Fatima, two students of Class IX of a school, together contributed ₹ 100 towards the Prime Minister's Relief Fund to help the earthquake victims. Write a linear equation which satisfies this data. (You may take their contributions as ₹ $x$ and ₹ $y$.) Draw the graph of the same.

8. In countries like USA and Canada, temperature is measured in Fahrenheit, whereas in countries like India, it is measured in Celsius. Here is a linear equation that converts Fahrenheit to Celsius:

$$F = \left(\frac{9}{5}\right)C + 32$$

(i) Draw the graph of the linear equation above using Celsius for $x$-axis and Fahrenheit for $y$-axis.

(ii) If the temperature is 30°C, what is the temperature in Fahrenheit?

(iii) If the temperature is 95°F, what is the temperature in Celsius?

(iv) If the temperature is 0°C, what is the temperature in Fahrenheit and if the temperature is 0°F, what is the temperature in Celsius?

(v) Is there a temperature which is numerically the same in both Fahrenheit and Celsius? If yes, find it.

## 4.5 Equations of Lines Parallel to the $x$-axis and $y$-axis

You have studied how to write the coordinates of a given point in the Cartesian plane. Do you know where the points (2, 0), (–3, 0), (4, 0) and ($n$, 0), for any real number $n$, lie in the Cartesian plane? Yes, they all lie on the $x$-axis. But do you know why? Because on the $x$-axis, the $y$-coordinate of each point is 0. In fact, every point on the $x$-axis is of the form ($x$, 0). Can you now guess the equation of the $x$-axis? It is given by $y = 0$. Note that $y = 0$ can be expressed as $0.x + 1.y = 0$. Similarly, observe that the equation of the $y$-axis is given by $x = 0$.

Now, consider the equation $x - 2 = 0$. If this is treated as an equation in one variable $x$ only, then it has the unique solution $x = 2$, which is a point on the number line. However, when treated as an equation in two variables, it can be expressed as

$x + 0.y - 2 = 0$. This has infinitely many solutions. In fact, they are all of the form $(2, r)$, where $r$ is any real number. Also, you can check that every point of the form $(2, r)$ is a solution of this equation. So as, an equation in two variables, $x - 2 = 0$ is represented by the line AB in the graph in Fig. 4.8.

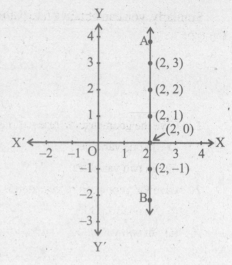

Fig. 4.8

**Example 9** : Solve the equation $2x + 1 = x - 3$, and represent the solution(s) on    (i) the number line,

    (ii) the Cartesian plane.

**Solution** : We solve $2x + 1 = x - 3$, to get

$$2x - x = -3 - 1$$

i.e.,                    $x = -4$

(i) The representation of the solution on the number line is shown in Fig. 4.9, where $x = -4$ is treated as an equation in one variable.

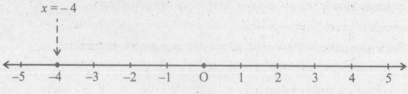

Fig. 4.9

(ii) We know that $x = -4$ can be written as

$$x + 0.y = -4$$

which is a linear equation in the variables $x$ and $y$. This is represented by a line. Now all the values of $y$ are permissible because $0.y$ is always 0. However, $x$ must satisfy the equation $x = -4$. Hence, two solutions of the given equation are $x = -4, y = 0$ and $x = -4, y = 2$.

Note that the graph AB is a line parallel to the $y$-axis and at a distance of 4 units to the left of it (see Fig. 4.10).

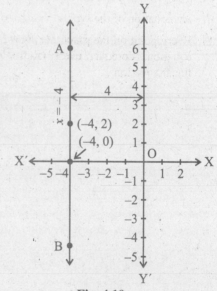

Fig. 4.10

Similarly, you can obtain a line parallel to the $x$-axis corresponding to equations of the type

$$y = 3 \quad \text{or} \quad 0.x + 1.y = 3$$

### EXERCISE 4.4

1. Give the geometric representations of $y = 3$ as an equation
   (i) in one variable
   (ii) in two variables
2. Give the geometric representations of $2x + 9 = 0$ as an equation
   (i) in one variable
   (ii) in two variables

## 4.6 Summary

In this chapter, you have studied the following points:

1. An equation of the form $ax + by + c = 0$, where $a$, $b$ and $c$ are real numbers, such that $a$ and $b$ are not both zero, is called a linear equation in two variables.
2. A linear equation in two variables has infinitely many solutions.
3. The graph of every linear equation in two variables is a straight line.
4. $x = 0$ is the equation of the $y$-axis and $y = 0$ is the equation of the $x$-axis.
5. The graph of $x = a$ is a straight line parallel to the $y$-axis.
6. The graph of $y = a$ is a straight line parallel to the $x$-axis.
7. An equation of the type $y = mx$ represents a line passing through the origin.
8. Every point on the graph of a linear equation in two variables is a solution of the linear equation. Moreover, every solution of the linear equation is a point on the graph of the linear equation.

# CHAPTER 5

# INTRODUCTION TO EUCLID'S GEOMETRY

## 5.1 Introduction

The word 'geometry' comes form the Greek words 'geo', meaning the 'earth', and 'metrein', meaning 'to measure'. Geometry appears to have originated from the need for measuring land. This branch of mathematics was studied in various forms in every ancient civilisation, be it in Egypt, Babylonia, China, India, Greece, the Incas, etc. The people of these civilisations faced several practical problems which required the development of geometry in various ways.

For example, whenever the river Nile overflowed, it wiped out the boundaries between the adjoining fields of different land owners. After such flooding, these boundaries had to be redrawn. For this purpose, the Egyptians developed a number of geometric techniques and rules for calculating simple areas and also for doing simple constructions. The knowledge of geometry was also used by them for computing volumes of granaries, and for constructing canals and pyramids. They also knew the correct formula to find the volume of a truncated pyramid (see Fig. 5.1). You know that a pyramid is a solid figure, the base of which is a triangle, or square, or some other polygon, and its side faces are triangles converging to a point at the top.

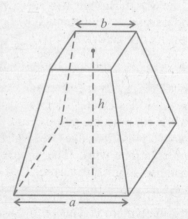

Fig. 5.1 : **A Truncated Pyramid**

In the Indian subcontinent, the excavations at Harappa and Mohenjo-Daro, etc. show that the Indus Valley Civilisation (about 3000 BCE) made extensive use of geometry. It was a highly organised society. The cities were highly developed and very well planned. For example, the roads were parallel to each other and there was an underground drainage system. The houses had many rooms of different types. This shows that the town dwellers were skilled in mensuration and practical arithmetic. The bricks used for constructions were kiln fired and the ratio length : breadth : thickness, of the bricks was found to be 4 : 2 : 1.

In ancient India, the *Sulbasutras* (800 BCE to 500 BCE) were the manuals of geometrical constructions. The geometry of the Vedic period originated with the construction of altars (or *vedis*) and fireplaces for performing Vedic rites. The location of the sacred fires had to be in accordance to the clearly laid down instructions about their shapes and areas, if they were to be effective instruments. Square and circular altars were used for household rituals, while altars whose shapes were combinations of rectangles, triangles and trapeziums were required for public worship. The *sriyantra* (given in the *Atharvaveda*) consists of nine interwoven isosceles triangles. These triangles are arranged in such a way that they produce 43 subsidiary triangles. Though accurate geometric methods were used for the constructions of altars, the principles behind them were not discussed.

These examples show that geometry was being developed and applied everywhere in the world. But this was happening in an unsystematic manner. What is interesting about these developments of geometry in the ancient world is that they were passed on from one generation to the next, either orally or through palm leaf messages, or by other ways. Also, we find that in some civilisations like Babylonia, geometry remained a very practical oriented discipline, as was the case in India and Rome. The geometry developed by Egyptians mainly consisted of the statements of results. There were no general rules of the procedure. In fact, Babylonians and Egyptians used geometry mostly for practical purposes and did very little to develop it as a systematic science. But in civilisations like Greece, the emphasis was on the *reasoning* behind why certain constructions work. The Greeks were interested in establishing the truth of the statements they discovered using deductive reasoning (see Appendix 1).

A Greek mathematician, Thales is credited with giving the first known proof. This proof was of the statement that a circle is bisected (i.e., cut into two equal parts) by its diameter. One of Thales' most famous pupils was Pythagoras (572 BCE), whom you have heard about. Pythagoras and his group discovered many geometric properties and developed the theory of geometry to a great extent. This process continued till 300 BCE. At that time Euclid, a teacher of mathematics at Alexandria in Egypt, collected all the known work and arranged it in his famous treatise,

**Thales**
**(640 BCE – 546 BCE)**
Fig. 5.2

called 'Elements'. He divided the 'Elements' into thirteen chapters, each called a book. These books influenced the whole world's understanding of geometry for generations to come.

In this chapter, we shall discuss Euclid's approach to geometry and shall try to link it with the present day geometry.

**Euclid (325 BCE – 265 BCE)**
**Fig. 5.3**

## 5.2 Euclid's Definitions, Axioms and Postulates

The Greek mathematicians of Euclid's time thought of geometry as an abstract model of the world in which they lived. The notions of point, line, plane (or surface) and so on were derived from what was seen around them. From studies of the space and solids in the space around them, an abstract geometrical notion of a solid object was developed. A solid has shape, size, position, and can be moved from one place to another. Its boundaries are called **surfaces.** They separate one part of the space from another, and are said to have no thickness. The boundaries of the surfaces are **curves** or straight **lines.** These lines end in **points**.

Consider the three steps from solids to points (solids-surfaces-lines-points). In each step we lose one extension, also called a **dimension**. So, a solid has three dimensions, a surface has two, a line has one and a point has none. Euclid summarised these statements as definitions. He began his exposition by listing 23 definitions in Book 1 of the 'Elements'. A few of them are given below :

1.   A **point**  is that which has no part.

2.   A **line** is breadthless length.

3.   The ends of a line are points.

4.   A **straight line** is a line which lies evenly with the points on itself.

5.   A **surface** is that which has length and breadth only.

6.   The edges of a surface are lines.

7.   A **plane surface** is a surface which lies evenly with the straight lines on itself.

If you carefully study these definitions, you find that some of the terms like part, breadth, length, evenly, etc. need to be further explained clearly. For example, consider his definition of a point. In this definition, 'a part' needs to be defined. Suppose if you define 'a part' to be that which occupies 'area', again 'an area' needs to be defined. So, to define one thing, you need to define many other things, and you may get a long chain of definitions without an end. For such reasons, mathematicians agree to leave some geometric terms *undefined*. However, we do have a intuitive feeling for the geometric concept of a point than what the 'definition' above gives us. So, we represent a point as a dot, even though a dot has some dimension.

A similar problem arises in Definition 2 above, since it refers to breadth and length, neither of which has been defined. Because of this, a few terms are kept undefined while developing any course of study. So, in geometry, we *take a point, a line and a plane (in Euclid's words a plane surface) as undefined terms*. The only thing is that we can represent them intuitively, or explain them with the help of 'physical models'.

Starting with his definitions, Euclid assumed certain properties, which were not to be proved. These assumptions are actually 'obvious universal truths'. He divided them into two types: axioms and postulates. He used the term **'postulate'** for the assumptions that were specific to geometry. Common notions (often called **axioms**), on the other hand, were assumptions used throughout mathematics and not specifically linked to geometry. For details about axioms and postulates, refer to Appendix 1. Some of **Euclid's axioms**, not in his order, are given below :

(1) Things which are equal to the same thing are equal to one another.

(2) If equals are added to equals, the wholes are equal.

(3) If equals are subtracted from equals, the remainders are equal.

(4) Things which coincide with one another are equal to one another.

(5) The whole is greater than the part.

(6) Things which are double of the same things are equal to one another.

(7) Things which are halves of the same things are equal to one another.

These 'common notions' refer to magnitudes of some kind. The first common notion could be applied to plane figures. For example, if an area of a triangle equals the area of a rectangle and the area of the rectangle equals that of a square, then the area of the triangle also equals the area of the square.

Magnitudes of the same kind can be compared and added, but magnitudes of different kinds cannot be compared. For example, a line cannot be added to a rectangle, nor can an angle be compared to a pentagon.

The 4th axiom given above seems to say that if two things are identical (that is, they are the same), then they are equal. In other words, everything equals itself. It is the justification of the principle of superposition. Axiom (5) gives us the definition of 'greater than'. For example, if a quantity B is a part of another quantity A, then A can be written as the sum of B and some third quantity C. Symbolically, $A > B$ means that there is some C such that $A = B + C$.

Now let us discuss **Euclid's five postulates.** They are :

**Postulate 1** : *A straight line may be drawn from any one point to any other point.*

Note that this postulate tells us that at least one straight line passes through two distinct points, but it does not say that there cannot be more than one such line. However, in his work, Euclid has frequently assumed, without mentioning, that there is a *unique* line joining two distinct points. We state this result in the form of an axiom as follows:

**Axiom 5.1** : *Given two distinct points, there is a unique line that passes through them.*

How many lines passing through P also pass through Q (see Fig. 5.4)? Only one, that is, the line PQ. How many lines passing through Q also pass through P? Only one, that is, the line PQ. Thus, the statement above is self-evident, and so is taken as an axiom.

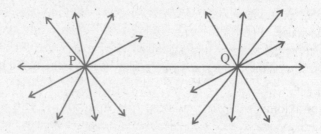

Fig. 5.4

**Postulate 2** : *A terminated line can be produced indefinitely.*

Note that what we call a line segment now-a-days is what Euclid called a terminated line. So, according to the present day terms, the second postulate says that a line segment can be extended on either side to form a line (see Fig. 5.5).

Fig. 5.5

**Postulate 3** : *A circle can be drawn with any centre and any radius.*

**Postulate 4** : *All right angles are equal to one another.*

**Postulate 5** : *If a straight line falling on two straight lines makes the interior angles on the same side of it taken together less than two right angles, then the two straight lines, if produced indefinitely, meet on that side on which the sum of angles is less than two right angles.*

For example, the line PQ in Fig. 5.6 falls on lines AB and CD such that the sum of the interior angles 1 and 2 is less than 180° on the left side of PQ. Therefore, the lines AB and CD will eventually intersect on the left side of PQ.

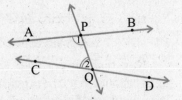

Fig. 5.6

A brief look at the five postulates brings to your notice that Postulate 5 is far more complex than any other postulate. On the other hand, Postulates 1 through 4 are so simple and obvious that these are taken as 'self-evident truths'. However, it is not possible to prove them. So, these statements are accepted without any proof (see Appendix 1). Because of its complexity, the fifth postulate will be given more attention in the next section.

Now-a-days, 'postulates' and 'axioms' are terms that are used interchangeably and in the same sense. 'Postulate' is actually a verb. When we say "let us postulate", we mean, "let us make some statement based on the observed phenomenon in the Universe". Its truth/validity is checked afterwards. If it is true, then it is accepted as a 'Postulate'.

A system of axioms is called **consistent** (see Appendix 1), if it is impossible to deduce from these axioms a statement that contradicts any axiom or previously proved statement. So, when any system of axioms is given, it needs to be ensured that the system is consistent.

After Euclid stated his postulates and axioms, he used them to prove other results. Then using these results, he proved some more results by applying deductive reasoning. The statements that were proved are called **propositions or theorems**. Euclid deduced 465 propositions in a logical chain using his axioms, postulates, definitions and theorems proved earlier in the chain. In the next few chapters on geometry, you will be using these axioms to prove some theorems.

Now, let us see in the following examples how Euclid used his axioms and postulates for proving some of the results:

**Example 1 :** If A, B and C are three points on a line, and B lies between A and C (see Fig. 5.7), then prove that AB + BC = AC.

Fig. 5.7

**Solution :** In the figure given above, AC coincides with AB + BC.

Also, Euclid's Axiom (4) says that things which coincide with one another are equal to one another. So, it can be deduced that

$$AB + BC = AC$$

Note that in this solution, it has been assumed that there is a unique line passing through two points.

**Example 2 :** Prove that an equilateral triangle can be constructed on any given line segment.

**Solution :** In the statement above, a line segment of any length is given, say AB [see Fig. 5.8(i)].

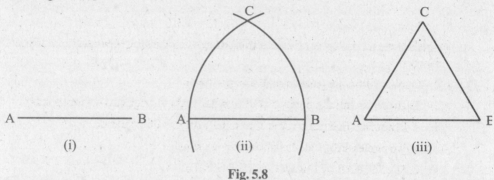

Fig. 5.8

Here, you need to do some construction. Using Euclid's Postulate 3, you can draw a circle with point A as the centre and AB as the radius [see Fig. 5.8(ii)]. Similarly, draw another circle with point B as the centre and BA as the radius. The two circles meet at a point, say C. Now, draw the line segments AC and BC to form Δ ABC [see Fig. 5.8 (iii)].

So, you have to prove that this triangle is equilateral, i.e., AB = AC = BC.

Now,        AB = AC, since they are the radii of the same circle                    (1)

Similarly,  AB = BC   (Radii of the same circle)                                    (2)

From these two facts, and Euclid's axiom that things which are equal to the same thing are equal to one another, you can conclude that AB = BC = AC.

So, Δ ABC is an equilateral triangle.

Note that here Euclid has assumed, without mentioning anywhere, that the two circles drawn with centres A and B will meet each other at a point.

Now we prove a theorem, which is frequently used in different results:

**Theorem 5.1** : *Two distinct lines cannot have more than one point in common.*

**Proof** : Here we are given two lines $l$ and $m$. We need to prove that they have only one point in common.

For the time being, let us suppose that the two lines intersect in two distinct points, say P and Q. So, you have two lines passing through two distinct points P and Q. But this assumption clashes with the axiom that only one line can pass through two distinct points. So, the assumption that we started with, that two lines can pass through two distinct points is wrong.

From this, what can we conclude? We are forced to conclude that two distinct lines cannot have more than one point in common.    ■

## EXERCISE 5.1

1. Which of the following statements are true and which are false? Give reasons for your answers.

   (i)   Only one line can pass through a single point.

   (ii)  There are an infinite number of lines which pass through two distinct points.

   (iii) A terminated line can be produced indefinitely on both the sides.

   (iv)  If two circles are equal, then their radii are equal.

   (v)   In Fig. 5.9, if AB = PQ and PQ = XY, then AB = XY.

Fig. 5.9

2. Give a definition for each of the following terms. Are there other terms that need to be defined first? What are they, and how might you define them?

   (i)   parallel lines          (ii)  perpendicular lines          (iii) line segment

   (iv)  radius of a circle       (v)   square

3. Consider two 'postulates' given below:

   (i)   Given any two distinct points A and B, there exists a third point C which is in between A and B.

   (ii)  There exist at least three points that are not on the same line.

   Do these postulates contain any undefined terms? Are these postulates consistent? Do they follow from Euclid's postulates? Explain.

4.  If a point C lies between two points A and B such that AC = BC, then prove that $AC = \dfrac{1}{2} AB$. Explain by drawing the figure.

5.  In Question 4, point C is called a mid-point of line segment AB. Prove that every line segment has one and only one mid-point.

6.  In Fig. 5.10, if AC = BD, then prove that AB = CD.

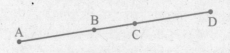

**Fig. 5.10**

7.  Why is Axiom 5, in the list of Euclid's axioms, considered a 'universal truth'? (Note that the question is not about the fifth postulate.)

## 5.3 Equivalent Versions of Euclid's Fifth Postulate

Euclid's fifth postulate is very significant in the history of mathematics. Recall it again from Section 5.2. We see that by implication, no intersection of lines will take place when the sum of the measures of the interior angles on the same side of the falling line is exactly 180°. There are several equivalent versions of this postulate. One of them is 'Playfair's Axiom' (given by a Scottish mathematician John Playfair in 1729), as stated below:

*'For every line l and for every point P not lying on l, there exists a unique line m passing through P and parallel to l'.*

From Fig. 5.11, you can see that of all the lines passing through the point P, only line *m* is parallel to line *l*.

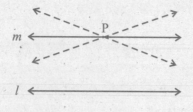

**Fig. 5.11**

This result can also be stated in the following form:

*Two distinct intersecting lines cannot be parallel to the same line.*

Euclid did not require his fifth postulate to prove his first 28 theorems. Many mathematicians, including him, were convinced that the fifth postulate is actually a theorem that can be proved using just the first four postulates and other axioms. However, all attempts to prove the fifth postulate as a theorem have failed. But these efforts have led to a great achievement – the creation of several other geometries. These geometries are quite different from Euclidean geometry. They are called *non-Euclidean geometries*. Their creation is considered a landmark in the history of thought because till then everyone had believed that Euclid's was the only geometry

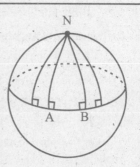

**Fig. 5.12**

and the world itself was Euclidean. Now the geometry of the universe we live in has been shown to be a non-Euclidean geometry. In fact, it is called *spherical geometry*. In spherical geometry, lines are not straight. They are parts of great circles (i.e., circles obtained by the intersection of a sphere and planes passing through the centre of the sphere).

In Fig. 5.12, the lines AN and BN (which are parts of great circles of a sphere) are perpendicular to the same line AB. But they are meeting each other, though the sum of the angles on the same side of line AB is not less than two right angles (in fact, it is 90° + 90° = 180°). Also, note that the sum of the angles of the triangle NAB is greater than 180°, as ∠A + ∠B = 180°. Thus, Euclidean geometry is valid only for the figures in the plane. On the curved surfaces, it fails.

Now, let us consider an example.

**Example 3 :** Consider the following statement : There exists a pair of straight lines that are everywhere equidistant from one another. Is this statement a direct consequence of Euclid's fifth postulate? Explain.

**Solution :** Take any line *l* and a point P not on *l*. Then, by Playfair's axiom, which is equivalent to the fifth postulate, we know that there is a unique line *m* through P which is parallel to *l*.

Now, the *distance of a point from a line* is the length of the perpendicular from the point to the line. This distance will be the same for any point on *m* from *l* and any point on *l* from *m*. So, these two lines are everywhere equidistant from one another.

**Remark :** The geometry that you will be studying in the next few chapters is Euclidean Geometry. However, the axioms and theorems used by us may be different from those of Euclid's.

## EXERCISE 5.2

1. How would you rewrite Euclid's fifth postulate so that it would be easier to understand?

2. Does Euclid's fifth postulate imply the existence of parallel lines? Explain.

## 5.4 Summary

In this chapter, you have studied the following points:

1. Though Euclid defined a point, a line, and a plane, the definitions are not accepted by mathematicians. Therefore, these terms are now taken as undefined.

2. Axioms or postulates are the assumptions which are obvious universal truths. They are not proved.

3. Theorems are statements which are proved, using definitions, axioms, previously proved statements and deductive reasoning.

4. Some of Euclid's axioms were :

   (1) Things which are equal to the same thing are equal to one another.

   (2) If equals are added to equals, the wholes are equal.

   (3) If equals are subtracted from equals, the remainders are equal.

   (4) Things which coincide with one another are equal to one another.

   (5) The whole is greater than the part.

   (6) Things which are double of the same things are equal to one another.

   (7) Things which are halves of the same things are equal to one another.

5. Euclid's postulates were :

   **Postulate 1 :** A straight line may be drawn from any one point to any other point.

   **Postulate 2 :** A terminated line can be produced indefinitely.

   **Postulate 3 :** A circle can be drawn with any centre and any radius.

   **Postulate 4 :** All right angles are equal to one another.

   **Postulate 5 :** If a straight line falling on two straight lines makes the interior angles on the same side of it taken together less than two right angles, then the two straight lines, if produced indefinitely, meet on that side on which the sum of angles is less than two right angles.

6. Two equivalent versions of Euclid's fifth postulate are:

   (i) 'For every line $l$ and for every point P not lying on $l$, there exists a unique line $m$ passing through P and parallel to $l$'.

   (ii) Two distinct intersecting lines cannot be parallel to the same line.

7. All the attempts to prove Euclid's fifth postulate using the first 4 postulates failed. But they led to the discovery of several other geometries, called non-Euclidean geometries.

# CHAPTER 6

# LINES AND ANGLES

## 6.1 Introduction

In Chapter 5, you have studied that a minimum of two points are required to draw a line. You have also studied some axioms and, with the help of these axioms, you proved some other statements. In this chapter, you will study the properties of the angles formed when two lines intersect each other, and also the properties of the angles formed when a line intersects two or more parallel lines at distinct points. Further you will use these properties to prove some statements using deductive reasoning (see Appendix 1). You have already verified these statements through some activities in the earlier classes.

In your daily life, you see different types of angles formed between the edges of plane surfaces. For making a similar kind of model using the plane surfaces, you need to have a thorough knowledge of angles. For instance, suppose you want to make a model of a hut to keep in the school exhibition using bamboo sticks. Imagine how you would make it? You would keep some of the sticks parallel to each other, and some sticks would be kept slanted. Whenever an architect has to draw a plan for a multistoried building, she has to draw intersecting lines and parallel lines at different angles. Without the knowledge of the properties of these lines and angles, do you think she can draw the layout of the building?

In science, you study the properties of light by drawing the ray diagrams. For example, to study the refraction property of light when it enters from one medium to the other medium, you use the properties of intersecting lines and parallel lines. When two or more forces act on a body, you draw the diagram in which forces are represented by directed line segments to study the net effect of the forces on the body. At that time, you need to know the relation between the angles when the rays (or line segments) are parallel to or intersect each other. To find the height of a tower or to find the distance of a ship from the light house, one needs to know the angle formed between the horizontal and the line of sight. Plenty of other examples can be given where lines and angles are used. In the subsequent chapters of geometry, you will be using these properties of lines and angles to deduce more and more useful properties.

Let us first revise the terms and definitions related to lines and angles learnt in earlier classes.

## 6.2 Basic Terms and Definitions

Recall that a part (or portion) of a line with two end points is called a **line-segment** and a part of a line with one end point is called a **ray**. Note that the line segment AB is denoted by $\overline{AB}$, and its length is denoted by AB. The ray AB is denoted by $\overrightarrow{AB}$, and a line is denoted by $\overleftrightarrow{AB}$. However, **we will not use these symbols**, and will denote the line segment AB, ray AB, length AB and line AB by the same symbol, AB. The meaning will be clear from the context. Sometimes small letters *l, m, n,* etc. will be used to denote lines.

If three or more points lie on the same line, they are called **collinear points**; otherwise they are called **non-collinear points**.

Recall that an **angle** is formed when two rays originate from the same end point. The rays making an angle are called the **arms** of the angle and the end point is called the **vertex** of the angle. You have studied different types of angles, such as acute angle, right angle, obtuse angle, straight angle and reflex angle in earlier classes (see Fig. 6.1).

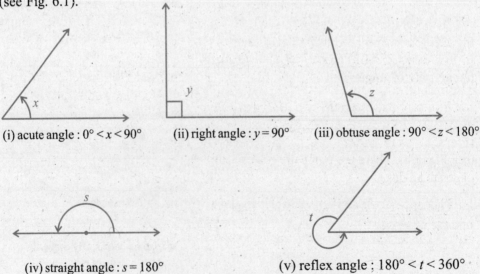

(i) acute angle : $0° < x < 90°$      (ii) right angle : $y = 90°$      (iii) obtuse angle : $90° < z < 180°$

(iv) straight angle : $s = 180°$          (v) reflex angle : $180° < t < 360°$

**Fig. 6.1 : Types of Angles**

An **acute** angle measures between 0° and 90°, whereas a **right angle** is exactly equal to 90°. An angle greater than 90° but less than 180° is called an **obtuse angle**. Also, recall that a **straight angle** is equal to 180°. An angle which is greater than 180° but less than 360° is called a **reflex angle**. Further, two angles whose sum is 90° are called **complementary angles**, and two angles whose sum is 180° are called **supplementary angles**.

You have also studied about adjacent angles in the earlier classes (see Fig. 6.2). Two angles are **adjacent**, if they have a common vertex, a common arm and their non-common arms are on different sides of the common arm. In Fig. 6.2, ∠ ABD and ∠ DBC are adjacent angles. Ray BD is their common arm and point B is their common vertex. Ray BA and ray BC are non common arms. Moreover, when two angles are adjacent, then their sum is always equal to the angle formed by the two non-common arms. So, we can write

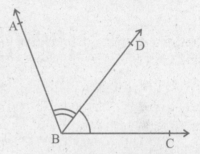

**Fig. 6.2 : Adjacent angles**

∠ ABC = ∠ ABD + ∠ DBC.

Note that ∠ ABC and ∠ ABD are not adjacent angles. Why? Because their non-common arms BD and BC lie on the same side of the common arm BA.

If the non-common arms BA and BC in Fig. 6.2, form a line then it will look like Fig. 6.3. In this case, ∠ ABD and ∠ DBC are called **linear pair of angles**.

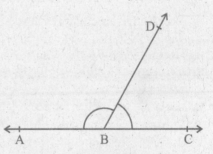

**Fig. 6.3 : Linear pair of angles**

You may also recall the **vertically opposite angles** formed when two lines, say AB and CD, intersect each other, say at the point O (see Fig. 6.4). There are two pairs of vertically opposite angles.

One pair is ∠AOD and ∠BOC. Can you find the other pair?

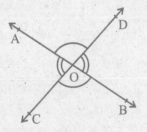

**Fig. 6.4 : Vertically opposite angles**

## 6.3 Intersecting Lines and Non-intersecting Lines

Draw two different lines PQ and RS on a paper. You will see that you can draw them in two different ways as shown in Fig. 6.5 (i) and Fig. 6.5 (ii).

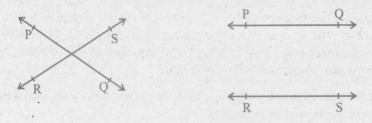

(i) Intersecting lines          (ii) Non-intersecting (parallel) lines

**Fig. 6.5 : Different ways of drawing two lines**

Recall the notion of a line, that it extends indefinitely in both directions. Lines PQ and RS in Fig. 6.5 (i) are intersecting lines and in Fig. 6.5 (ii) are parallel lines. Note that the lengths of the common perpendiculars at different points on these parallel lines is the same. This equal length is called the *distance between two parallel lines*.

## 6.4 Pairs of Angles

In Section 6.2, you have learnt the definitions of some of the pairs of angles such as complementary angles, supplementary angles, adjacent angles, linear pair of angles, etc. Can you think of some relations between these angles? Now, let us find out the relation between the angles formed when a ray stands on a line. Draw a figure in which a ray stands on a line as shown in Fig. 6.6. Name the line as AB and the ray as OC. What are the angles formed at the point O? They are $\angle$ AOC, $\angle$ BOC and $\angle$ AOB.

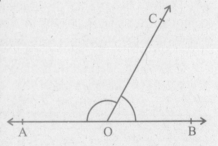

**Fig. 6.6 : Linear pair of angles**

Can we write $\angle$ AOC + $\angle$ BOC = $\angle$ AOB?                                    (1)

Yes! (Why? Refer to adjacent angles in Section 6.2)

What is the measure of $\angle$ AOB? It is 180°.   (Why?)                              (2)

From (1) and (2), can you say that $\angle$ AOC + $\angle$ BOC = 180°?   Yes! (Why?)

From the above discussion, we can state the following Axiom:

**Axiom 6.1** : *If a ray stands on a line, then the sum of two adjacent angles so formed is* 180°.

Recall that when the sum of two adjacent angles is 180°, then they are called a **linear pair of angles**.

In Axiom 6.1, it is given that 'a ray stands on a line'. From this 'given', we have concluded that 'the sum of two adjacent angles so formed is 180°'. Can we write Axiom 6.1 the other way? That is, take the 'conclusion' of Axiom 6.1 as 'given' and the 'given' as the 'conclusion'. So it becomes:

(A) If the sum of two adjacent angles is 180°, then a ray stands on a line (that is, the non-common arms form a line).

Now you see that the Axiom 6.1 and statement (A) are in a sense the reverse of each others. We call each as converse of the other. We do not know whether the statement (A) is true or not. Let us check. Draw adjacent angles of different measures as shown in Fig. 6.7. Keep the ruler along one of the non-common arms in each case. Does the other non-common arm also lie along the ruler?

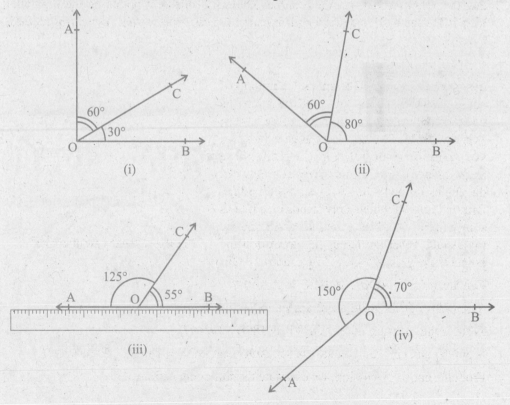

**Fig. 6.7 : Adjacent angles with different measures**

You will find that only in Fig. 6.7 (iii), both the non-common arms lie along the ruler, that is, points A, O and B lie on the same line and ray OC stands on it. Also see that $\angle AOC + \angle COB = 125° + 55° = 180°$. From this, you may conclude that statement (A) is true. So, you can state in the form of an axiom as follows:

**Axiom 6.2** : *If the sum of two adjacent angles is 180°, then the non-common arms of the angles form a line.*

For obvious reasons, the two axioms above together is called the **Linear Pair Axiom**.

Let us now examine the case when two lines intersect each other.

Recall, from earlier classes, that when two lines intersect, the vertically opposite angles are equal. Let us prove this result now. See Appendix 1 for the ingredients of a proof, and keep those in mind while studying the proof given below.

**Theorem 6.1** : *If two lines intersect each other, then the vertically opposite angles are equal.*

**Proof** : In the statement above, it is given that 'two lines intersect each other'. So, let AB and CD be two lines intersecting at O as shown in Fig. 6.8. They lead to two pairs of vertically opposite angles, namely,

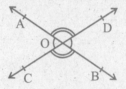

(i) $\angle$ AOC and $\angle$ BOD (ii) $\angle$ AOD and $\angle$ BOC.

**Fig. 6.8 : Vertically opposite angles**

We need to prove that $\angle$ AOC = $\angle$ BOD and $\angle$ AOD = $\angle$ BOC.

Now, ray OA stands on line CD.

Therefore, $\angle$ AOC + $\angle$ AOD = 180°                     (Linear pair axiom)  (1)

Can we write $\angle$ AOD + $\angle$ BOD = 180°? Yes! (Why?)                                (2)

From (1) and (2), we can write

$$\angle AOC + \angle AOD = \angle AOD + \angle BOD$$

This implies that $\angle$ AOC = $\angle$ BOD    (Refer Section 5.2, Axiom 3)

Similarly, it can be proved that $\angle$AOD = $\angle$BOC    ■

Now, let us do some examples based on Linear Pair Axiom and Theorem 6.1.

**Example 1 :** In Fig. 6.9, lines PQ and RS intersect each other at point O. If $\angle$ POR : $\angle$ ROQ = 5 : 7, find all the angles.

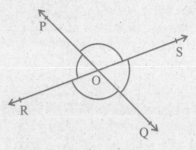

Fig. 6.9

**Solution :**  $\angle$ POR + $\angle$ ROQ = 180°
                                       (Linear pair of angles)

But   $\angle$ POR : $\angle$ ROQ = 5 : 7
                                       (Given)

Therefore,       $\angle$ POR = $\dfrac{5}{12} \times 180° = 75°$

Similarly,       $\angle$ ROQ = $\dfrac{7}{12} \times 180° = 105°$

Now,                $\angle$ POS = $\angle$ROQ = 105°     (Vertically opposite angles)

and                 $\angle$ SOQ = $\angle$POR = 75°      (Vertically opposite angles)

**Example 2 :** In Fig. 6.10, ray OS stands on a line POQ. Ray OR and ray OT are angle bisectors of $\angle$ POS and $\angle$ SOQ, respectively. If $\angle$ POS = x, find $\angle$ ROT.

**Solution :** Ray OS stands on the line POQ.

Therefore,           $\angle$ POS + $\angle$ SOQ = 180°

But,                        $\angle$ POS = x

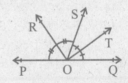

Fig. 6.10

Therefore,           $x + \angle$ SOQ = 180°

So,                         $\angle$ SOQ = 180° – x

Now, ray OR bisects $\angle$ POS, therefore,

$$\angle ROS = \frac{1}{2} \times \angle POS$$

$$= \frac{1}{2} \times x = \frac{x}{2}$$

Similarly,                $\angle$ SOT = $\dfrac{1}{2} \times \angle$ SOQ

$$= \frac{1}{2} \times (180° - x)$$

$$= 90° - \frac{x}{2}$$

Now,                              $\angle \text{ROT} = \angle \text{ROS} + \angle \text{SOT}$

$$= \frac{x}{2} + 90° - \frac{x}{2}$$

$$= 90°$$

**Example 3 :** In Fig. 6.11, OP, OQ, OR and OS are four rays. Prove that $\angle \text{POQ} + \angle \text{QOR} + \angle \text{SOR} + \angle \text{POS} = 360°$.

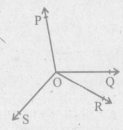

Fig. 6.11

**Solution :** In Fig. 6.11, you need to produce any of the rays OP, OQ, OR or OS backwards to a point. Let us produce ray OQ backwards to a point T so that TOQ is a line (see Fig. 6.12).

Now, ray OP stands on line TOQ.

Therefore,           $\angle \text{TOP} + \angle \text{POQ} = 180°$     (1)

(Linear pair axiom)

Similarly, ray OS stands on line TOQ.

Therefore,           $\angle \text{TOS} + \angle \text{SOQ} = 180°$     (2)

But                       $\angle \text{SOQ} = \angle \text{SOR} + \angle \text{QOR}$

So, (2) becomes

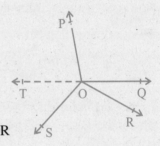

Fig. 6.12

$\angle \text{TOS} + \angle \text{SOR} + \angle \text{QOR} = 180°$                                                     (3)

Now, adding (1) and (3), you get

$\angle \text{TOP} + \angle \text{POQ} + \angle \text{TOS} + \angle \text{SOR} + \angle \text{QOR} = 360°$                          (4)

But                                $\angle \text{TOP} + \angle \text{TOS} = \angle \text{POS}$

Therefore, (4) becomes

$\angle \text{POQ} + \angle \text{QOR} + \angle \text{SOR} + \angle \text{POS} = 360°$

## EXERCISE 6.1

1.  In Fig. 6.13, lines AB and CD intersect at O. If $\angle \text{AOC} + \angle \text{BOE} = 70°$ and $\angle \text{BOD} = 40°$, find $\angle \text{BOE}$ and reflex $\angle \text{COE}$.

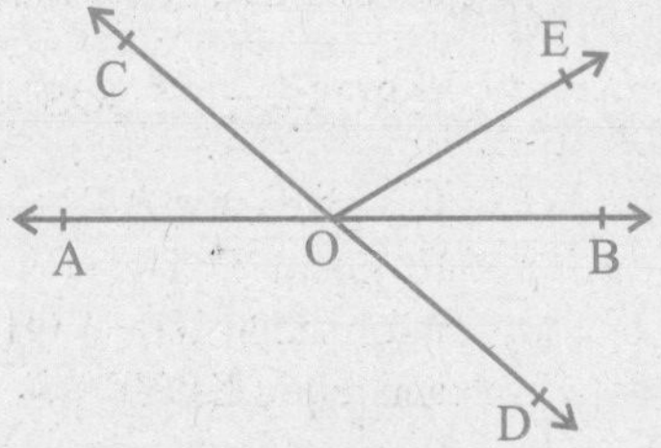

Fig. 6.13

2. In Fig. 6.14, lines XY and MN intersect at O. If
   $\angle POY = 90°$ and $a : b = 2 : 3$, find $c$.

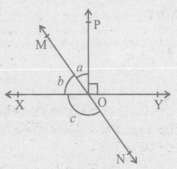

Fig. 6.14

3. In Fig. 6.15, $\angle PQR = \angle PRQ$, then prove that
   $\angle PQS = \angle PRT$.

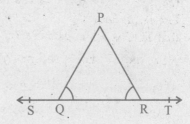

Fig. 6.15

4. In Fig. 6.16, if $x + y = w + z$, then prove that AOB
   is a line.

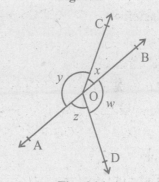

Fig. 6.16

5. In Fig. 6.17, POQ is a line. Ray OR is perpendicular
   to line PQ. OS is another ray lying between rays
   OP and OR. Prove that

   $$\angle ROS = \frac{1}{2} (\angle QOS - \angle POS).$$

6. It is given that $\angle XYZ = 64°$ and XY is produced
   to point P. Draw a figure from the given
   information. If ray YQ bisects $\angle ZYP$, find $\angle XYQ$
   and reflex $\angle QYP$.

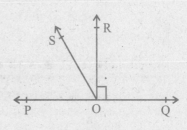

Fig. 6.17

## 6.5 Parallel Lines and a Transversal

Recall that a line which intersects two or more lines at distinct points is called a **transversal** (see Fig. 6.18). Line *l* intersects lines *m* and *n* at points P and Q respectively. Therefore, line *l* is a transversal for lines *m* and *n*. Observe that four angles are formed at each of the points P and Q.

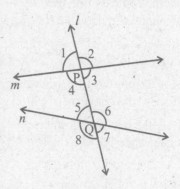

Let us name these angles as $\angle 1, \angle 2, \ldots, \angle 8$ as shown in Fig. 6.18.

$\angle 1, \angle 2, \angle 7$ and $\angle 8$ are called **exterior angles**, while $\angle 3, \angle 4, \angle 5$ and $\angle 6$ are called **interior angles**.

**Fig. 6.18**

Recall that in the earlier classes, you have named some pairs of angles formed when a transversal intersects two lines. These are as follows:

(a) **Corresponding angles :**

   (i) $\angle 1$ and $\angle 5$                (ii) $\angle 2$ and $\angle 6$

   (iii) $\angle 4$ and $\angle 8$             (iv) $\angle 3$ and $\angle 7$

(b) **Alternate interior angles :**

   (i) $\angle 4$ and $\angle 6$                (ii) $\angle 3$ and $\angle 5$

(c) **Alternate exterior angles:**

   (i) $\angle 1$ and $\angle 7$                (ii) $\angle 2$ and $\angle 8$

(d) **Interior angles on the same side of the transversal:**

   (i) $\angle 4$ and $\angle 5$                (ii) $\angle 3$ and $\angle 6$

Interior angles on the same side of the transversal are also referred to as **consecutive interior** angles or **allied** angles or **co-interior** angles. Further, many a times, we simply use the words alternate angles for alternate interior angles.

Now, let us find out the relation between the angles in these pairs when line *m* is parallel to line *n*. You know that the ruled lines of your notebook are parallel to each other. So, with ruler and pencil, draw two parallel lines along any two of these lines and a transversal to intersect them as shown in Fig. 6.19.

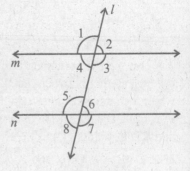

**Fig. 6.19**

Now, measure any pair of corresponding angles and find out the relation between them. You may find that : $\angle 1 = \angle 5, \angle 2 = \angle 6, \angle 4 = \angle 8$ and $\angle 3 = \angle 7$. From this, you may conclude the following axiom.

**Axiom 6.3 :** *If a transversal intersects two parallel lines, then each pair of corresponding angles is equal.*

Axiom 6.3 is also referred to as the **corresponding angles axiom**. Now, let us discuss the converse of this axiom which is as follows:

If a transversal intersects two lines such that a pair of corresponding angles is equal, then the two lines are parallel.

Does this statement hold true? It can be verified as follows: Draw a line AD and mark points B and C on it. At B and C, construct $\angle$ ABQ and $\angle$ BCS equal to each other as shown in Fig. 6.20 (i).

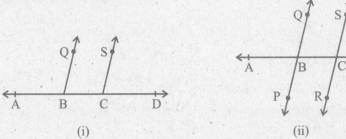

(i)                                    (ii)

**Fig. 6.20**

Produce QB and SC on the other side of AD to form two lines PQ and RS [see Fig. 6.20 (ii)]. You may observe that the two lines do not intersect each other. You may also draw common perpendiculars to the two lines PQ and RS at different points and measure their lengths. You will find it the same everywhere. So, you may conclude that the lines are parallel. Therefore, the converse of corresponding angles axiom is also true. So, we have the following axiom:

**Axiom 6.4 :** *If a transversal intersects two lines such that a pair of corresponding angles is equal, then the two lines are parallel to each other.*

Can we use corresponding angles axiom to find out the relation between the alternate interior angles when a transversal intersects two parallel lines? In Fig. 6.21, transveral PS intersects parallel lines AB and CD at points Q and R respectively.

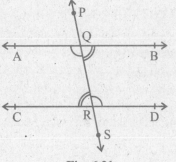

Is $\angle$ BQR $= \angle$ QRC and $\angle$ AQR $= \angle$ QRD?

You know that $\angle$ PQA $= \angle$ QRC        (1)

(Corresponding angles axiom)

**Fig. 6.21**

Is                    ∠ PQA = ∠ BQR? Yes! (Why ?)                    (2)

So, from (1) and (2), you may conclude that

∠ BQR = ∠ QRC.

Similarly,                    ∠ AQR = ∠ QRD.

This result can be stated as a theorem given below:

**Theorem 6.2** : *If a transversal intersects two parallel lines, then each pair of alternate interior angles is equal.*

Now, using the converse of the corresponding angles axiom, can we show the two lines parallel if a pair of alternate interior angles is equal? In Fig. 6.22, the transversal PS intersects lines AB and CD at points Q and R respectively such that ∠ BQR = ∠ QRC.

Is AB ∥ CD?

∠ BQR = ∠ PQA        (Why?)    (1)

But,     ∠ BQR = ∠ QRC        (Given)    (2)

So, from (1) and (2), you may conclude that

∠ PQA = ∠ QRC

But they are corresponding angles.

So, AB ∥ CD    (Converse of corresponding angles axiom)

This result can be stated as a theorem given below:

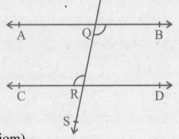

Fig. 6.22

**Theorem 6.3** : *If a transversal intersects two lines such that a pair of alternate interior angles is equal, then the two lines are parallel.*

In a similar way, you can obtain the following two theorems related to interior angles on the same side of the transversal.

**Theorem 6.4** : *If a transversal intersects two parallel lines, then each pair of interior angles on the same side of the transversal is supplementary.*

**Theorem 6.5** : *If a transversal intersects two lines such that a pair of interior angles on the same side of the transversal is supplementary, then the two lines are parallel.*

You may recall that you have verified all the above axioms and theorems in earlier classes through activities. You may repeat those activities here also.

## 6.6 Lines Parallel to the Same Line

If two lines are parallel to the same line, will they be parallel to each other? Let us check it. See Fig. 6.23 in which line $m \parallel$ line $l$ and line $n \parallel$ line $l$.

Let us draw a line $t$ transversal for the lines, $l$, $m$ and $n$. It is given that line $m \parallel$ line $l$ and line $n \parallel$ line $l$.

Therefore, $\angle 1 = \angle 2$ and $\angle 1 = \angle 3$

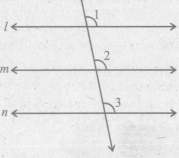

(Corresponding angles axiom)

So,    $\angle 2 = \angle 3$ (Why?)

But $\angle 2$ and $\angle 3$ are corresponding angles and they are equal.

Therefore, you can say that

Line $m \parallel$ Line $n$

(Converse of corresponding angles axiom)        Fig. 6.23

This result can be stated in the form of the following theorem:

**Theorem 6.6** : *Lines which are parallel to the same line are parallel to each other.*

**Note** : The property above can be extended to more than two lines also.

Now, let us solve some examples related to parallel lines.

**Example 4 :** In Fig. 6.24, if PQ $\parallel$ RS, $\angle$ MXQ $= 135°$ and $\angle$ MYR $= 40°$, find $\angle$ XMY.

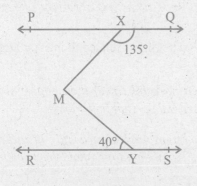
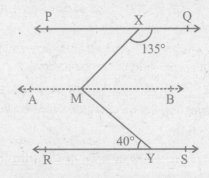

Fig. 6.24                    Fig. 6.25

**Solution :** Here, we need to draw a line AB parallel to line PQ, through point M as shown in Fig. 6.25. Now, AB $\parallel$ PQ and PQ $\parallel$ RS.

Therefore,                          AB ∥ RS    (Why?)

Now,                    ∠ QXM + ∠ XMB = 180°

                    (AB ∥ PQ, Interior angles on the same side of the transversal XM)

But                              ∠ QXM = 135°

So,              135° + ∠ XMB = 180°

Therefore,                    ∠ XMB = 45°                                              (1)

Now,                              ∠ BMY = ∠ MYR          (AB ∥ RS, Alternate angles)

Therefore,                    ∠ BMY = 40°                                              (2)

Adding (1) and (2), you get

                    ∠ XMB + ∠ BMY = 45° + 40°

That is,                          ∠ XMY = 85°

**Example 5 :** If a transversal intersects two lines such that the bisectors of a pair of corresponding angles are parallel, then prove that the two lines are parallel.

**Solution :** In Fig. 6.26, a transversal AD intersects two lines PQ and RS at points B and C respectively. Ray BE is the bisector of ∠ ABQ and ray CG is the bisector of ∠ BCS; and BE ∥ CG.

We are to prove that PQ ∥ RS.

It is given that ray BE is the bisector of ∠ ABQ.

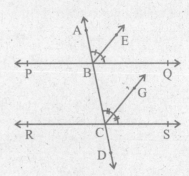

Therefore,     $\angle ABE = \dfrac{1}{2} \angle ABQ$         (1)

Similarly, ray CG is the bisector of ∠ BCS.

Therefore,     $\angle BCG = \dfrac{1}{2} \angle BCS$         (2)

But BE ∥ CG and AD is the transversal.

Therefore,     ∠ ABE = ∠ BCG

               (Corresponding angles axiom)         (3)

**Fig. 6.26**

Substituting (1) and (2) in (3), you get

$$\frac{1}{2} \angle ABQ = \frac{1}{2} \angle BCS$$

That is,                          ∠ ABQ = ∠ BCS

But, they are the corresponding angles formed by transversal AD with PQ and RS; and are equal.

Therefore,                                  PQ ∥ RS

                                (Converse of corresponding angles axiom)

**Example 6 :** In Fig. 6.27, AB ∥ CD and CD ∥ EF. Also EA ⊥ AB. If ∠ BEF = 55°, find the values of $x$, $y$ and $z$.

Solution :   $y + 55° = 180°$

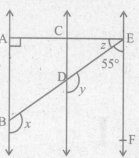

   (Interior angles on the same side of the transversal ED)

Therefore,          $y = 180° - 55° = 125°$

Again              $x = y$

   (AB ∥ CD, Corresponding angles axiom)

Therefore          $x = 125°$

Now, since AB ∥ CD and CD ∥ EF, therefore, AB ∥ EF.

**Fig. 6.27**

So,                    ∠ EAB + ∠ FEA = 180°

(Interior angles on the same side of the transversal EA)

Therefore,              $90° + z + 55° = 180°$

Which gives                  $z = 35°$

## EXERCISE 6.2

1.  In Fig. 6.28, find the values of $x$ and $y$ and then show that AB ∥ CD.

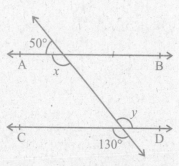

**Fig. 6.28**

**2.** In Fig. 6.29, if AB ∥ CD, CD ∥ EF and $y : z = 3 : 7$, find $x$.

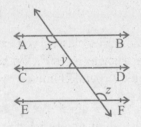

**Fig. 6.29**

**3.** In Fig. 6.30, if AB ∥ CD, EF ⊥ CD and ∠ GED = 126°, find ∠ AGE, ∠ GEF and ∠ FGE.

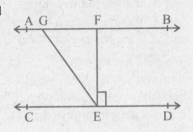

**Fig. 6.30**

**4.** In Fig. 6.31, if PQ ∥ ST, ∠ PQR = 110° and ∠ RST = 130°, find ∠ QRS.

[**Hint :** Draw a line parallel to ST through point R.]

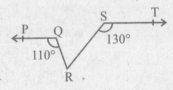

**Fig. 6.31**

**5.** In Fig. 6.32, if AB ∥ CD, ∠ APQ = 50° and ∠ PRD = 127°, find $x$ and $y$.

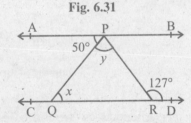

**Fig. 6.32**

**6.** In Fig. 6.33, PQ and RS are two mirrors placed parallel to each other. An incident ray AB strikes the mirror PQ at B, the reflected ray moves along the path BC and strikes the mirror RS at C and again reflects back along CD. Prove that AB ∥ CD.

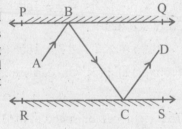

**Fig. 6.33**

## 6.7 Angle Sum Property of a Triangle

In the earlier classes, you have studied through activities that the sum of all the angles of a triangle is 180°. We can prove this statement using the axioms and theorems related to parallel lines.

**Theorem 6.7** : *The sum of the angles of a triangle is 180°.*

**Proof** : Let us see what is given in the statement above, that is, the hypothesis and what we need to prove. We are given a triangle PQR and ∠ 1, ∠ 2 and ∠ 3 are the angles of Δ PQR (see Fig. 6.34).

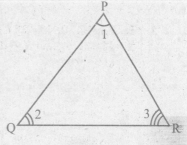

Fig. 6.34

We need to prove that ∠ 1 + ∠ 2 + ∠ 3 = 180°. Let us draw a line XPY parallel to QR through the opposite vertex P, as shown in Fig. 6.35, so that we can use the properties related to parallel lines.

Now, XPY is a line.

Therefore,     ∠ 4 + ∠ 1 + ∠ 5 = 180°     (1)

But XPY ‖ QR and PQ, PR are transversals.

So,          ∠ 4 = ∠ 2   and   ∠ 5 = ∠ 3
                   (Pairs of alternate angles)

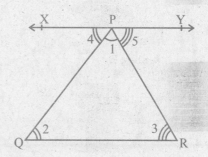

Substituting ∠ 4 and ∠ 5 in (1), we get

          ∠ 2 + ∠ 1 + ∠ 3 = 180°

That is,          ∠ 1 + ∠ 2 + ∠ 3 = 180°     ∎

Fig. 6.35

Recall that you have studied about the formation of an exterior angle of a triangle in the earlier classes (see Fig. 6.36). Side QR is produced to point S, ∠ PRS is called an exterior angle of ΔPQR.

Is          ∠ 3 + ∠ 4 = 180°? (Why?)     (1)

Also, see that

     ∠ 1 + ∠ 2 + ∠ 3 = 180° (Why?)     (2)

From (1) and (2), you can see that

          ∠ 4 = ∠ 1 + ∠ 2.

This result can be stated in the form of a theorem as given below:

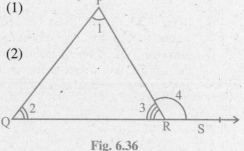

Fig. 6.36

**Theorem 6.8 :** *If a side of a triangle is produced, then the exterior angle so formed is equal to the sum of the two interior opposite angles.*

It is obvious from the above theorem that an *exterior angle of a triangle is greater than either of its interior apposite angles.*

Now, let us take some examples based on the above theorems.

**Example 7 :** In Fig. 6.37, if QT ⊥ PR, ∠ TQR = 40° and ∠ SPR = 30°, find $x$ and $y$.

**Solution :** In Δ TQR, $90° + 40° + x = 180°$

　　　　　　(Angle sum property of a triangle)

Therefore,　　$x = 50°$

Now,　　　　$y = ∠ SPR + x$　(Theorem 6.8)

Therefore,　　$y = 30° + 50°$

　　　　　　　$= 80°$

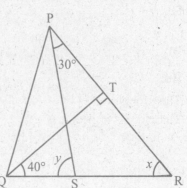

Fig. 6.37

**Example 8 :** In Fig. 6.38, the sides AB and AC of ΔABC are produced to points E and D respectively. If bisectors BO and CO of ∠ CBE and ∠ BCD respectively meet at point O, then prove that

$∠ BOC = 90° - \dfrac{1}{2} ∠BAC.$

**Solution :** Ray BO is the bisector of ∠ CBE.

Therefore,　　　　$∠ CBO = \dfrac{1}{2} ∠ CBE$

　　　　　　　　　$= \dfrac{1}{2} (180° - y)$

　　　　　　　　　$= 90° - \dfrac{y}{2}$　(1)

Similarly, ray CO is the bisector of ∠ BCD.

Therefore,　　　　　　$∠ BCO = \dfrac{1}{2} ∠ BCD$

　　　　　　　　　　　$= \dfrac{1}{2} (180° - z)$

　　　　　　　　　　　$= 90° - \dfrac{z}{2}$　(2)

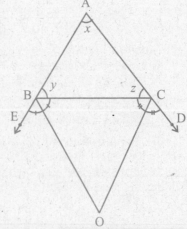

Fig. 6.38

In $\triangle$ BOC, $\angle$ BOC + $\angle$ BCO + $\angle$ CBO = 180°                    (3)

Substituting (1) and (2) in (3), you get

$$\angle \text{BOC} + 90° - \frac{z}{2} + 90° - \frac{y}{2} = 180°$$

So,                                 $$\angle \text{BOC} = \frac{z}{2} + \frac{y}{2}$$

or,                                 $$\angle \text{BOC} = \frac{1}{2}\,(y + z)$$                    (4)

But,                     $x + y + z = 180°$      (Angle sum property of a triangle)

Therefore,               $y + z = 180° - x$

Therefore, (4) becomes

$$\angle \text{BOC} = \frac{1}{2}\,(180° - x)$$

$$= 90° - \frac{x}{2}$$

$$= 90° - \frac{1}{2}\,\angle \text{BAC}$$

## EXERCISE 6.3

1.  In Fig. 6.39, sides QP and RQ of $\triangle$ PQR are produced to points S and T respectively. If $\angle$ SPR = 135° and $\angle$ PQT = 110°, find $\angle$ PRQ.

2.  In Fig. 6.40, $\angle$ X = 62°, $\angle$ XYZ = 54°. If YO and ZO are the bisectors of $\angle$ XYZ and $\angle$ XZY respectively of $\triangle$ XYZ, find $\angle$ OZY and $\angle$ YOZ.

3.  In Fig. 6.41, if AB ∥ DE, $\angle$ BAC = 35° and $\angle$ CDE = 53°, find $\angle$ DCE.

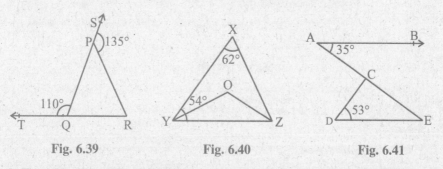

Fig. 6.39                    Fig. 6.40                    Fig. 6.41

4.  In Fig. 6.42, if lines PQ and RS intersect at point T, such that $\angle$ PRT = 40°, $\angle$ RPT = 95° and $\angle$ TSQ = 75°, find $\angle$ SQT.

**5.** In Fig. 6.43, if PQ ⊥ PS, PQ ∥ SR, ∠ SQR = 28° and ∠ QRT = 65°, then find the values of $x$ and $y$.

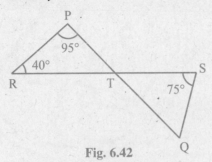

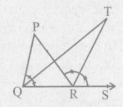

Fig. 6.42                                                                      Fig. 6.43

**6.** In Fig. 6.44, the side QR of Δ PQR is produced to a point S. If the bisectors of ∠ PQR and ∠ PRS meet at point T, then prove that

$$\angle QTR = \frac{1}{2} \angle QPR.$$

Fig. 6.44

## 6.8 Summary

In this chapter, you have studied the following points:

1. If a ray stands on a line, then the sum of the two adjacent angles so formed is 180° and vice-versa. This property is called as the Linear pair axiom.

2. If two lines intersect each other, then the vertically opposite angles are equal.

3. If a transversal intersects two parallel lines, then

   (i)   each pair of corresponding angles is equal,

   (ii)  each pair of alternate interior angles is equal,

   (iii) each pair of interior angles on the same side of the transversal is supplementary.

4. If a transversal intersects two lines such that, either

   (i)   any one pair of corresponding angles is equal, or

   (ii)  any one pair of alternate interior angles is equal, or

   (iii) any one pair of interior angles on the same side of the transversal is supplementary,
         then the lines are parallel.

5. Lines which are parallel to a given line are parallel to each other.

6. The sum of the three angles of a triangle is 180°.

7. If a side of a triangle is produced, the exterior angle so formed is equal to the sum of the two interior opposite angles.

# CHAPTER 7

# TRIANGLES

## 7.1 Introduction

You have studied about triangles and their various properties in your earlier classes. You know that a closed figure formed by three intersecting lines is called a triangle. ('Tri' means 'three'). A triangle has three sides, three angles and three vertices. For example, in triangle ABC, denoted as △ ABC (see Fig. 7.1); AB, BC, CA are the three sides, ∠ A, ∠ B, ∠ C are the three angles and A, B, C are three vertices.

In Chapter 6, you have also studied some properties of triangles. In this chapter, you will study in details about the congruence of triangles, rules of congruence, some more properties of triangles and inequalities in a triangle. You have already verified most of these properties in earlier classes. We will now prove some of them.

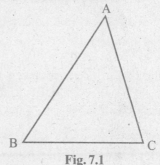

Fig. 7.1

## 7.2 Congruence of Triangles

You must have observed that two copies of your photographs of the same size are identical. Similarly, two bangles of the same size, two ATM cards issued by the same bank are identical. You may recall that on placing a one rupee coin on another minted in the same year, they cover each other completely.

Do you remember what such figures are called? Indeed they are called **congruent figures** ('congruent' means equal in all respects or figures whose shapes and sizes are both the same).

Now, draw two circles of the same radius and place one on the other. What do you observe? They cover each other completely and we call them as congruent circles.

Repeat this activity by placing one square on the other with sides of the same measure (see Fig. 7.2) or by placing two equilateral triangles of equal sides on each other. You will observe that the squares are congruent to each other and so are the equilateral triangles.

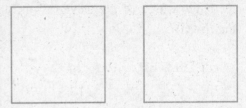

Fig. 7.2

You may wonder why we are studying congruence. You all must have seen the ice tray in your refrigerator. Observe that the moulds for making ice are all congruent. The cast used for moulding in the tray also has congruent depressions (may be all are rectangular or all circular or all triangular). So, whenever identical objects have to be produced, the concept of congruence is used in making the cast.

Sometimes, you may find it difficult to replace the refill in your pen by a new one and this is so when the new refill is not of the same size as the one you want to remove. Obviously, if the two refills are identical or congruent, the new refill fits.

So, you can find numerous examples where congruence of objects is applied in daily life situations.

Can you think of some more examples of congruent figures?

Now, which of the following figures are not congruent to the square in Fig 7.3 (i) :

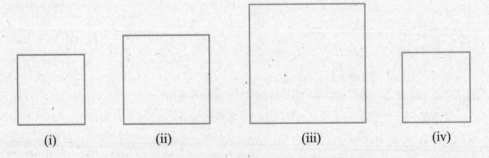

(i)                  (ii)                  (iii)                  (iv)

Fig. 7.3

The large squares in Fig. 7.3 (ii) and (iii) are obviously not congruent to the one in Fig 7.3 (i), but the square in Fig 7.3 (iv) is congruent to the one given in Fig 7.3 (i).

Let us now discuss the congruence of two triangles.

You already know that two triangles are congruent if the sides and angles of one triangle are equal to the corresponding sides and angles of the other triangle.

Now, which of the triangles given below are congruent to triangle ABC in Fig. 7.4 (i)?

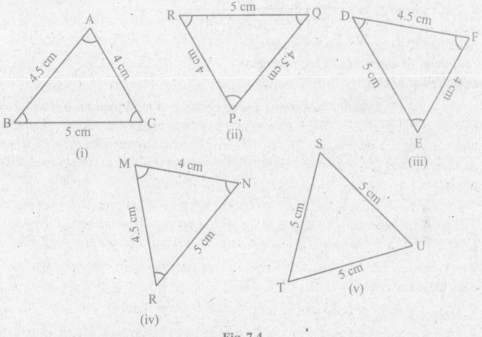

Fig. 7.4

Cut out each of these triangles from Fig. 7.4 (ii) to (v) and turn them around and try to cover △ ABC. Observe that triangles in Fig. 7.4 (ii), (iii) and (iv) are congruent to △ ABC while △ TSU of Fig 7.4 (v) is not congruent to △ ABC.

If △ PQR is congruent to △ ABC, we write △ PQR ≅ △ ABC.

Notice that when △ PQR ≅ △ ABC, then sides of △ PQR fall on corresponding equal sides of △ ABC and so is the case for the angles.

That is, PQ covers AB, QR covers BC and RP covers CA; ∠ P covers ∠ A, ∠ Q covers ∠ B and ∠ R covers ∠ C. Also, there is a one-one correspondence between the vertices. That is, P corresponds to A, Q to B, R to C and so on which is written as

$$P \leftrightarrow A, Q \leftrightarrow B, R \leftrightarrow C$$

Note that under this correspondence, △ PQR ≅ △ ABC; but it will not be correct to write △QRP ≅ △ ABC.

Similarly, for Fig. 7.4 (iii),

FD ↔ AB, DE ↔ BC  and EF ↔ CA

and   F ↔ A, D ↔ B  and E ↔ C

So, Δ FDE ≅ Δ ABC but writing Δ DEF ≅ Δ ABC is not correct.

Give the correspondence between the triangle in Fig. 7.4 (iv) and Δ ABC.

So, it is necessary to write the correspondence of vertices correctly for writing of congruence of triangles in symbolic form.

Note that in **congruent triangles corresponding parts** are **equal** and we write in short 'CPCT' for *corresponding parts of congruent triangles*.

## 7.3 Criteria for Congruence of Triangles

In earlier classes, you have learnt four criteria for congruence of triangles. Let us recall them.

Draw two triangles with one side 3 cm. Are these triangles congruent? Observe that they are not congruent (see Fig. 7.5).

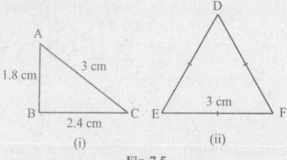

Fig. 7.5

Now, draw two triangles with one side 4 cm and one angle 50° (see Fig. 7.6). Are they congruent?

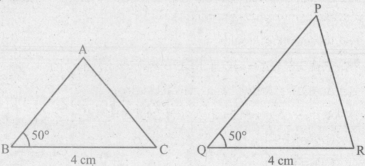

Fig. 7.6

See that these two triangles are not congruent.

Repeat this activity with some more pairs of triangles.

So, equality of one pair of sides or one pair of sides and one pair of angles is not sufficient to give us congruent triangles.

What would happen if the other pair of arms (sides) of the equal angles are also equal?

In Fig 7.7, BC = QR, ∠ B = ∠ Q and also, AB = PQ. Now, what can you say about congruence of Δ ABC and Δ PQR?

Recall from your earlier classes that, in this case, the two triangles are congruent. Verify this for Δ ABC and Δ PQR in Fig. 7.7.

Repeat this activity with other pairs of triangles. Do you observe that the equality of two sides and the included angle is enough for the congruence of triangles? Yes, it is enough.

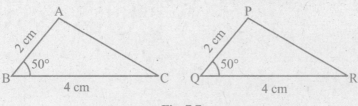

Fig. 7.7

This is the first criterion for congruence of triangles.

**Axiom 7.1 (SAS congruence rule) :** *Two triangles are congruent if two sides and the included angle of one triangle are equal to the two sides and the included angle of the other triangle.*

This result cannot be proved with the help of previously known results and so it is accepted true as an axiom (see Appendix 1).

Let us now take some examples.

**Example 1 :** In Fig. 7.8, OA = OB and OD = OC. Show that

      (i) Δ AOD ≅ Δ BOC and   (ii) AD ∥ BC.

**Solution :** (i) You may observe that in Δ AOD and Δ BOC,

$$\left.\begin{array}{l} OA = OB \\ OD = OC \end{array}\right\} \quad \text{(Given)}$$

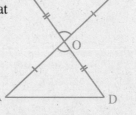

Fig. 7.8

Also, since ∠ AOD and ∠ BOC form a pair of vertically opposite angles, we have

$$\angle \text{AOD} = \angle \text{BOC}.$$

So,                                    Δ AOD ≅ Δ BOC        (by the SAS congruence rule)

(ii) In congruent triangles AOD and BOC, the other corresponding parts are also equal.

So,   ∠ OAD = ∠ OBC and these form a pair of alternate angles for line segments AD and BC.

Therefore,                      AD ‖ BC.

**Example 2 :** AB is a line segment and line *l* is its perpendicular bisector. If a point P lies on *l*, show that P is equidistant from A and B.

**Solution :** Line *l* ⊥ AB and passes through C which is the mid-point of AB (see Fig. 7.9). You have to show that PA = PB. Consider Δ PCA and Δ PCB.

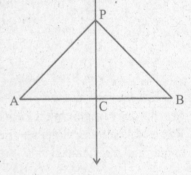

We have    AC = BC    (C is the mid-point of AB)

∠ PCA = ∠ PCB = 90°        (Given)

PC = PC        (Common)

So,   Δ PCA ≅ Δ PCB (SAS rule)

and so, PA = PB, as they are corresponding sides of congruent triangles.

**Fig. 7.9**

Now, let us construct two triangles, whose sides are 4 cm and 5 cm and one of the angles is 50° and this angle is not included in between the equal sides (see Fig. 7.10). Are the two triangles congruent?

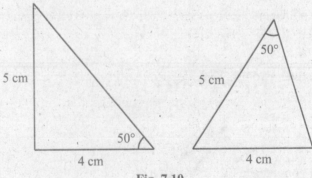

**Fig. 7.10**

Notice that the two triangles are not congruent.

Repeat this activity with more pairs of triangles. You will observe that for triangles to be congruent, it is very important that the equal angles are included between the pairs of equal sides.

So, SAS *congruence rule holds* but not ASS or SSA rule.

Next, try to construct the two triangles in which two angles are 60° and 45° and the side included between these angles is 4 cm (see Fig. 7.11).

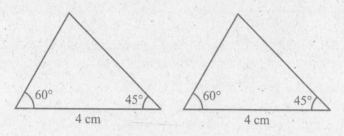

**Fig. 7.11**

Cut out these triangles and place one triangle on the other. What do you observe? See that one triangle covers the other completely; that is, the two triangles are congruent. Repeat this activity with more pairs of triangles. You will observe that equality of two angles and the included side is sufficient for congruence of triangles.

This result is the **Angle-Side-Angle** criterion for congruence and is written as **ASA** criterion. You have verified this criterion in earlier classes, but let us state and prove this result.

Since this result can be proved, it is called a theorem and to prove it, we use the SAS axiom for congruence.

**Theorem 7.1 (ASA congruence rule) :** *Two triangles are congruent if two angles and the included side of one triangle are equal to two angles and the included side of other triangle.*

**Proof :** We are given two triangles ABC and DEF in which:

$$\angle B = \angle E, \angle C = \angle F$$

and $$BC = EF$$

We need to prove that $$\Delta ABC \cong \Delta DEF$$

For proving the congruence of the two triangles see that three cases arise.

**Case (i)** : Let AB = DE (see Fig. 7.12).

Now what do you observe? You may observe that

$$AB = DE \qquad \text{(Assumed)}$$
$$\angle B = \angle E \qquad \text{(Given)}$$
$$BC = EF \qquad \text{(Given)}$$

So,    $\Delta$ ABC $\cong$ $\Delta$ DEF    (By SAS rule)

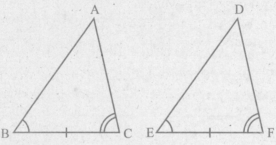

**Fig. 7.12**

**Case (ii)** : Let if possible AB > DE. So, we can take a point P on AB such that PB = DE. Now consider $\Delta$ PBC and $\Delta$ DEF (see Fig. 7.13).

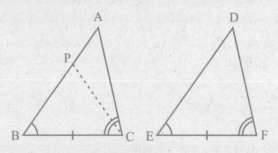

**Fig. 7.13**

Observe that in $\Delta$ PBC and $\Delta$ DEF,

$$PB = DE \qquad \text{(By construction)}$$
$$\angle B = \angle E \qquad \text{(Given)}$$
$$BC = EF \qquad \text{(Given)}$$

So, we can conclude that:

$\Delta$ PBC $\cong$ $\Delta$ DEF, by the SAS axiom for congruence.

Since the triangles are congruent, their corresponding parts will be equal.

So, $\angle$ PCB = $\angle$ DFE

But, we are given that

$\angle$ ACB = $\angle$ DFE

So, $\angle$ ACB = $\angle$ PCB

Is this possible?

This is possible only if P coincides with A.

or, BA = ED

So, $\triangle$ ABC $\cong$ $\triangle$ DEF (by SAS axiom)

**Case (iii)** : If AB < DE, we can choose a point M on DE such that ME = AB and repeating the arguments as given in Case (ii), we can conclude that AB = DE and so, $\triangle$ ABC $\cong$ $\triangle$ DEF. ■

Suppose, now in two triangles two pairs of angles and one pair of corresponding sides are equal but the side is not included between the corresponding equal pairs of angles. Are the triangles still congruent? You will observe that they are congruent. Can you reason out why?

You know that the sum of the three angles of a triangle is 180°. So if two pairs of angles are equal, the third pair is also equal (180° – sum of equal angles).

So, two *triangles are congruent if any two pairs of angles and one pair of corresponding sides are equal*. We may call it as the **AAS Congruence Rule**.

Now let us perform the following activity :

Draw triangles with angles 40°, 50° and 90°. How many such triangles can you draw?

In fact, you can draw as many triangles as you want with different lengths of sides (see Fig. 7.14).

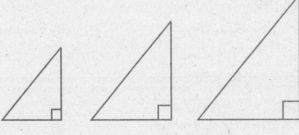

**Fig. 7.14**

Observe that the triangles may or may not be congruent to each other.

So, equality of three angles is not sufficient for congruence of triangles. Therefore, for congruence of triangles out of three equal parts, one has to be a side.

Let us now take some more examples.

**Example 3 :** Line-segment AB is parallel to another line-segment CD. O is the mid-point of AD (see Fig. 7.15). Show that (i) ΔAOB ≅ ΔDOC (ii) O is also the mid-point of BC.

**Solution :** (i) Consider Δ AOB and Δ DOC.

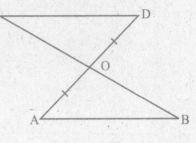

∠ ABO = ∠ DCO

(Alternate angles as AB ∥ CD

and BC is the transversal)

∠ AOB = ∠ DOC

(Vertically opposite angles)

OA = OD          (Given)

Fig. 7.15

Therefore,     ΔAOB ≅ ΔDOC     (AAS rule)

(ii)               OB = OC        (CPCT)

So, O is the mid-point of BC.


## EXERCISE 7.1

1. In quadrilateral ACBD,

   AC = AD and AB bisects ∠ A (see Fig. 7.16). Show that Δ ABC ≅ Δ ABD.

   What can you say about BC and BD?

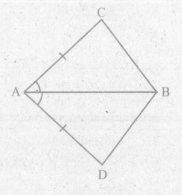

Fig. 7.16

2. ABCD is a quadrilateral in which AD = BC and
   ∠ DAB = ∠ CBA (see Fig. 7.17). Prove that

   (i)   △ ABD ≅ △ BAC

   (ii)  BD = AC

   (iii) ∠ ABD = ∠ BAC.

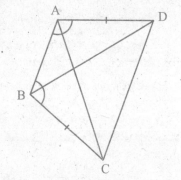

Fig. 7.17

3. AD and BC are equal perpendiculars to a line
   segment AB (see Fig. 7.18). Show that CD bisects
   AB.

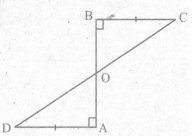

Fig. 7.18

4. *l* and *m* are two parallel lines intersected by
   another pair of parallel lines *p* and *q*
   (see Fig. 7.19). Show that △ ABC ≅ △ CDA.

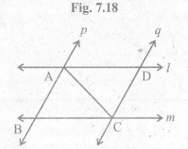

Fig. 7.19

5. Line *l* is the bisector of an angle ∠ A and B is any
   point on *l*. BP and BQ are perpendiculars from B
   to the arms of ∠ A (see Fig. 7.20). Show that:

   (i)  △ APB ≅ △ AQB

   (ii) BP = BQ or B is equidistant from the arms
        of ∠ A.

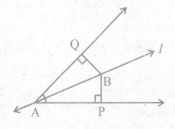

Fig. 7.20

6. In Fig. 7.21, AC = AE, AB = AD and
   ∠BAD = ∠EAC. Show that BC = DE.

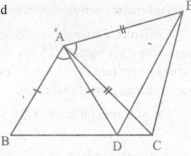

Fig. 7.21

7. AB is a line segment and P is its mid-point. D and
   E are points on the same side of AB such that
   ∠ BAD = ∠ ABE and ∠ EPA = ∠ DPB
   (see Fig. 7.22). Show that

   (i)   Δ DAP ≅ Δ EBP

   (ii)  AD = BE

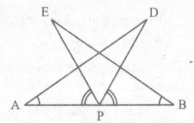

Fig. 7.22

8. In right triangle ABC, right angled at C, M is
   the mid-point of hypotenuse AB. C is joined
   to M and produced to a point D such that
   DM = CM. Point D is joined to point B
   (see Fig. 7.23). Show that:

   (i)   Δ AMC ≅ Δ BMD

   (ii)  ∠ DBC is a right angle.

   (iii) Δ DBC ≅ Δ ACB

   (iv)  CM = $\dfrac{1}{2}$ AB

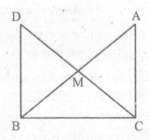

Fig. 7.23

## 7.4 Some Properties of a Triangle

In the above section you have studied two criteria for congruence of triangles. Let us
now apply these results to study some properties related to a triangle whose two sides
are equal.

Perform the activity given below:

Construct a triangle in which two sides are equal, say each equal to 3.5 cm and the third side equal to 5 cm (see Fig. 7.24). You have done such constructions in earlier classes.

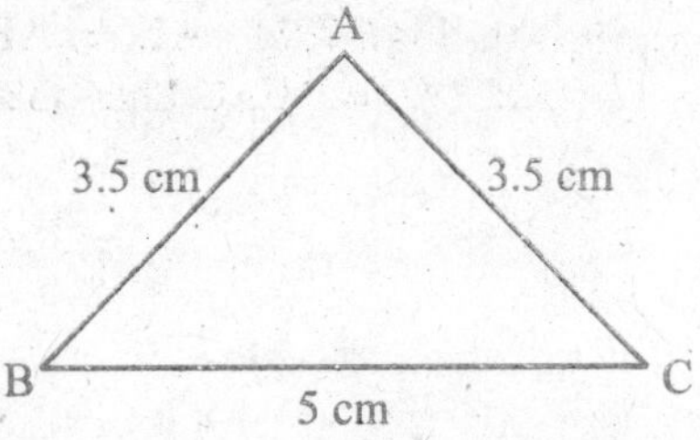

Do you remember what is such a triangle called?

A triangle in which two sides are equal is called an **isosceles triangle**. So, △ ABC of Fig. 7.24 is an isosceles triangle with AB = AC.

**Fig. 7.24**

Now, measure ∠ B and ∠ C. What do you observe?

Repeat this activity with other isosceles triangles with different sides.

You may observe that in each such triangle, the angles opposite to the equal sides are equal.

This is a very important result and is indeed true for any isosceles triangle. It can be proved as shown below.

**Theorem 7.2** : *Angles opposite to equal sides of an isosceles triangle are equal.*

This result can be proved in many ways. One of the proofs is given here.

**Proof :** We are given an isosceles triangle ABC in which AB = AC. We need to prove that ∠ B = ∠ C.

Let us draw the bisector of ∠ A and let D be the point of intersection of this bisector of ∠ A and BC (see Fig. 7.25).

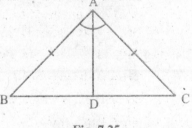

**Fig. 7.25**

In △ BAD and △ CAD,

|  |  |  |
| --- | --- | --- |
| | AB = AC | (Given) |
| | ∠ BAD = ∠ CAD | (By construction) |
| | AD = AD | (Common) |
| So, | △ BAD ≅ △ CAD | (By SAS rule) |

So, ∠ ABD = ∠ ACD, since they are corresponding angles of congruent triangles.

So,                                         ∠ B = ∠ C     ∎

Is the converse also true? That is:

If two angles of any triangle are equal, can we conclude that the sides opposite to them are also equal?

Perform the following activity.

Construct a triangle ABC with BC of any length and ∠ B = ∠ C = 50°. Draw the bisector of ∠ A and let it intersect BC at D (see Fig. 7.26).

Cut out the triangle from the sheet of paper and fold it along AD so that vertex C falls on vertex B.

What can you say about sides AC and AB?

Observe that AC covers AB completely

So,                    AC = AB

Repeat this activity with some more triangles. Each time you will observe that the sides opposite to equal angles are equal. So we have the following:

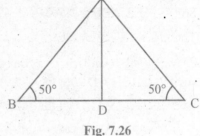

Fig. 7.26

**Theorem 7.3** : *The sides opposite to equal angles of a triangle are equal.*

This is the converse of Theorem 7.2.

You can prove this theorem by ASA congruence rule.

Let us take some examples to apply these results.

**Example 4 :** In △ ABC, the bisector AD of ∠ A is perpendicular to side BC (see Fig. 7.27). Show that AB = AC and △ ABC is isosceles.

**Solution :** In △ABD and △ACD,

|  |  |  |
|---|---|---|
| ∠ BAD = ∠ CAD | (Given) |
| AD = AD | (Common) |
| ∠ ADB = ∠ ADC = 90° | (Given) |
| So,   △ ABD ≅ △ ACD | (ASA rule) |
| So,      AB = AC | (CPCT) |

or, △ ABC is an isosceles triangle.

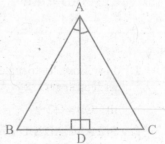

Fig. 7.27

**Example 5 :** E and F are respectively the mid-points of equal sides AB and AC of △ ABC (see Fig. 7.28). Show that BF = CE.

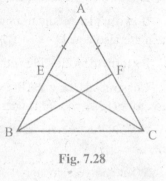

Fig. 7.28

**Solution :** In △ ABF and △ ACE,

| | | |
|---|---|---|
| AB = AC | (Given) |
| ∠ A = ∠ A | (Common) |
| AF = AE | (Halves of equal sides) |

So,      △ ABF ≅ △ ACE      (SAS rule)

Therefore,      BF = CE      (CPCT)

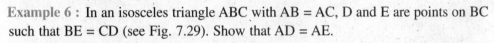

**Example 6 :** In an isosceles triangle ABC with AB = AC, D and E are points on BC such that BE = CD (see Fig. 7.29). Show that AD = AE.

**Solution :** In △ ABD and △ ACE,

       AB = AC      (Given)    (1)

       ∠ B = ∠ C

     (Angles opposite to equal sides)    (2)

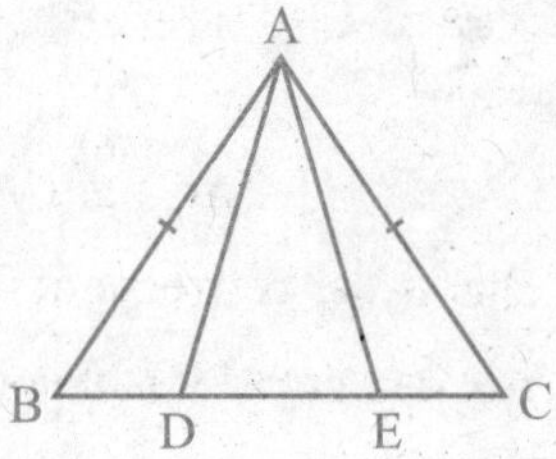

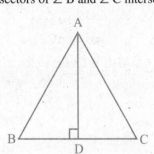

Fig. 7.29

Also,      BE = CD

So,      BE – DE = CD – DE

That is,      BD = CE           (3)

So,      △ ABD ≅ △ ACE

       (Using (1), (2), (3) and SAS rule).

This gives      AD = AE      (CPCT)

## EXERCISE 7.2

1. In an isosceles triangle ABC, with AB = AC, the bisectors of ∠ B and ∠ C intersect each other at O. Join A to O. Show that :

     (i)   OB = OC        (ii) AO bisects ∠ A

2. In △ ABC, AD is the perpendicular bisector of BC (see Fig. 7.30). Show that △ ABC is an isosceles triangle in which AB = AC.

Fig. 7.30

**3.** ABC is an isosceles triangle in which altitudes BE and CF are drawn to equal sides AC and AB respectively (see Fig. 7.31). Show that these altitudes are equal.

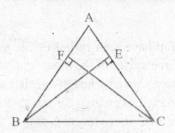

**Fig. 7.31**

**4.** ABC is a triangle in which altitudes BE and CF to sides AC and AB are equal (see Fig. 7.32). Show that

(i)   $\triangle\,ABE \cong \triangle\,ACF$

(ii)  AB = AC, i.e., ABC is an isosceles triangle.

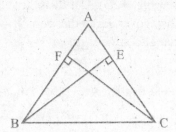

**Fig. 7.32**

**5.** ABC and DBC are two isosceles triangles on the same base BC (see Fig. 7.33). Show that $\angle\,ABD = \angle\,ACD$.

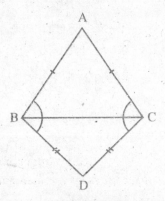

**Fig. 7.33**

**6.** $\triangle ABC$ is an isosceles triangle in which AB = AC. Side BA is produced to D such that AD = AB (see Fig. 7.34). Show that $\angle\,BCD$ is a right angle.

**7.** ABC is a right angled triangle in which $\angle\,A = 90°$ and AB = AC. Find $\angle\,B$ and $\angle\,C$.

**8.** Show that the angles of an equilateral triangle are 60° each.

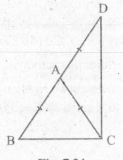

**Fig. 7.34**

## 7.5 Some More Criteria for Congruence of Triangles

You have seen earlier in this chapter that equality of three angles of one triangle to three angles of the other is not sufficient for the congruence of the two triangles. You may wonder whether equality of three sides of one triangle to three sides of another triangle is enough for congruence of the two triangles. You have already verified in earlier classes that this is indeed true.

To be sure, construct two triangles with sides 4 cm, 3.5 cm and 4.5 cm (see Fig. 7.35). Cut them out and place them on each other. What do you observe? They cover each other completely, if the equal sides are placed on each other. So, the triangles are congruent.

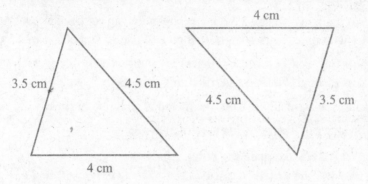

Fig. 7.35

Repeat this activity with some more triangles. We arrive at another rule for congruence.

**Theorem 7.4 (SSS congruence rule) :** *If three sides of one triangle are equal to the three sides of another triangle, then the two triangles are congruent.*

This theorem can be proved using a suitable construction.

You have already seen that in the SAS congruence rule, the pair of equal angles has to be the included angle between the pairs of corresponding pair of equal sides and if this is not so, the two triangles may not be congruent.

Perform this activity:

Construct two right angled triangles with hypotenuse equal to 5 cm and one side equal to 4 cm each (see Fig. 7.36).

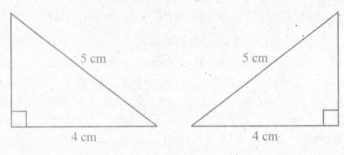

Fig. 7.36

Cut them out and place one triangle over the other with equal side placed on each other. Turn the triangles, if necessary. What do you observe?

The two triangles cover each other completely and so they are congruent. Repeat this activity with other pairs of right triangles. What do you observe?

You will find that two right triangles are congruent if one pair of sides and the hypotenuse are equal. You have verified this in earlier classes.

Note that, the right angle is *not* the included angle in this case.

So, you arrive at the following congruence rule:

**Theorem 7.5 (RHS congruence rule) :** *If in two right triangles the hypotenuse and one side of one triangle are equal to the hypotenuse and one side of the other triangle, then the two triangles are congruent.*

Note that RHS stands for **Right angle - Hypotenuse - Side.**

Let us now take some examples.

**Example 7 :** AB is a line-segment. P and Q are points on opposite sides of AB such that each of them is equidistant from the points A and B (see Fig. 7.37). Show that the line PQ is the perpendicular bisector of AB.

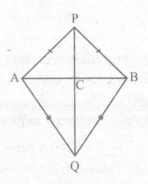

Fig. 7.37

**Solution :** You are given that PA = PB and QA = QB and you are to show that PQ ⊥ AB and PQ bisects AB. Let PQ intersect AB at C.

Can you think of two congruent triangles in this figure?

Let us take Δ PAQ and Δ PBQ.

In these triangles,

|  | AP = BP | (Given) |
|---|---|---|
|  | AQ = BQ | (Given) |
|  | PQ = PQ | (Common) |
| So, | $\triangle$ PAQ $\cong$ $\triangle$ PBQ | (SSS rule) |
| Therefore, | $\angle$ APQ = $\angle$ BPQ | (CPCT). |

Now let us consider $\triangle$ PAC and $\triangle$ PBC.

| You have : | AP = BP | (Given) |
|---|---|---|
|  | $\angle$ APC = $\angle$ BPC($\angle$ APQ = $\angle$ BPQ proved above) | |
|  | PC = PC | (Common) |
| So, | $\triangle$ PAC $\cong$ $\triangle$ PBC | (SAS rule) |
| Therefore, | AC = BC | (CPCT) (1) |
| and | $\angle$ ACP = $\angle$ BCP | (CPCT) |
| Also, | $\angle$ ACP + $\angle$ BCP = 180° | (Linear pair) |
| So, | 2$\angle$ ACP = 180° | |
| or, | $\angle$ ACP = 90° | (2) |

From (1) and (2), you can easily conclude that PQ is the perpendicular bisector of AB.

[Note that, without showing the congruence of $\triangle$ PAQ and $\triangle$ PBQ, you cannot show that $\triangle$ PAC $\cong$ $\triangle$ PBC even though AP = BP           (Given)

PC = PC           (Common)

and           $\angle$ PAC = $\angle$ PBC(Angles opposite to equal sides in

$\triangle$APB)

It is because these results give us SSA rule which is not always valid or true for congruence of triangles. Also the angle is not included between the equal pairs of sides.]

Let us take some more examples.

**Example 8 :** P is a point equidistant from two lines *l* and *m* intersecting at point A (see Fig. 7.38). Show that the line AP bisects the angle between them.

**Solution :** You are given that lines *l* and *m* intersect each other at A. Let PB $\perp$ *l*, PC $\perp$ *m*. It is given that PB = PC.

You are to show that $\angle$ PAB = $\angle$ PAC.

Let us consider △ PAB and △ PAC. In these two triangles,

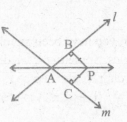

Fig. 7.38

| | |
|---|---|
| PB = PC | (Given) |
| ∠ PBA = ∠ PCA = 90° | (Given) |
| PA = PA | (Common) |

So,        △ PAB ≅ △ PAC        (RHS rule)

So,        ∠ PAB = ∠ PAC        (CPCT)

Note that this result is the converse of the result proved in Q.5 of Exercise 7.1.

## EXERCISE 7.3

1. △ ABC and △ DBC are two isosceles triangles on the same base BC and vertices A and D are on the same side of BC (see Fig. 7.39). If AD is extended to intersect BC at P, show that

   (i)   △ ABD ≅ △ ACD

   (ii)  △ ABP ≅ △ ACP

   (iii) AP bisects ∠ A as well as ∠ D.

   (iv)  AP is the perpendicular bisector of BC.

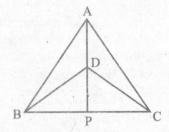

Fig. 7.39

2. AD is an altitude of an isosceles triangle ABC in which AB = AC. Show that

   (i)   AD bisects BC           (ii) AD bisects ∠ A.

3. Two sides AB and BC and median AM of one triangle ABC are respectively equal to sides PQ and QR and median PN of △ PQR (see Fig. 7.40). Show that:

   (i)   △ ABM ≅ △ PQN

   (ii)  △ ABC ≅ △ PQR

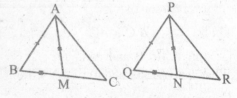

Fig. 7.40

4. BE and CF are two equal altitudes of a triangle ABC. Using RHS congruence rule, prove that the triangle ABC is isosceles.

5. ABC is an isosceles triangle with AB = AC. Draw AP ⊥ BC to show that ∠ B = ∠ C.

## 7.6 Inequalities in a Triangle

So far, you have been mainly studying the equality of sides and angles of a triangle or triangles. Sometimes, we do come across unequal objects, we need to compare them. For example, line-segment AB is greater in length as compared to line segment CD in Fig. 7.41 (i) and ∠ A is greater than ∠ B in Fig 7.41 (ii).

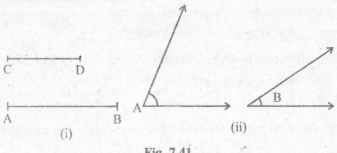

**Fig. 7.41**

Let us now examine whether there is any relation between unequal sides and unequal angles of a triangle. For this, let us perform the following activity:

**Activity :** Fix two pins on a drawing board say at B and C and tie a thread to mark a side BC of a triangle.

Fix one end of another thread at C and tie a pencil at the other (free) end . Mark a point A with the pencil and draw △ ABC (see Fig 7.42). Now, shift the pencil and mark another point A′ on CA beyond A (new position of it)

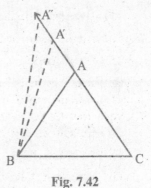

So,        A′C > AC   (Comparing the lengths)

Join A′ to B and complete the triangle A′BC. What can you say about ∠ A′BC and ∠ ABC?

Compare them. What do you observe?

**Fig. 7.42**

Clearly,   ∠ A′BC > ∠ ABC

Continue to mark more points on CA (extended) and draw the triangles with the side BC and the points marked.

You will observe that as the length of the side AC is increased (by taking different positions of A), the angle opposite to it, that is, ∠ B also increases.

Let us now perform another activity :

**Activity :** Construct a scalene triangle (that is a triangle in which all sides are of different lengths). Measure the lengths of the sides.

Now, measure the angles. What do you observe?

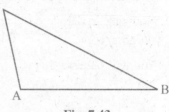

In Δ ABC of Fig 7.43, BC is the longest side and AC is the shortest side.

Also, ∠ A is the largest and ∠ B is the smallest.

Repeat this activity with some other triangles.

Fig. 7.43

We arrive at a very important result of inequalities in a triangle. It is stated in the form of a theorem as shown below:

**Theorem 7.6 :** *If two sides of a triangle are unequal, the angle opposite to the longer side is larger (or greater).*

You may prove this theorem by taking a point P on BC such that CA = CP in Fig. 7.43.

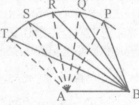

Now, let us perform another activity :

**Activity :** Draw a line-segment AB. With A as centre and some radius, draw an arc and mark different points say P, Q, R, S, T on it.

Fig. 7.44

Join each of these points with A as well as with B (see Fig. 7.44). Observe that as we move from P to T, ∠ A is becoming larger and larger. What is happening to the length of the side opposite to it? Observe that the length of the side is also increasing; that is ∠ TAB > ∠ SAB > ∠ RAB > ∠ QAB > ∠ PAB and TB > SB > RB > QB > PB.

Now, draw any triangle with all angles unequal to each other. Measure the lengths of the sides (see Fig. 7.45).

Observe that the side opposite to the largest angle is the longest. In Fig. 7.45, ∠ B is the largest angle and AC is the longest side.

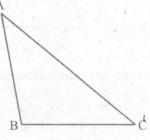

Repeat this activity for some more triangles and we see that the converse of Theorem 7.6 is also true. In this way, we arrive at the following theorem:

Fig. 7.45

**Theorem 7.7** : *In any triangle, the side opposite to the larger (greater) angle is longer.*

This theorem can be proved by the method of contradiction.

Now take a triangle ABC and in it, find AB + BC, BC + AC and AC + AB. What do you observe?

You will observe that $\qquad$ AB + BC > AC,

$$BC + AC > AB \text{ and } AC + AB > BC.$$

Repeat this activity with other triangles and with this you can arrive at the following theorem :

**Theorem 7.8** : *The sum of any two sides of a triangle is greater than the third side.*

In Fig. 7.46, observe that the side BA of △ ABC has been produced to a point D such that AD = AC. Can you show that ∠ BCD > ∠ BDC and BA + AC > BC? Have you arrived at the proof of the above theorem.

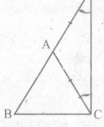

Fig. 7.46

Let us now take some examples based on these results.

**Example 9** : D is a point on side BC of △ ABC such that AD = AC (see Fig. 7.47). Show that AB > AD.

**Solution** : In △ DAC,

$\qquad$ AD = AC $\qquad$ (Given)

So, $\qquad$ ∠ ADC = ∠ ACD

$\qquad$ (Angles opposite to equal sides)

Now, $\qquad$ ∠ ADC is an exterior angle for △ABD.

So, $\qquad$ ∠ ADC > ∠ ABD

or, $\qquad$ ∠ ACD > ∠ ABD

or, $\qquad$ ∠ ACB > ∠ ABC

So, $\qquad$ AB > AC (Side opposite to larger angle in △ ABC)

or, $\qquad$ AB > AD (AD = AC)

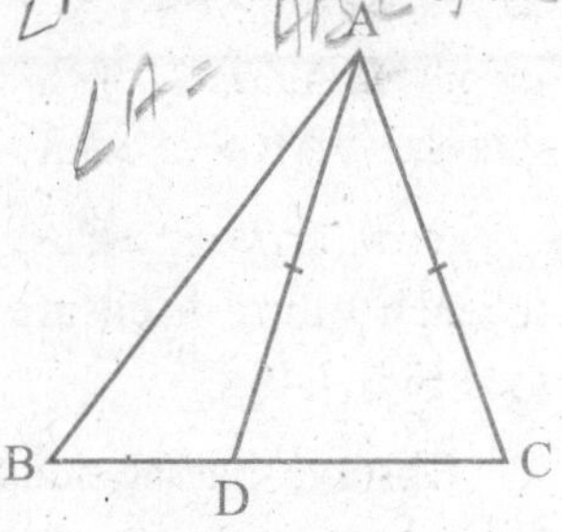

Fig. 7.47

## EXERCISE 7.4

1. Show that in a right angled triangle, the hypotenuse is the longest side.

2. In Fig. 7.48, sides AB and AC of △ ABC are extended to points P and Q respectively. Also, ∠ PBC < ∠ QCB. Show that AC > AB.

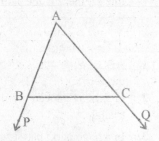

Fig. 7.48

3. In Fig. 7.49, ∠ B < ∠ A and ∠ C < ∠ D. Show that AD < BC.

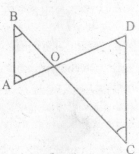

Fig. 7.49

4. AB and CD are respectively the smallest and longest sides of a quadrilateral ABCD (see Fig. 7.50). Show that ∠ A > ∠ C and ∠ B > ∠ D.

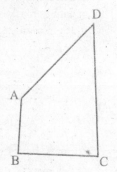

Fig. 7.50

5. In Fig 7.51, PR > PQ and PS bisects ∠ QPR. Prove that ∠ PSR > ∠ PSQ.

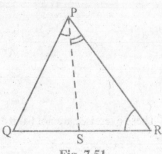

Fig. 7.51

**6.** Show that of all line segments drawn from a given point not on it, the perpendicular line segment is the shortest.

## EXERCISE 7.5 (Optional)∗

**1.** ABC is a triangle. Locate a point in the interior of Δ ABC which is equidistant from all the vertices of Δ ABC.

**2.** In a triangle locate a point in its interior which is equidistant from all the sides of the triangle.

**3.** In a huge park, people are concentrated at three points (see Fig. 7.52):

    A : where there are different slides and swings for children,

    B : near which a man-made lake is situated,

    C : which is near to a large parking and exit.

Where should an icecream parlour be set up so that maximum number of persons can approach it?

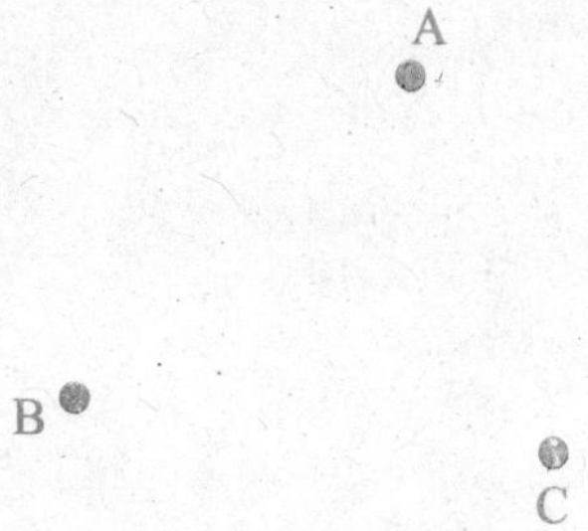

**Fig. 7.52**

(*Hint* : The parlour should be equidistant from A, B and C)

**4.** Complete the hexagonal and star shaped Rangolies [see Fig. 7.53 (i) and (ii)] by filling them with as many equilateral triangles of side 1 cm as you can. Count the number of triangles in each case. Which has more triangles?

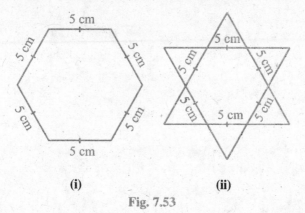

(i)                (ii)

**Fig. 7.53**

---

∗These exercises are not from examination point of view.

## 7.7 Summary

In this chapter, you have studied the following points :

1.  Two figures are congruent, if they are of the same shape and of the same size.

2.  Two circles of the same radii are congruent.

3.  Two squares of the same sides are congruent.

4.  If two triangles ABC and PQR are congruent under the correspondence A $\leftrightarrow$ P, B $\leftrightarrow$ Q and C $\leftrightarrow$ R, then symbolically, it is expressed as $\Delta$ ABC $\cong$ $\Delta$ PQR.

5.  If two sides and the included angle of one triangle are equal to two sides and the included angle of the other triangle, then the two triangles are congruent (SAS Congruence Rule).

6.  If two angles and the included side of one triangle are equal to two angles and the included side of the other triangle, then the two triangles are congruent (ASA Congruence Rule).

7.  If two angles and one side of one triangle are equal to two angles and the corresponding side of the other triangle, then the two triangles are congruent (AAS Congruence Rule).

8.  Angles opposite to equal sides of a triangle are equal.

9.  Sides opposite to equal angles of a triangle are equal.

10. Each angle of an equilateral triangle is of 60°.

11. If three sides of one triangle are equal to three sides of the other triangle, then the two triangles are congruent (SSS Congruence Rule).

12. If in two right triangles, hypotenuse and one side of a triangle are equal to the hypotenuse and one side of other triangle, then the two triangles are congruent (RHS Congruence Rule).

13. In a triangle, angle opposite to the longer side is larger (greater).

14. In a triangle, side opposite to the larger (greater) angle is longer.

15. Sum of any two sides of a triangle is greater than the third side.

# CHAPTER 8

# QUADRILATERALS

## 8.1 Introduction

You have studied many properties of a triangle in Chapters 6 and 7 and you know that on joining three non-collinear points in pairs, the figure so obtained is a triangle. Now, let us mark four points and see what we obtain on joining them in pairs in some order.

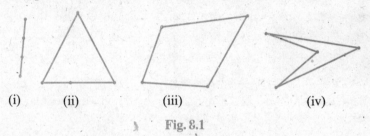

(i)          (ii)          (iii)          (iv)

Fig. 8.1

Note that if all the points are collinear (in the same line), we obtain a line segment [see Fig. 8.1 (i)], if three out of four points are collinear, we get a triangle [see Fig. 8.1 (ii)], and if no three points out of four are collinear, we obtain a closed figure with four sides [see Fig. 8.1 (iii) and (iv)].

Such a figure formed by joining four points in an order is called a *quadrilateral*. In this book, we will consider only quadrilaterals of the type given in Fig. 8.1 (iii) but not as given in Fig. 8.1 (iv).

A quadrilateral has four sides, four angles and four vertices [see Fig. 8.2 (i)].

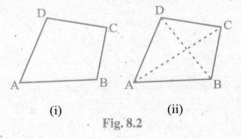

(i)          (ii)

Fig. 8.2

In quadrilateral ABCD, AB, BC, CD and DA are the four sides; A, B, C and D are the four vertices and ∠ A, ∠ B, ∠ C and ∠ D are the four angles formed at the vertices.

Now join the opposite vertices A to C and B to D [see Fig. 8.2 (ii)].

AC and BD are the two diagonals of the quadrilateral ABCD.

In this chapter, we will study more about different types of quadrilaterals, their properties and especially those of parallelograms.

You may wonder why should we study about quadrilaterals (or parallelograms) Look around you and you will find so many objects which are of the shape of a quadrilateral - the floor, walls, ceiling, windows of your classroom, the blackboard, each face of the duster, each page of your book, the top of your study table etc. Some of these are given below (see Fig. 8.3).

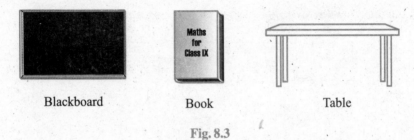

Blackboard                          Book                              Table

Fig. 8.3

Although most of the objects we see around are of the shape of special quadrilateral called rectangle, we shall study more about quadrilaterals and especially parallelograms because a rectangle is also a parallelogram and all properties of a parallelogram are true for a rectangle as well.

## 8.2 Angle Sum Property of a Quadrilateral

Let us now recall the angle sum property of a quadrilateral.

The sum of the angles of a quadrilateral is 360°. This can be verified by drawing a diagonal and dividing the quadrilateral into two triangles.

Let ABCD be a quadrilateral and AC be a diagonal (see Fig. 8.4).

What is the sum of angles in ∆ ADC?

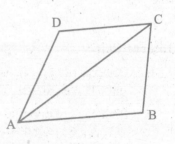

Fig. 8.4

You know that

$$\angle\,DAC + \angle\,ACD + \angle\,D = 180° \qquad (1)$$

Similarly, in $\triangle ABC$,

$$\angle\,CAB + \angle\,ACB + \angle\,B = 180° \qquad (2)$$

Adding (1) and (2), we get

$$\angle\,DAC + \angle\,ACD + \angle\,D + \angle\,CAB + \angle\,ACB + \angle\,B = 180° + 180° = 360°$$

Also,   $\angle\,DAC + \angle\,CAB = \angle\,A$ and $\angle\,ACD + \angle\,ACB = \angle\,C$

So,      $\angle\,A + \angle\,D + \angle\,B + \angle\,C = 360°$.

i.e., *the sum of the angles of a quadrilateral is 360°.*

## 8.3 Types of Quadrilaterals

Look at the different quadrilaterals drawn below:

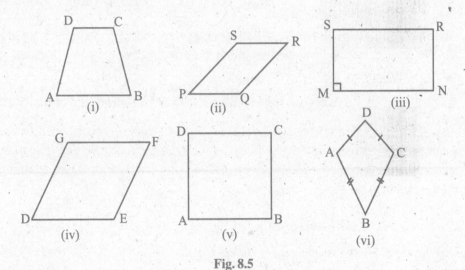

**Fig. 8.5**

**Observe that :**

- One pair of opposite sides of quadrilateral ABCD in Fig. 8.5 (i) namely, AB and CD are parallel. You know that it is called a *trapezium.*

- Both pairs of opposite sides of quadrilaterals given in Fig. 8.5 (ii), (iii) , (iv) and (v) are parallel. Recall that such quadrilaterals are called *parallelograms.*

  So, quadrilateral PQRS of Fig. 8.5 (ii) is a parallelogram.

Similarly, all quadrilaterals given in Fig. 8.5 (iii), (iv) and (v) are parallelograms.

● In parallelogram MNRS of Fig. 8.5 (iii), note that one of its angles namely ∠ M is a right angle. What is this special parallelogram called? Try to recall. It is called a *rectangle*.

● The parallelogram DEFG of Fig. 8.5 (iv) has all sides equal and we know that it is called a *rhombus*.

● The parallelogram ABCD of Fig. 8.5 (v) has ∠ A = 90° and all sides equal; it is called a *square*.

● In quadrilateral ABCD of Fig. 8.5 (vi), AD = CD and AB = CB i.e., two pairs of adjacent sides are equal. It is not a parallelogram. It is called a *kite*.

Note that a square, rectangle and rhombus are all parallelograms.

● A square is a rectangle and also a rhombus.

● A parallelogram is a trapezium.

● A kite is not a parallelogram.

● A trapezium is not a parallelogram (as only one pair of opposite sides is parallel in a trapezium and we require both pairs to be parallel in a parallelogram).

● A rectangle or a rhombus is not a square.

Look at the Fig. 8.6. We have a rectangle and a parallelogram with same perimeter 14 cm.

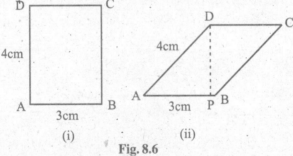

Fig. 8.6

Here the area of the parallelogram is DP × AB and this is less than the area of the rectangle, i.e., AB × AD as DP < AD. Generally sweet shopkeepers cut 'Burfis' in the shape of a parallelogram to accomodate more pieces in the same tray (see the shape of the Burfi before you eat it next time!).

Let us now review some properties of a parallelogram learnt in earlier classes.

## 8.4 Properties of a Parallelogram

Let us perform an activity.

Cut out a parallelogram from a sheet of paper and cut it along a diagonal (see Fig. 8.7). You obtain two triangles. What can you say about these triangles?

Place one triangle over the other. Turn one around, if necessary. What do you observe?

Observe that the two triangles are congruent to each other.

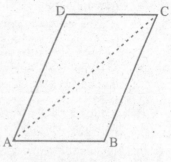

Fig. 8.7

Repeat this activity with some more parallelograms. Each time you will observe that each diagonal divides the parallelogram into two congruent triangles.

Let us now prove this result.

**Theorem 8.1** : *A diagonal of a parallelogram divides it into two congruent triangles.*

**Proof** : Let ABCD be a parallelogram and AC be a diagonal (see Fig. 8.8). Observe that the diagonal AC divides parallelogram ABCD into two triangles, namely, $\triangle$ ABC and $\triangle$ CDA. We need to prove that these triangles are congruent.

In $\triangle$ ABC and $\triangle$ CDA, note that BC ‖ AD and AC is a transversal.

So,      $\angle$ BCA = $\angle$ DAC  (Pair of alternate angles)

Also,    AB ‖ DC and AC is a transversal.

So,      $\angle$ BAC = $\angle$ DCA  (Pair of alternate angles)

and      AC = CA                    (Common)

So,      $\triangle$ ABC $\cong$ $\triangle$ CDA          (ASA rule)

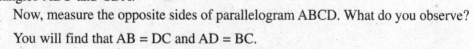

Fig. 8.8

or,    diagonal AC divides parallelogram ABCD into two congruent triangles ABC and CDA.    ∎

Now, measure the opposite sides of parallelogram ABCD. What do you observe?

You will find that AB = DC and AD = BC.

This is another property of a parallelogram stated below:

**Theorem 8.2** : *In a parallelogram, opposite sides are equal.*

You have already proved that a diagonal divides the parallelogram into two congruent triangles; so what can you say about the corresponding parts say, the corresponding sides? They are equal.

So,    AB = DC   and   AD = BC

Now what is the converse of this result? You already know that whatever is given in a theorem, the same is to be proved in the converse and whatever is proved in the theorem it is given in the converse. Thus, Theorem 8.2 can be stated as given below :

If a quadrilateral is a parallelogram, then each pair of its opposite sides is equal. So its converse is :

**Theorem 8.3 :** *If each pair of opposite sides of a quadrilateral is equal, then it is a parallelogram.*

Can you reason out why?

Let sides AB and CD of the quadrilateral ABCD be equal and also  AD = BC (see Fig. 8.9). Draw diagonal AC.

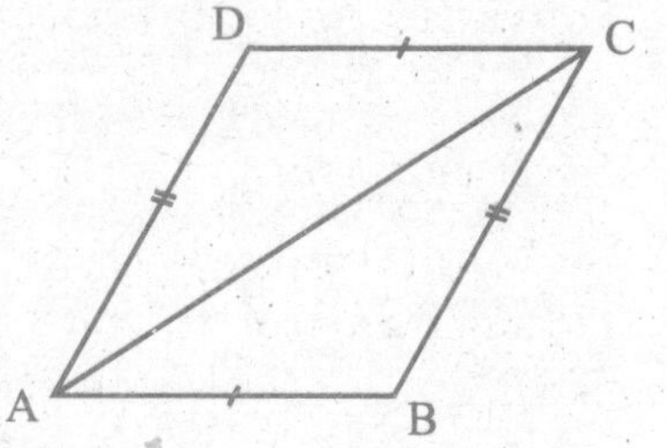

Clearly,     $\triangle$ ABC $\cong$ $\triangle$ CDA          (Why?)

So,           $\angle$ BAC = $\angle$ DCA

and          $\angle$ BCA = $\angle$ DAC          (Why?)

Fig. 8.9

Can you now say that ABCD is a parallelogram? Why?

You have just seen that in a parallelogram each pair of opposite sides is equal and conversely if each pair of opposite sides of a quadrilateral is equal, then it is a parallelogram. Can we conclude the same result for the pairs of opposite angles?

Draw a parallelogram and measure its angles. What do you observe?

Each pair of opposite angles is equal.

Repeat this with some more parallelograms. We arrive at yet another result as given below.

**Theorem 8.4 :** *In a parallelogram, opposite angles are equal.*

Now, is the converse of this result also true? Yes. Using the angle sum property of a quadrilateral and the results of parallel lines intersected by a transversal, we can see that the converse is also true. So, we have the following theorem :

**Theorem 8.5 :** *If in a quadrilateral, each pair of opposite angles is equal, then it is a parallelogram.*

There is yet another property of a parallelogram. Let us study the same. Draw a parallelogram ABCD and draw both its diagonals intersecting at the point O (see Fig. 8.10).

Measure the lengths of OA, OB, OC and OD.

What do you observe? You will observe that

$$OA = OC \quad \text{and} \quad OB = OD.$$

or, O is the mid-point of both the diagonals.

Repeat this activity with some more parallelograms.

Each time you will find that O is the mid-point of both the diagonals.

So, we have the following theorem :

**Theorem 8.6 :** *The diagonals of a parallelogram bisect each other.*

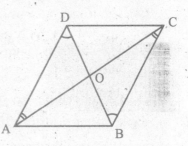

Now, what would happen, if in a quadrilateral the diagonals bisect each other? Will it be a parallelogram? Indeed this is true.

This result is the converse of the result of Theorem 8.6. It is given below:

**Fig. 8.10**

**Theorem 8.7 :** *If the diagonals of a quadrilateral bisect each other, then it is a parallelogram.*

You can reason out this result as follows:

Note that in Fig. 8.11, it is given that OA = OC and OB = OD.

So, $\triangle$ AOB $\cong$ $\triangle$ COD (Why?)

Therefore, $\angle$ ABO = $\angle$ CDO (Why?)

From this, we get AB || CD

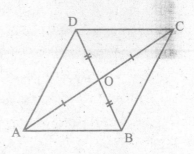

Similarly, BC || AD

**Fig. 8.11**

Therefore ABCD is a parallelogram.

Let us now take some examples.

**Example 1 :** Show that each angle of a rectangle is a right angle.

**Solution :** Let us recall what a rectangle is.

A rectangle is a parallelogram in which one angle is a right angle.

Let ABCD be a rectangle in which $\angle A = 90°$.

We have to show that $\angle B = \angle C = \angle D = 90°$

We have, AD ∥ BC and AB is a transversal (see Fig. 8.12).

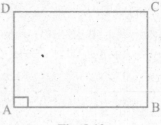

So,     $\angle A + \angle B = 180°$   (Interior angles on the same side of the transversal)

Fig. 8.12

But,          $\angle A = 90°$

So,          $\angle B = 180° - \angle A = 180° - 90° = 90°$

Now,                    $\angle C = \angle A$ and $\angle D = \angle B$

(Opposite angles of the parallellogram)

So,                    $\angle C = 90°$ and $\angle D = 90°$.

Therefore, each of the angles of a rectangle is a right angle.

**Example 2 :** Show that the diagonals of a rhombus are perpendicular to each other.

**Solution :** Consider the rhombus ABCD (see Fig. 8.13).

You know that  AB = BC = CD = DA (Why?)

Now, in $\triangle$ AOD and $\triangle$ COD,

        OA = OC (Diagonals of a parallelogram
                    bisect each other)

        OD = OD                 (Common)

        AD = CD

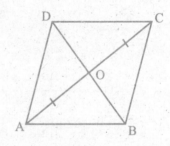

Therefore, $\triangle$ AOD $\cong$ $\triangle$ COD

                    (SSS congruence rule)

Fig. 8.13

This gives, $\angle$ AOD = $\angle$ COD       (CPCT)

But, $\angle$ AOD + $\angle$ COD = 180° (Linear pair)

So,        2$\angle$ AOD = 180°

or,          $\angle$ AOD = 90°

So, the diagonals of a rhombus are perpendicular to each other.

**Example 3 :** ABC is an isosceles triangle in which AB = AC. AD bisects exterior angle PAC and CD ∥ AB (see Fig. 8.14). Show that

(i) ∠ DAC = ∠ BCA and   (ii) ABCD is a parallelogram.

**Solution** : (i) Δ ABC is isosceles in which AB = AC (Given)

So,    ∠ ABC = ∠ ACB   (Angles opposite to equal sides)

Also,  ∠ PAC = ∠ ABC + ∠ ACB

(Exterior angle of a triangle)

or,    ∠ PAC = 2∠ ACB                (1)

Now, AD bisects ∠ PAC.

So,´   ∠ PAC = 2∠ DAC                (2)

Therefore,

2∠ DAC = 2∠ ACB   [From (1) and (2)]

or,    ∠ DAC = ∠ ACB

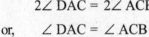

Fig. 8.14

(ii) Now, these equal angles form a pair of alternate angles when line segments BC and AD are intersected by a transversal AC.

So,    BC ∥ AD

Also,  BA ∥ CD                (Given)

Now, both pairs of opposite sides of quadrilateral ABCD are parallel.

So, ABCD is a parallelogram.

**Example 4** : Two parallel lines $l$ and $m$ are intersected by a transversal $p$ (see Fig. 8.15). Show that the quadrilateral formed by the bisectors of interior angles is a rectangle.

**Solution** : It is given that PS ∥ QR and transversal $p$ intersects them at points A and C respectively.

The bisectors of ∠ PAC and ∠ ACQ intersect at B and bisectors of ∠ ACR and ∠ SAC intersect at D.

We are to show that quadrilateral ABCD is a rectangle.

Now,    ∠ PAC = ∠ ACR

(Alternate angles as $l$ ∥ $m$ and $p$ is a transversal)

So,    $\frac{1}{2}$∠ PAC = $\frac{1}{2}$ ∠ ACR

i.e.,    ∠ BAC = ∠ ACD

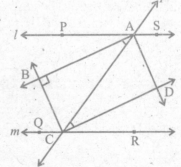

Fig. 8.15

These form a pair of alternate angles for lines AB and DC with AC as transversal and they are equal also.

So,                                         AB ∥ DC

Similarly,                                 BC ∥ AD      (Considering ∠ ACB and ∠ CAD)

Therefore, quadrilateral ABCD is a parallelogram.

Also,                         ∠ PAC + ∠ CAS = 180°    (Linear pair)

So,                $\frac{1}{2}$ ∠ PAC + $\frac{1}{2}$ ∠ CAS = $\frac{1}{2}$ × 180° = 90°

or,                         ∠ BAC + ∠ CAD = 90°

or,                                 ∠ BAD = 90°

So, ABCD is a parallelogram in which one angle is 90°.

Therefore, ABCD is a rectangle.

**Example 5 :** Show that the bisectors of angles of a parallelogram form a rectangle.

**Solution :** Let P, Q, R and S be the points of intersection of the bisectors of ∠ A and ∠ B, ∠ B and ∠ C, ∠ C and ∠ D, and ∠ D and ∠ A respectively of parallelogram ABCD (see Fig. 8.16).

In Δ ASD, what do you observe?

Since DS bisects ∠ D and AS bisects ∠ A, therefore,

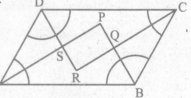

**Fig. 8.16**

$$\angle DAS + \angle ADS = \frac{1}{2} \angle A + \frac{1}{2} \angle D$$

$$= \frac{1}{2} (\angle A + \angle D)$$

$$= \frac{1}{2} \times 180° \quad (\angle A \text{ and } \angle D \text{ are interior angles}$$

on the same side of the transversal)

$$= 90°$$

Also, ∠ DAS + ∠ ADS + ∠ DSA = 180°          (Angle sum property of a triangle)

or,                 90° + ∠ DSA = 180°

or,                         ∠ DSA = 90°

So,                         ∠ PSR = 90°          (Being vertically opposite to ∠ DSA)

Similarly, it can be shown that $\angle$ APB = 90° or $\angle$ SPQ = 90° (as it was shown for $\angle$ DSA). Similarly, $\angle$ PQR = 90° and $\angle$ SRQ = 90°.

So, PQRS is a quadrilateral in which all angles are right angles.

Can we conclude that it is a rectangle? Let us examine. We have shown that $\angle$ PSR = $\angle$ PQR = 90° and $\angle$ SPQ = $\angle$ SRQ = 90°. So both pairs of opposite angles are equal.

Therefore, PQRS is a parallelogram in which one angle (in fact all angles) is 90° and so, PQRS is a rectangle.

## 8.5 Another Condition for a Quadrilateral to be a Parallelogram

You have studied many properties of a parallelogram in this chapter and you have also verified that if in a quadrilateral any one of those properties is satisfied, then it becomes a parallelogram.

We now study yet another condition which is the least required condition for a quadrilateral to be a parallelogram.

It is stated in the form of a theorem as given below:

**Theorem 8.8** : *A quadrilateral is a parallelogram if a pair of opposite sides is equal and parallel.*

Look at Fig 8.17 in which AB = CD and AB ‖ CD. Let us draw a diagonal AC. You can show that $\triangle$ ABC $\cong$ $\triangle$ CDA by SAS congruence rule.

So, BC ‖ AD (Why?)

Let us now take an example to apply this property of a parallelogram.

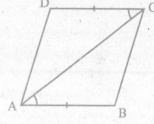

Fig. 8.17

**Example 6** : ABCD is a parallelogram in which P and Q are mid-points of opposite sides AB and CD (see Fig. 8.18). If AQ intersects DP at S and BQ intersects CP at R, show that:

(i)   APCQ is a parallelogram.

(ii)  DPBQ is a parallelogram.

(iii) PSQR is a parallelogram.

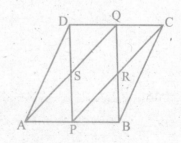

Fig. 8.18

**Solution :** (i) In quadrilateral APCQ,

$$AP \parallel QC \qquad\qquad \text{(Since AB} \parallel \text{CD)} \quad (1)$$

$$AP = \frac{1}{2} AB, \quad CQ = \frac{1}{2} CD \qquad\qquad \text{(Given)}$$

Also,  $\qquad\qquad AB = CD$  (Why?)

So,  $\qquad\qquad AP = QC$  (2)

Therefore, APCQ is a parallelogram  $\qquad$ [From (1) and (2) and Theorem 8.8]

(ii)   Similarly, quadrilateral DPBQ is a parallelogram, because

$$DQ \parallel PB \ \text{ and } DQ = PB$$

(iii)   In quadrilateral PSQR,

$$SP \parallel QR \ \text{(SP is a part of DP and QR is a part of QB)}$$

Similarly,  $\qquad\qquad SQ \parallel PR$

So, PSQR is a parallelogram.

## EXERCISE 8.1

1.  The angles of quadrilateral are in the ratio 3 : 5 : 9 : 13. Find all the angles of the quadrilateral.

2.  If the diagonals of a parallelogram are equal, then show that it is a rectangle.

3.  Show that if the diagonals of a quadrilateral bisect each other at right angles, then it is a rhombus.

4.  Show that the diagonals of a square are equal and bisect each other at right angles.

5.  Show that if the diagonals of a quadrilateral are equal and bisect each other at right angles, then it is a square.

6.  Diagonal AC of a parallelogram ABCD bisects $\angle$ A (see Fig. 8.19). Show that

    (i)   it bisects $\angle$ C also,

    (ii)   ABCD is a rhombus.

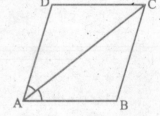

Fig. 8.19

7.  ABCD is a rhombus. Show that diagonal AC bisects $\angle$ A as well as $\angle$ C and diagonal BD bisects $\angle$ B as well as $\angle$ D.

8.  ABCD is a rectangle in which diagonal AC bisects $\angle$ A as well as $\angle$ C. Show that:
    (i) ABCD is a square (ii) diagonal BD bisects $\angle$ B as well as $\angle$ D.

9.  In parallelogram ABCD, two points P and Q are
    taken on diagonal BD such that DP = BQ
    (see Fig. 8.20). Show that:

    (i)   $\triangle APD \cong \triangle CQB$

    (ii)  AP = CQ

    (iii) $\triangle AQB \cong \triangle CPD$

    (iv)  AQ = CP

    (v)   APCQ is a parallelogram

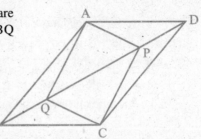

Fig. 8.20

10. ABCD is a parallelogram and AP and CQ are
    perpendiculars from vertices A and C on diagonal
    BD (see Fig. 8.21). Show that

    (i)   $\triangle APB \cong \triangle CQD$

    (ii)  AP = CQ

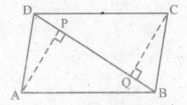

Fig. 8.21

11. In $\triangle ABC$ and $\triangle DEF$, AB = DE, AB ∥ DE, BC = EF
    and BC ∥ EF. Vertices A, B and C are joined to
    vertices D, E and F respectively (see Fig. 8.22).
    Show that

    (i)   quadrilateral ABED is a parallelogram

    (ii)  quadrilateral BEFC is a parallelogram

    (iii) AD ∥ CF and AD = CF

    (iv)  quadrilateral ACFD is a parallelogram

    (v)   AC = DF

    (vi)  $\triangle ABC \cong \triangle DEF$.

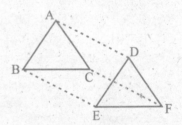

Fig. 8.22

12. ABCD is a trapezium in which AB ∥ CD and
    AD = BC (see Fig. 8.23). Show that

    (i)   $\angle A = \angle B$

    (ii)  $\angle C = \angle D$

    (iii) $\triangle ABC \cong \triangle BAD$

    (iv)  diagonal AC = diagonal BD

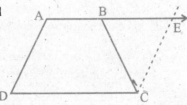

Fig. 8.23

    [*Hint*: Extend AB and draw a line through C
          parallel to DA intersecting AB produced at E.]

## 8.6 The Mid-point Theorem

You have studied many properties of a triangle as well as a quadrilateral. Now let us study yet another result which is related to the mid-point of sides of a triangle. Perform the following activity.

Draw a triangle and mark the mid-points E and F of two sides of the triangle. Join the points E and F (see Fig. 8.24).

Measure EF and BC. Measure $\angle$ AEF and $\angle$ ABC.

What do you observe? You will find that :

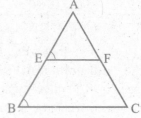

$$EF = \frac{1}{2} \ BC \ \text{and} \ \angle AEF = \angle ABC$$

so,   EF ∥ BC

Repeat this activity with some more triangles.

**Fig. 8.24**

So,  you arrive at the following theorem:

**Theorem 8.9** : *The line segment joining the mid-points of two sides of a triangle is parallel to the third side.*

You can prove this theorem using the following clue:

Observe Fig 8.25 in which E and F are mid-points of AB and AC respectively and CD ∥ BA.

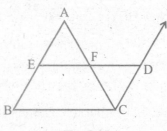

$$\Delta \ AEF \cong \Delta \ CDF \quad \text{(ASA Rule)}$$

So,    EF = DF and BE = AE = DC   (Why?)

Therefore, BCDE is a parallelogram.   (Why?)

This gives EF ∥ BC.

**Fig. 8.25**

In this case, also note that $EF = \frac{1}{2} \ ED = \frac{1}{2} BC$.

Can you state the converse of Theorem 8.9? Is the converse true?

You will see that converse of the above theorem is also true which is stated as below:

**Theorem 8.10** : *The line drawn through the mid-point of one side of a triangle, parallel to another side bisects the third side.*

In Fig 8.26, observe that E is the mid-point of AB, line $l$ is passsing through E and is parallel to BC and CM ∥ BA.

Prove that AF = CF by using the congruence of Δ AEF and Δ CDF.

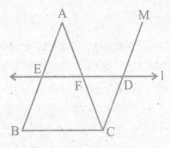

Fig. 8.26

**Example 7 :** In Δ ABC, D, E and F are respectively the mid-points of sides AB, BC and CA (see Fig. 8.27). Show that Δ ABC is divided into four congruent triangles by joining D, E and F.

**Solution :** As D and E are mid-points of sides AB and BC of the triangle ABC, by Theorem 8.9,

DE ∥ AC

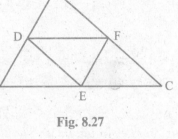

Fig. 8.27

Similarly,      DF ∥ BC and EF ∥ AB

Therefore ADEF, BDFE and DFCE are all parallelograms.

Now DE is a diagonal of the parallelogram BDFE,

therefore,      Δ BDE ≅ Δ FED

Similarly      Δ DAF ≅ Δ FED

and            Δ EFC ≅ Δ FED

So, all the four triangles are congruent.

**Example 8 :** $l$, $m$ and $n$ are three parallel lines intersected by transversals $p$ and $q$ such that $l$, $m$ and $n$ cut off equal intercepts AB and BC on $p$ (see Fig. 8.28). Show that $l$, $m$ and $n$ cut off equal intercepts DE and EF on $q$ also.

**Solution :** We are given that AB = BC and have to prove that DE = EF.

Let us join A to F intersecting $m$ at G..

The trapezium ACFD is divided into two triangles;

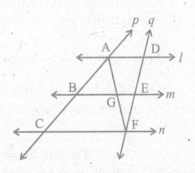

Fig. 8.28

namely $\triangle$ ACF and $\triangle$ AFD.

In $\triangle$ ACF, it is given that B is the mid-point of AC (AB = BC)

and        BG ∥ CF    (since *m* ∥ *n*).

So, G is the mid-point of AF    (by using Theorem 8.10)

Now, in $\triangle$ AFD, we can apply the same argument as G is the mid-point of AF, GE ∥ AD and so by Theorem 8.10, E is the mid-point of DF,

i.e.,        DE = EF.

In other words, *l*, *m* and *n* cut off equal intercepts on *q* also.

**EXERCISE 8.2**

1.   ABCD is a quadrilateral in which P, Q, R and S are mid-points of the sides AB, BC, CD and DA (see Fig 8.29). AC is a diagonal. Show that :

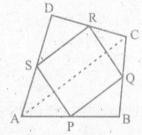

   (i)    SR ∥ AC and SR = $\dfrac{1}{2}$ AC

   (ii)   PQ = SR

   (iii)  PQRS is a parallelogram.

Fig. 8.29

2.   ABCD is a rhombus and P, Q, R and S are ©wthe mid-points of the sides AB, BC, CD and DA respectively. Show that the quadrilateral PQRS is a rectangle.

3.   ABCD is a rectangle and P, Q, R and S are mid-points of the sides AB, BC, CD and DA respectively. Show that the quadrilateral PQRS is a rhombus.

4.   ABCD is a trapezium in which AB ∥ DC, BD is a diagonal and E is the mid-point of AD. A line is drawn through E parallel to AB intersecting BC at F (see Fig. 8.30). Show that F is the mid-point of BC.

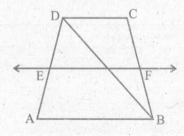

Fig. 8.30

5.  In a parallelogram ABCD, E and F are the mid-points of sides AB and CD respectively (see Fig. 8.31). Show that the line segments AF and EC trisect the diagonal BD.

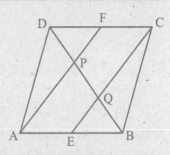

Fig. 8.31

6.  Show that the line segments joining the mid-points of the opposite sides of a quadrilateral bisect each other.

7.  ABC is a triangle right angled at C. A line through the mid-point M of hypotenuse AB and parallel to BC intersects AC at D. Show that

    (i)   D is the mid-point of AC          (ii) $MD \perp AC$

    (iii) $CM = MA = \dfrac{1}{2} AB$

## 8.7 Summary

In this chapter, you have studied the following points :

1.  Sum of the angles of a quadrilateral is 360°.

2.  A diagonal of a parallelogram divides it into two congruent triangles.

3.  In a parallelogram,

    (i)   opposite sides are equal          (ii) opposite angles are equal

    (iii) diagonals bisect each other

4.  A quadrilateral is a parallelogram, if

    (i)   opposite sides are equal      or      (ii) opposite angles are equal

    or (iii) diagonals bisect each other

    or (iv)a pair of opposite sides is equal and parallel

5.  Diagonals of a rectangle bisect each other and are equal and vice-versa.

6.  Diagonals of a rhombus bisect each other at right angles and vice-versa.

7.  Diagonals of a square bisect each other at right angles and are equal, and vice-versa.

8.  The line-segment joining the mid-points of any two sides of a triangle is parallel to the third side and is half of it.

9.  A line through the mid-point of a side of a triangle parallel to another side bisects the third side.

10. The quadrilateral formed by joining the mid-points of the sides of a quadrilateral, in order, is a parallelogram.

# CHAPTER 9

# AREAS OF PARALLELOGRAMS AND TRIANGLES

## 9.1 Introduction

In Chapter 5, you have seen that the study of Geometry, originated with the measurement of earth (lands) in the process of recasting boundaries of the fields and dividing them into appropriate parts. For example, a farmer *Budhia* had a triangular field and she wanted to divide it equally among her two daughters and one son. Without actually calculating the area of the field, she just divided one side of the triangular field into three equal parts and joined the two points of division to the opposite vertex. In this way, the field was divided into three parts and she gave one part to each of her children. Do you think that all the three parts so obtained by her were, in fact, equal in area? To get answers to this type of questions and other related problems, there is a need to have a relook at areas of plane figures, which you have already studied in earlier classes.

You may recall that the part of the plane enclosed by a simple closed figure is called a *planar region* corresponding to that figure. The magnitude or measure of this planar region is called its *area*. This magnitude or measure is always expressed with the help of a number (in some unit) such as 5 cm², 8 m², 3 hectares etc. So, we can say that area of a figure is a number (in some unit) associated with the part of the plane enclosed by the figure.

We are also familiar with the concept of congruent figures from earlier classes and from Chapter 7. *Two figures are called congruent, if they have the same shape and the same size.* In other words, if two figures A and B are congruent (see Fig. 9.1), then using a tracing paper,

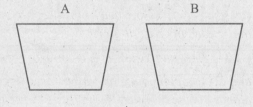

Fig. 9.1

you can superpose one figure over the other such that it will cover the other completely. So *if two figures A and B are congruent, they must have equal areas.* However, the converse of this statement is *not true.* In other words, *two figures having equal areas need not be congruent.* For example, in Fig. 9.2, rectangles ABCD and EFGH have equal areas ($9 \times 4$ cm$^2$ and $6 \times 6$ cm$^2$) but clearly they are not congruent. (Why?)

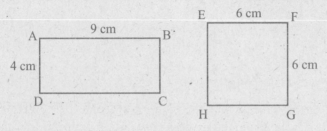

Fig. 9.2

Now let us look at Fig. 9.3 given below:

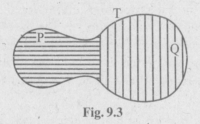

Fig. 9.3

You may observe that planar region formed by figure T is made up of two planar regions formed by figures P and Q. You can easily see that

Area of figure T = Area of figure P + Area of figure Q.

You may denote the area of figure A as ar(A), area of figure B as ar(B), area of figure T as ar(T), and so on. Now you can say that *area of a figure is a number (in some unit) associated with the part of the plane enclosed by the figure with the following two properties:*

(1) *If* A *and* B *are two congruent figures, then* ar(A) = ar(B);

and (2) *if a planar region formed by a figure* T *is made up of two non-overlapping planar regions formed by figures* P *and* Q, *then* ar(T) = ar(P) + ar(Q).

You are also aware of some formulae for finding the areas of different figures such as rectangle, square, parallelogram, triangle etc., from your earlier classes. In this chapter, attempt shall be made to consolidate the knowledge about these formulae by studying some relationship between the areas of these geometric figures under the condition when they lie on the same base and between the same parallels. This study will also be useful in the understanding of some results on 'similarity of triangles'.

## 9.2 Figures on the Same Base and Between the Same Parallels

Look at the following figures:

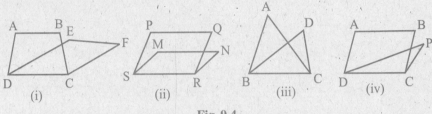

Fig. 9.4

In Fig. 9.4(i), trapezium ABCD and parallelogram EFCD have a common side DC. We say that trapezium ABCD and parallelogram EFCD *are on the same base* DC. Similarly, in Fig. 9.4 (ii), parallelograms PQRS and MNRS are on the same base SR; in Fig. 9.4(iii), triangles ABC and DBC are on the same base BC and in Fig. 9.4(iv), parallelogram ABCD and triangle PDC are on the same base DC.

Now look at the following figures:

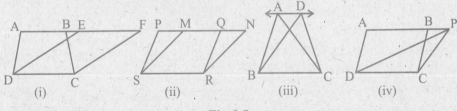

Fig. 9.5

In Fig. 9.5(i), clearly trapezium ABCD and parallelogram EFCD are on the *same base* DC. In addition to the above, the vertices A and B (of trapezium ABCD) opposite to base DC and the vertices E and F (of parallelogram EFCD) opposite to base DC lie on a line AF parallel to DC. We say that trapezium ABCD and parallelogram EFCD are on *the same base* DC *and between the same parallels* AF and DC. Similarly, parallelograms PQRS and MNRS are on the same base SR and between the same parallels PN and SR [see Fig.9.5 (ii)] as vertices P and Q of PQRS and vertices M and N of MNRS lie on a line PN parallel to base SR. In the same way, triangles ABC and DBC lie on the same base BC and between the same parallels AD and BC [see Fig. 9.5 (iii)] and parallelogram ABCD and triangle PCD lie on the same base DC and between the same parallels AP and DC [see Fig. 9.5(iv)].

So, *two figures are said to be on the same base and between the same parallels, if they have a common base (side) and the vertices (or the vertex) opposite to the common base of each figure lie on a line parallel to the base.*

Keeping in view the above statement, you cannot say that $\triangle$ PQR and $\triangle$ DQR of Fig. 9.6(i) lie between the same parallels $l$ and QR. Similarly, you cannot say that

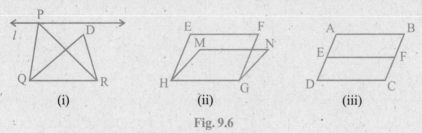

Fig. 9.6

parallelograms EFGH and MNGH of Fig. 9.6(ii) lie between the same parallels EF and HG and that parallelograms ABCD and EFCD of Fig. 9.6(iii) lie between the same parallels AB and DC (even though they have a common base DC and lie between the parallels AD and BC). So, it should clearly be noted that *out of the two parallels, one must be the line containing the common base.* Note that $\triangle$ABC and $\triangle$DBE of Fig. 9.7(i) are not on the

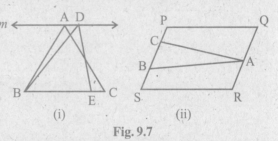

Fig. 9.7

common base. Similarly, $\triangle$ABC and parallelogram PQRS of Fig. 9.7(ii) are also not on the same base.

## EXERCISE 9.1

1. Which of the following figures lie on the same base and between the same parallels. In such a case, write the common base and the two parallels.

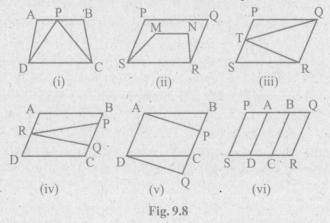

Fig. 9.8

## 9.3 Parallelograms on the same Base and Between the same Parallels

Now let us try to find a relation, if any, between the areas of two parallelograms on the same base and between the same parallels. For this, let us perform the following activities:

**Activity 1 :** Let us take a graph sheet and draw two parallelograms ABCD and PQCD on it as shown in Fig. 9.9.

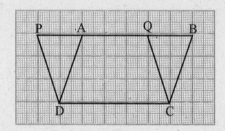

Fig. 9.9

The above two parallelograms are on the same base DC and between the same parallels PB and DC. You may recall the method of finding the areas of these two parallelograms by counting the squares.

In this method, the area is found by counting the number of complete squares enclosed by the figure, the number of squares a having more than half their parts enclosed by the figure and the number of squares having half their parts enclosed by the figure. The squares whose less than half parts are enclosed by the figure are ignored. You will find that areas of both the parallelograms are (approximately) 15cm². Repeat this activity* by drawing some more pairs of parallelograms on the graph sheet. What do you observe? Are the areas of the two parallelograms different or equal? If fact, they are equal. So, this may lead you to conclude that *parallelograms on the same base and between the same parallels are equal in area.* However, remember that this is just a verification.

**Activity 2 :** Draw a parallelogram ABCD on a thick sheet of paper or on a cardboard sheet. Now, draw a line-segment DE as shown in Fig. 9.10.

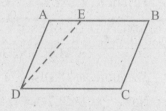

Fig. 9.10

---

*This activity can also be performed by using a Geoboard.

Next, cut a triangle A′ D′ E′ congruent to triangle ADE on a separate sheet with the help of a tracing paper and place $\triangle$ A′D′E′ in such a way that A′D′ coincides with BC as shown in Fig 9.11. Note that there are two parallelograms ABCD and EE′CD on the same base DC and between the same parallels AE′ and DC. What can you say about their areas?

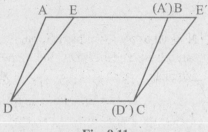

**Fig. 9.11**

As $\qquad$ $\triangle$ ADE $\cong$ $\triangle$ A′D′E′

Therefore $\qquad$ ar (ADE) = ar (A′D′E′)

Also $\qquad$ ar (ABCD) = ar (ADE) + ar (EBCD)

$\qquad\qquad\qquad\qquad$ = ar (A′D′E′) + ar (EBCD)

$\qquad\qquad\qquad\qquad$ = ar (EE′CD)

So, the two parallelograms are equal in area.

Let us now try to prove this relation between the two such parallelograms.

**Theorem 9.1** : *Parallelograms on the same base and between the same parallels are equal in area.*

**Proof :** Two parallelograms ABCD and EFCD, on the same base DC and between the same parallels AF and DC are given (see Fig.9.12).

We need to prove that ar (ABCD) = ar (EFCD).

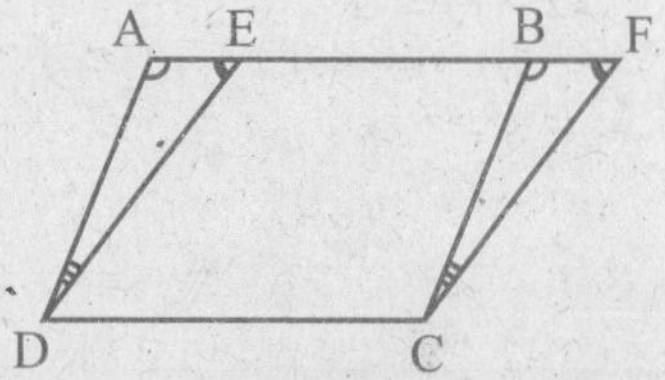

**Fig. 9.12**

In $\triangle$ ADE and $\triangle$ BCF,

$\angle$ DAE = $\angle$ CBF (Corresponding angles from AD ∥ BC and transversal AF) $\qquad$ (1)

$\angle$ AED = $\angle$ BFC (Corresponding angles from ED ∥ FC and transversal AF) $\qquad$ (2)

Therefore, $\angle$ ADE = $\angle$ BCF (Angle sum property of a triangle) $\qquad$ (3)

Also, $\qquad\qquad$ AD = BC (Opposite sides of the parallelogram ABCD) $\qquad$ (4)

So, $\qquad$ $\triangle$ ADE $\cong$ $\triangle$ BCF $\qquad\qquad$ [By ASA rule, using (1), (3), and (4)]

Therefore, ar (ADE) = ar (BCF) (Congruent figures have equal areas) $\qquad$ (5)

Now, $\quad$ ar (ABCD) = ar (ADE) + ar (EDCB)

$\qquad\qquad\qquad$ = ar (BCF) + ar (EDCB) $\qquad\qquad\qquad\qquad$ [From(5)]

$\qquad\qquad\qquad$ = ar (EFCD)

So, parallelograms ABCD and EFCD are equal in area. $\quad\blacksquare$

Let us now take some examples to illustrate the use of the above theorem.

Example 1 : In Fig. 9.13, ABCD is a parallelogram and EFCD is a rectangle.

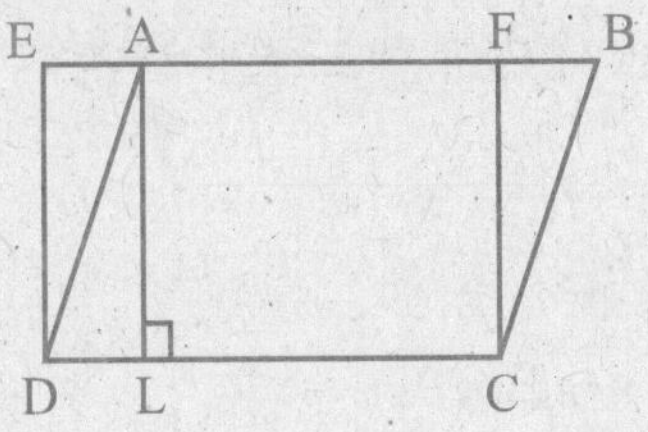

Also, AL ⊥ DC. Prove that

(i) ar (ABCD) = ar (EFCD)

(ii) ar (ABCD) = DC × AL

Fig. 9.13

Solution : (i) As a rectangle is also a parallelogram,

therefore,          ar (ABCD) = ar (EFCD)          (Theorem 9.1)

(ii) From above result,

ar (ABCD) = DC × FC (Area of the rectangle = length × breadth)   (1)

As            AL ⊥ DC, therefore, AFCL is also a rectangle

So,          AL = FC                                                              (2)

Therefore,  ar (ABCD) = DC × AL                              [From (1) and (2)]

Can you see from the Result (ii) above *that area of a parallelogram is the product of its any side and the coresponding altitude.* Do you remember that you have studied this formula for area of a parallelogram in Class VII. On the basis of this formula, Theorem 9.1 can be rewritten as *parallelograms on the same base or equal bases and between the same parallels are equal in area.*

Can you write the converse of the above statement? It is as follows: *Parallelograms on the same base (or equal bases) and having  equal areas lie between the same parallels.* Is the converse true? Prove the converse using the formula for area of the parallelogram.

Example 2 : If a triangle and a parallelogram are on the same base and between the same parallels, then prove that the area of the triangle is equal to half the area of the parallelogram.

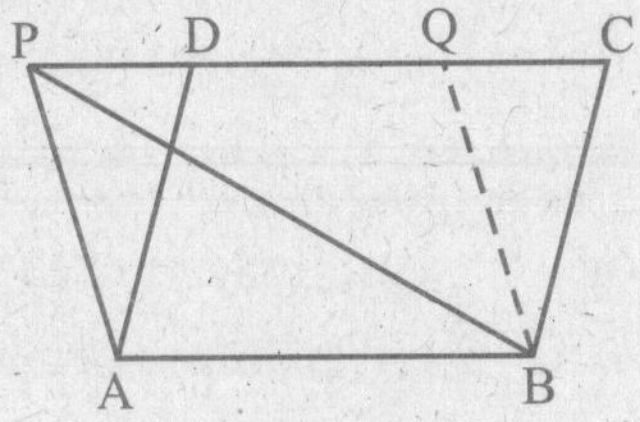

Solution : Let △ ABP and parallelogram ABCD be on the same base AB and between the same parallels AB and PC (see Fig. 9.14).

Fig. 9.14

You wish to prove that ar (PAB) = $\frac{1}{2}$ ar (ABCD)

Draw BQ ∥ AP to obtain another parallelogram ABQP. Now parallelograms ABQP and ABCD are on the same base AB and between the same parallels AB and PC.

Therefore,                    ar (ABQP) = ar (ABCD)              (By Theorem 9.1) (1)

But $\triangle$ PAB $\cong$ $\triangle$ BQP (Diagonal PB divides parallelogram ABQP into two congruent triangles.)

So,                         ar (PAB) = ar (BQP)                              (2)

Therefore,                 ar (PAB) = $\dfrac{1}{2}$ ar (ABQP)   [From (2)]              (3)

This gives                 ar (PAB) = $\dfrac{1}{2}$ ar (ABCD)              [From (1) and (3)]

## EXERCISE 9.2

1.  In Fig. 9.15, ABCD is a parallelogram, AE $\perp$ DC and CF $\perp$ AD. If AB = 16 cm, AE = 8 cm and CF = 10 cm, find AD.

2.  If E,F,G and H are respectively the mid-points of the sides of a parallelogram ABCD, show that

    ar (EFGH) = $\dfrac{1}{2}$ ar (ABCD) .

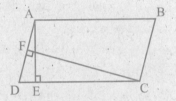

Fig. 9.15

3.  P and Q are any two points lying on the sides DC and AD respectively of a parallelogram ABCD. Show that ar (APB) = ar (BQC).

4.  In Fig. 9.16, P is a point in the interior of a parallelogram ABCD. Show that

    (i)   ar (APB) + ar (PCD) = $\dfrac{1}{2}$ ar (ABCD)

    (ii)  ar (APD) + ar (PBC) = ar (APB) + ar (PCD)

    [*Hint* : Through P, draw a line parallel to AB.]

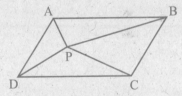

Fig. 9.16

5.  In Fig. 9.17, PQRS and ABRS are parallelograms and X is any point on side BR. Show that

    (i) ar (PQRS) = ar (ABRS)

    (ii) ar (AX S) = $\dfrac{1}{2}$ ar (PQRS)

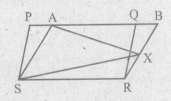

Fig. 9.17

6.  A farmer was having a field in the form of a parallelogram PQRS. She took any point A on RS and joined it to points P and Q. In how many parts the fields is divided? What are the shapes of these parts? The farmer wants to sow wheat and pulses in equal portions of the field separately. How should she do it?

## 9.4 Triangles on the same Base and between the same Parallels

Let us look at Fig. 9.18. In it, you have two triangles ABC and PBC on the same base BC and between the same parallels BC and AP. What can you say about the areas of such triangles? To answer this question, you may perform the activity of drawing several pairs of triangles on the same base and between the same parallels on the graph sheet and find their areas by the method of counting the squares. Each time, you will find that the areas of the two triangles are (approximately) equal. This activity can be performed using a geoboard also. You will again find that the two areas are (approximately) equal.

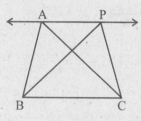

Fig. 9.18

To obtain a logical answer to the above question, you may proceed as follows:

In Fig. 9.18, draw CD ∥ BA and CR ∥ BP such that D and R lie on line AP(see Fig.9.19).

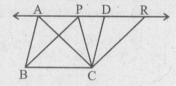

Fig. 9.19

From this, you obtain two parallelograms PBCR and ABCD on the same base BC and between the same parallels BC and AR.

Therefore,　　　　　　　ar (ABCD) = ar (PBCR)　(Why?)

Now　　　　　　　　　$\triangle$ ABC $\cong$ $\triangle$ CDA and $\triangle$ PBC $\cong$ $\triangle$ CRP　(Why?)

So,　　ar (ABC) = $\frac{1}{2}$ ar (ABCD) and ar (PBC) = $\frac{1}{2}$ ar (PBCR)　(Why?)

Therefore,　　　　　　　ar (ABC) = ar (PBC)

In this way, you have arrived at the following theorem:

**Theorem 9.2** : *Two triangles on the same base (or equal bases) and between the same parallels are equal in area.*

Now, suppose ABCD is a parallelogram whose one of the diagonals is AC (see Fig. 9.20). Let AN $\perp$ DC. Note that

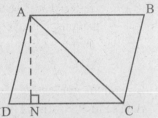

$$\Delta\, ADC \cong\, \Delta\, CBA \qquad \text{(Why?)}$$

So, ar (ADC) = ar (CBA)  (Why?)

Therefore, ar (ADC) = $\dfrac{1}{2}$ ar (ABCD)

$$= \dfrac{1}{2}\,(DC \times AN) \qquad \text{(Why?)}$$

**Fig. 9.20**

So, area of $\Delta$ ADC = $\dfrac{1}{2}$ × base DC × corresponding altitude AN

In other words, *area of a triangle is half the product of its base (or any side) and the corresponding altitude (or height)*. Do you remember that you have learnt this formula for area of a triangle in Class VII ? From this formula, you can see that *two triangles with same base (or equal bases) and equal areas will have equal corresponding altitudes*.

For having equal corresponding altitudes, the triangles must lie between the same parallels. From this, you arrive at the following converse of Theorem 9.2 .

**Theorem 9.3** : *Two triangles having the same base (or equal bases) and equal areas lie between the same parallels.*

Let us now take some examples to illustrate the use of the above results.

**Example 3** : Show that a median of a triangle divides it into two triangles of equal areas.

**Solution** : Let ABC be a triangle and let AD be one of its medians (see Fig. 9.21).

You wish to show that

ar (ABD) = ar (ACD).

Since the formula for area involves altitude, let us draw AN $\perp$ BC.

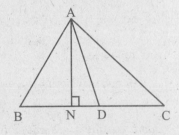

Now  ar(ABD) = $\dfrac{1}{2}$ × base × altitude (of $\Delta$ ABD)

$$= \dfrac{1}{2} \times BD \times AN$$

**Fig. 9.21**

$$= \frac{1}{2} \times CD \times AN \quad (\text{As } BD = CD)$$

$$= \frac{1}{2} \times \text{base} \times \text{altitude (of } \triangle ACD)$$

$$= ar(ACD)$$

**Example 4 :** In Fig. 9.22, ABCD is a quadrilateral and BE ∥ AC and also BE meets DC produced at E. Show that area of △ ADE is equal to the area of the quadrilateral ABCD.

**Solution :** Observe the figure carefully .

△ BAC and △ EAC lie on the same base AC and between the same parallels AC and BE.

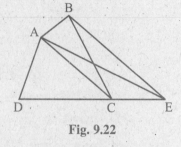

Fig. 9.22

Therefore,      ar(BAC) = ar(EAC)                    (By Theorem 9.2)

So, ar(BAC) + ar(ADC) = ar(EAC) + ar(ADC)   (Adding same areas on both sides)

or              ar(ABCD) = ar(ADE)

## EXERCISE 9.3

1. In Fig.9.23, E is any point on median AD of a △ ABC. Show that ar (ABE) = ar (ACE).

2. In a triangle ABC, E is the mid-point of median AD. Show that ar (BED) = $\frac{1}{4}$ ar(ABC) .

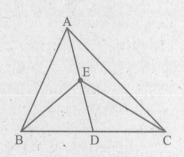

Fig. 9.23

3. Show that the diagonals of a parallelogram divide it into four triangles of equal area.

4. In Fig. 9.24, ABC and ABD are two triangles on the same base AB. If line- segment CD is bisected by AB at O, show that ar(ABC) = ar (ABD).

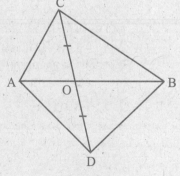

Fig. 9.24

**5.** D, E and F are respectively the mid-points of the sides BC, CA and AB of a △ ABC. Show that

(i) BDEF is a parallelogram.  (ii) ar (DEF) = $\frac{1}{4}$ ar (ABC)

(iii) ar (BDEF) = $\frac{1}{2}$ ar (ABC)

**6.** In Fig. 9.25, diagonals AC and BD of quadrilateral ABCD intersect at O such that OB = OD. If AB = CD, then show that:

(i) ar (DOC) = ar (AOB)

(ii) ar (DCB) = ar (ACB)

(iii) DA ∥ CB or ABCD is a parallelogram.

[*Hint* : From D and B, draw perpendiculars to AC.]

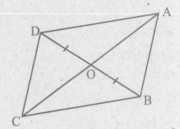

Fig. 9.25

**7.** D and E are points on sides AB and AC respectively of △ ABC such that ar (DBC) = ar (EBC). Prove that DE ∥ BC.

**8.** XY is a line parallel to side BC of a triangle ABC. If BE ∥ AC and CF ∥ AB meet XY at E and F respectively, show that

ar (ABE) = ar (ACF)

**9.** The side AB of a parallelogram ABCD is produced to any point P. A line through A and parallel to CP meets CB produced at Q and then parallelogram PBQR is completed (see Fig. 9.26). Show that ar (ABCD) = ar (PBQR).

[*Hint* : Join AC and PQ. Now compare ar (ACQ) and ar (APQ).]

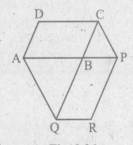

Fig. 9.26

**10.** Diagonals AC and BD of a trapezium ABCD with AB ∥ DC intersect each other at O. Prove that ar (AOD) = ar (BOC).

**11.** In Fig. 9.27, ABCDE is a pentagon. A line through B parallel to AC meets DC produced at F. Show that

(i) ar (ACB) = ar (ACF)

(ii) ar (AEDF) = ar (ABCDE)

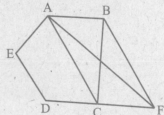

Fig. 9.27

**12.** A villager Itwaari has a plot of land of the shape of a quadrilateral. The Gram Panchayat of the village decided to take over some portion of his plot from one of the corners to construct a Health Centre. Itwaari agrees to the above proposal with the condition that he should be given equal amount of land in lieu of his land adjoining his plot so as to form a triangular plot. Explain how this proposal will be implemented.

**13.** ABCD is a trapezium with AB ∥ DC. A line parallel to AC intersects AB at X and BC at Y. Prove that ar (ADX) = ar (ACY).

[*Hint* : Join CX.]

**14.** In Fig.9.28, AP ∥ BQ ∥ CR. Prove that

ar (AQC) = ar (PBR).

**15.** Diagonals AC and BD of a quadrilateral ABCD intersect at O in such a way that ar (AOD) = ar (BOC). Prove that ABCD is a trapezium.

**16.** In Fig.9.29, ar (DRC) = ar (DPC) and ar (BDP) = ar (ARC). Show that both the quadrilaterals ABCD and DCPR are trapeziums.

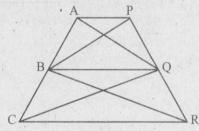

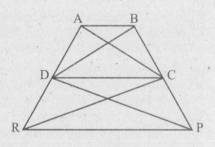

Fig. 9.28

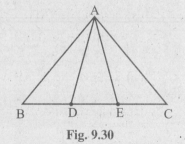

Fig. 9.29

# EXERCISE 9.4 (Optional)*

**1.** Parallelogram ABCD and rectangle ABEF are on the same base AB and have equal areas. Show that the perimeter of the parallelogram is greater than that of the rectangle.

**2.** In Fig. 9.30, D and E are two points on BC such that BD = DE = EC. Show that ar (ABD) = ar (ADE) = ar (AEC).

Can you now answer the question that you have left in the 'Introduction' of this chapter, whether the field of *Budhia* has been actually divided into three parts of equal area?

Fig. 9.30

*These exercises are not from examination point of view.

[**Remark:** Note that by taking BD = DE = EC, the triangle ABC is divided into three triangles ABD, ADE and AEC of equal areas. In the same way, by dividing BC into *n* equal parts and joining the points of division so obtained to the opposite vertex of BC, you can divide ΔABC into *n* triangles of equal areas.]

3. In Fig. 9.31, ABCD, DCFE and ABFE are parallelograms. Show that ar (ADE) = ar (BCF).

4. In Fig. 9.32, ABCD is a parallelogram and BC is produced to a point Q such that AD = CQ. If AQ intersect DC at P, show that ar (BPC) = ar (DPQ).

   [*Hint* : Join AC.]

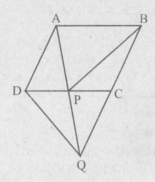

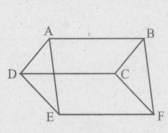

Fig. 9.31                      Fig. 9.32

5. In Fig.9.33, ABC and BDE are two equilateral triangles such that D is the mid-point of BC. If AE intersects BC at F, show that

   (i)   ar (BDE) = $\dfrac{1}{4}$ ar (ABC)

   (ii)  ar (BDE) = $\dfrac{1}{2}$ ar (BAE)

   (iii) ar (ABC) = 2 ar (BEC)

   (iv) ar (BFE) = ar (AFD)

   (v)  ar (BFE) = 2 ar (FED)

   (vi) ar (FED) = $\dfrac{1}{8}$ ar (AFC)

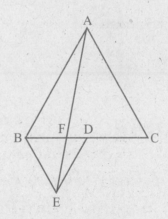

Fig. 9.33

[*Hint* : Join EC and AD. Show that BE ∥ AC and DE ∥ AB, etc.]

6.  Diagonals AC and BD of a quadrilateral ABCD intersect each other at P. Show that
    ar (APB) × ar (CPD) = ar (APD) × ar (BPC).

    [*Hint* : From A and C, draw perpendiculars to BD.]

7.  P and Q are respectively the mid-points of sides AB and BC of a triangle ABC and R
    is the mid-point of AP, show that

    (i) ar (PRQ) = $\dfrac{1}{2}$ ar (ARC)          (ii) ar (RQC) = $\dfrac{3}{8}$ ar (ABC)

    (iii) ar (PBQ) = ar (ARC)

8.  In Fig. 9.34, ABC is a right triangle right angled at A. BCED, ACFG and ABMN are
    squares on the sides BC, CA and AB respectively. Line segment AX ⊥ DE meets BC
    at Y. Show that:

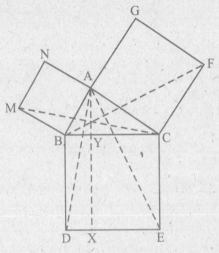

Fig. 9.34

(i) Δ MBC ≅ Δ ABD                    (ii) ar (BYXD) = 2 ar (MBC)

(iii) ar (BYXD) = ar (ABMN)          (iv) Δ FCB ≅ Δ ACE

(v) ar (CYXE) = 2 ar (FCB)           (vi) ar (CYXE) = ar (ACFG)

(vii) ar (BCED) = ar (ABMN) + ar (ACFG)

**Note :** Result (vii) is the famous *Theorem of Pythagoras*. You shall learn a simpler
proof of this theorem in Class X.

## 9.5 Summary

In this chapter, you have studied the following points :

1. Area of a figure is a number (in some unit) associated with the part of the plane enclosed by that figure.

2. Two congruent figures have equal areas but the converse need not be true.

3. If a planar region formed by a figure T is made up of two non-overlapping planar regions formed by figures P and Q, then ar (T) = ar (P) + ar (Q), where ar (X) denotes the area of figure X.

4. Two figures are said to be on the same base and between the same parallels, if they have a common base (side) and the vertices, (or the vertex) opposite to the common base of each figure lie on a line parallel to the base.

5. Parallelograms on the same base (or equal bases) and between the same parallels are equal in area.

6. Area of a parallelogram is the product of its base and the corresponding altitude.

7. Parallelograms on the same base (or equal bases) and having equal areas lie between the same parallels.

8. If a parallelogram and a triangle are on the same base and between the same parallels, then area of the triangle is half the area of the parallelogram.

9. Triangles on the same base (or equal bases) and between the same parallels are equal in area.

10. Area of a triangle is half the product of its base and the corresponding altitude.

11. Triangles on the same base (or equal bases) and having equal areas lie between the same parallels.

12. A median of a triangle divides it into two triangles of equal areas.

# CHAPTER 10

# CIRCLES

## 10.1 Introduction

You may have come across many objects in daily life, which are round in shape, such as wheels of a vehicle, bangles, dials of many clocks, coins of denominations 50 p, Re 1 and Rs 5, key rings, buttons of shirts, etc. (see Fig.10.1). In a clock, you might have observed that the second's hand goes round the dial of the clock rapidly and its tip moves in a round path. This path traced by the tip of the second's hand is called a *circle*. In this chapter, you will study about circles, other related terms and some properties of a circle.

Wheel        Clock        Key Ring        Button

Bangle

Fig. 10.1

## 10.2 Circles and Its Related Terms: A Review

Take a compass and fix a pencil in it. Put its pointed leg on a point on a sheet of a paper. Open the other leg to some distance. Keeping the pointed leg on the same point, rotate the other leg through one revolution. What is the closed figure traced by the pencil on paper? As you know, it is a circle (see Fig.10.2). How did you get a circle? You kept one point fixed (A in Fig.10.2) and drew all the points that were at a fixed distance from A. This gives us the following definition:

Fig. 10.2

*The collection of all the points in a plane, which are at a fixed distance from a fixed point in the plane, is called a circle.*

The fixed point is called the *centre* of the circle and the fixed distance is called the *radius* of the circle. In Fig.10.3, O is the centre and the length OP is the radius of the circle.

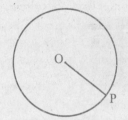

Fig. 10.3

**Remark :** Note that the line segment joining the centre and any point on the circle is also called a *radius* of the circle. That is, 'radius' is used in two senses-in the sense of a line segment and also in the sense of its length.

You are already familiar with some of the following concepts from Class VI. We are just recalling them.

A circle divides the plane on which it lies into three parts. They are: (i) inside the circle, which is also called the *interior* of the circle; (ii) the *circle* and (iii) outside the circle, which is also called the *exterior* of the circle (see Fig.10.4). The circle and its interior make up the *circular region*.

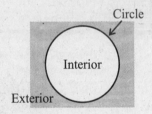

Fig. 10.4

If you take two points P and Q on a circle, then the line segment PQ is called a *chord* of the circle (see Fig. 10.5). The chord, which passes through the centre of the circle, is called a *diameter* of the circle. As in the case of radius, the word 'diameter' is also used in two senses, that is, as a line segment and also as its length. Do you find any other chord of the circle longer than a diameter? No, you see that a *diameter is the longest chord and all diameters have the same length, which is equal to two times the radius.* In Fig.10.5, AOB is a diameter of the circle. How many diameters does a circle have? Draw a circle and see how many diameters you can find.

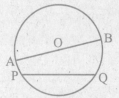

Fig. 10.5

A piece of a circle between two points is called an *arc*. Look at the pieces of the circle between two points P and Q in Fig.10.6. You find that there are two pieces, one longer and the other smaller (see Fig.10.7). The longer one is called the *major arc PQ* and the shorter one is called the *minor arc PQ*. The minor arc PQ is also denoted by $\overset{\frown}{PQ}$ and the major arc PQ by $\overset{\frown}{PRQ}$, where R is some point on the arc between P and Q. Unless otherwise stated, arc PQ or $\overset{\frown}{PQ}$ stands for minor arc PQ. When P and Q are ends of a diameter, then both arcs are equal and each is called a *semicircle*.

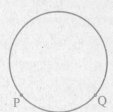

Fig. 10.6

The length of the complete circle is called its *circumference*. The region between a chord and either of its arcs is called a *segment* of the circular region or simply a *segment* of the circle. You will find that there are two types of segments also, which are the *major segment* and the *minor segment* (see Fig. 10.8). The region between an arc and the two radii, joining the centre to the end points of the arc is called a *sector*. Like segments, you find that

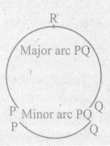

Fig. 10.7

the minor arc corresponds to the *minor sector* and the major arc corresponds to the *major sector*. In Fig. 10.9, the region OPQ is the minor sector and remaining part of the circular region is the major sector. When two arcs are equal, that is, each is a semicircle, then both segments and both sectors become the same and each is known as a *semicircular region*.

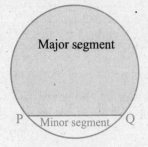

Fig. 10.8

Fig. 10.9

## EXERCISE 10.1

1. Fill in the blanks:

   (i) The centre of a circle lies in _____ of the circle. (exterior/ interior)

   (ii) A point, whose distance from the centre of a circle is greater than its radius lies in _____ of the circle. (exterior/ interior)

   (iii) The longest chord of a circle is a _____ of the circle.

   (iv) An arc is a _____ when its ends are the ends of a diameter.

   (v) Segment of a circle is the region between an arc and _____ of the circle.

   (vi) A circle divides the plane, on which it lies, in _____ parts.

2. Write True or False: Give reasons for your answers.

   (i) Line segment joining the centre to any point on the circle is a radius of the circle.

   (ii) A circle has only finite number of equal chords.

   (iii) If a circle is divided into three equal arcs, each is a major arc.

   (iv) A chord of a circle, which is twice as long as its radius, is a diameter of the circle.

   (v) Sector is the region between the chord and its corresponding arc.

   (vi) A circle is a plane figure.

## 10.3 Angle Subtended by a Chord at a Point

Take a line segment PQ and a point R not on the line containing PQ. Join PR and QR (see Fig. 10.10). Then ∠ PRQ is called the angle subtended by the line segment PQ at the point R. What are angles POQ, PRQ and PSQ called in Fig. 10.11? ∠ POQ is the angle subtended by the chord PQ at the centre O, ∠ PRQ and ∠ PSQ are respectively the angles subtended by PQ at points R and S on the major and minor arcs PQ.

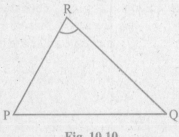

Fig. 10.10

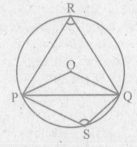

Fig. 10.11

Let us examine the relationship between the size of the chord and the angle subtended by it at the centre. You may see by drawing different chords of a circle and

angles subtended by them at the centre that the longer
is the chord, the bigger will be the angle subtended
by it at the centre. What will happen if you take two
equal chords of a circle? Will the angles subtended at
the centre be the same or not?

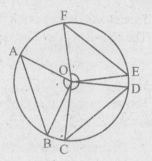

Draw two or more equal chords of a circle and
measure the angles subtended by them at the centre
(see Fig.10.12). You will find that the angles subtended
by them at the centre are equal. Let us give a proof
of this fact.

Fig. 10.12

**Theorem 10.1 :** *Equal chords of a circle subtend equal angles at the centre.*

**Proof :** You are given two equal chords AB and CD
of a circle with centre O (see Fig.10.13). You want
to prove that ∠ AOB = ∠ COD.

In triangles AOB and COD,

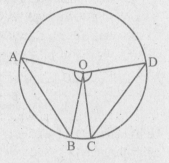

|  |  |  |
|---|---|---|
| OA = OC | (Radii of a circle) | |
| OB = OD | (Radii of a circle) | |
| AB = CD | (Given) | |

Therefore,  Δ AOB ≅ Δ COD  (SSS rule)

This gives  ∠ AOB = ∠ COD

(Corresponding parts of congruent triangles) ∎

Fig. 10.13

**Remark :** For convenience, the abbreviation CPCT will be used in place of
'Corresponding parts of congruent triangles', because we use this very frequently as
you will see.

Now if two chords of a circle subtend equal angles at the centre, what can you
say about the chords? Are they equal or not? Let us examine this by the following
activity:

Take a tracing paper and trace a circle on it. Cut
it along the circle to get a disc. At its centre O, draw
an angle AOB where A, B are points on the circle.
Make another angle POQ at the centre equal to
∠AOB. Cut the disc along AB and PQ
(see Fig. 10.14). You will get two segments ACB
and PRQ of the circle. If you put one on the other,
what do you observe? They cover each other, i.e.,
they are congruent. So AB = PQ.

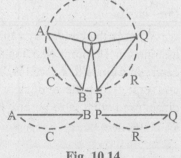

Fig. 10.14

Though you have seen it for this particular case, try it out for other equal angles too. The chords will all turn out to be equal because of the following theorem:

**Theorem 10.2 :** *If the angles subtended by the chords of a circle at the centre are equal, then the chords are equal.*

The above theorem is the converse of the Theorem 10.1. Note that in Fig. 10.13, if you take $\angle$ AOB = $\angle$ COD, then

$$\Delta \text{ AOB} \cong \Delta \text{ COD (Why?)}$$

Can you now see that AB = CD?

### EXERCISE 10.2

1. Recall that two circles are congruent if they have the same radii. Prove that equal chords of congruent circles subtend equal angles at their centres.

2. Prove that if chords of congruent circles subtend equal angles at their centres, then the chords are equal.

## 10.4 Perpendicular from the Centre to a Chord

**Activity :** Draw a circle on a tracing paper. Let O be its centre. Draw a chord AB. Fold the paper along a line through O so that a portion of the chord falls on the other. Let the crease cut AB at the point M. Then, $\angle$ OMA = $\angle$ OMB = 90° or OM is perpendicular to AB. Does the point B coincide with A (see Fig.10.15)?

Yes it will. So MA = MB.

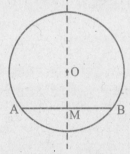

Fig. 10.15

Give a proof yourself by joining OA and OB and proving the right triangles OMA and OMB to be congruent. This example is a particular instance of the following result:

**Theorem 10.3 :** *The perpendicular from the centre of a circle to a chord bisects the chord.*

What is the converse of this theorem? To write this, first let us be clear what is assumed in Theorem 10.3 and what is proved. Given that the perpendicular from the centre of a circle to a chord is drawn and to prove that it bisects the chord. Thus in the converse, what the hypothesis is 'if a line from the centre bisects a chord of a circle' and what is to be proved is 'the line is perpendicular to the chord'. So the converse is:

**Theorem 10.4** : *The line drawn through the centre of a circle to bisect a chord is perpendicular to the chord.*

Is this true? Try it for few cases and see. You will see that it is true for these cases. See if it is true, in general, by doing the following exercise. We will write the stages and you give the reasons.

Let AB be a chord of a circle with centre O and O is joined to the mid-point M of AB. You have to prove that OM ⊥ AB. Join OA and OB (see Fig. 10.16). In triangles OAM and OBM,

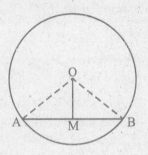

Fig. 10.16

| | |
|---|---|
| OA = OB | (Why ?) |
| AM = BM | (Why ?) |
| OM = OM | (Common) |
| Therefore, ΔOAM ≅ ΔOBM | (How ?) |
| This gives ∠OMA = ∠OMB = 90° | (Why ?) |

## 10.5 Circle through Three Points

You have learnt in Chapter 6, that two points are sufficient to determine a line. That is, there is one and only one line passing through two points. A natural question arises. How many points are sufficient to determine a circle?

Take a point P. How many circles can be drawn through this point? You see that there may be as many circles as you like passing through this point [see Fig. 10.17(i)]. Now take two points P and Q. You again see that there may be an infinite number of circles passing through P and Q [see Fig.10.17(ii)]. What will happen when you take three points A, B and C? Can you draw a circle passing through three collinear points?

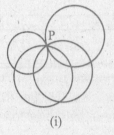

(i)

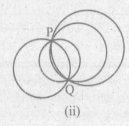

(ii)

Fig. 10. 17

No. If the points lie on a line, then the third point will lie inside or outside the circle passing through two points (see Fig 10.18).

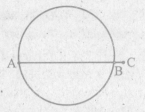

Fig. 10.18

So, let us take three points A, B and C, which are not on the same line, or in other words, they are not collinear [see Fig. 10.19(i)]. Draw perpendicular bisectors of AB and BC say, PQ and RS respectively. Let these perpendicular bisectors intersect at one point O. (Note that PQ and RS will intersect because they are not parallel) [see Fig. 10.19(ii)].

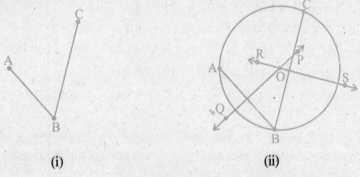

(i)                                              (ii)

Fig. 10.19

Now O lies on the perpendicular bisector PQ of AB, you have OA = OB, as every point on the perpendicular bisector of a line segment is equidistant from its end points, proved in Chapter 7.

Similarly, as O lies on the perpendicular bisector RS of BC, you get

OB = OC

So OA = OB = OC, which means that the points A, B and C are at equal distances from the point O. So if you draw a circle with centre O and radius OA, it will also pass through B and C. This shows that there is a circle passing through the three points A, B and C. You know that two lines (perpendicular bisectors) can intersect at only one point, so you can draw only one circle with radius OA. In other words, there is a unique circle passing through A, B and C. You have now proved the following theorem:

**Theorem 10.5** : *There is one and only one circle passing through three given non-collinear points.*

**Remark :** If ABC is a triangle, then by Theorem 10.5, there is a unique circle passing through the three vertices A, B and C of the triangle. This circle is called the *circumcircle* of the △ ABC. Its centre and radius are called respectively the *circumcentre* and the *circumradius* of the triangle.

**Example 1 :** Given an arc of a circle, complete the circle.

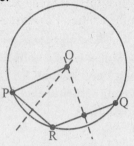

**Solution :** Let arc PQ of a circle be given. We have to complete the circle, which means that we have to find its centre and radius. Take a point R on the arc. Join PR and RQ. Use the construction that has been used in proving Theorem 10.5, to find the centre and radius.

Taking the centre and the radius so obtained, we can complete the circle (see Fig. 10.20).

**Fig. 10.20**

## EXERCISE 10.3

1.  Draw different pairs of circles. How many points does each pair have in common? What is the maximum number of common points?

2.  Suppose you are given a circle. Give a construction to find its centre.

3.  If two circles intersect at two points, prove that their centres lie on the perpendicular bisector of the common chord.

## 10.6 Equal Chords and Their Distances from the Centre

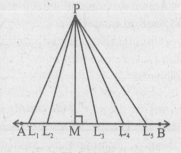

Let AB be a line and P be a point. Since there are infinite numbers of points on a line, if you join these points to P, you will get infinitely many line segments $PL_1$, $PL_2$, PM, $PL_3$, $PL_4$, etc. Which of these is the distance of AB from P? You may think a while and get the answer. Out of these line segments, the perpendicular from P to AB, namely PM in Fig. 10.21, will be the least. In Mathematics, we define this least length PM to be **the distance of AB from P**. So you may say that:

**Fig. 10.21**

*The length of the perpendicular from a point to a line is the distance of the line from the point.*

Note that if the point lies on the line, the distance of the line from the point is zero.

A circle can have infinitely many chords. You may observe by drawing chords of a circle that longer chord is nearer to the centre than the smaller chord. You may observe it by drawing several chords of a circle of different lengths and measuring their distances from the centre. What is the distance of the diameter, which is the longest chord from the centre? Since the centre lies on it, the distance is zero. Do you think that there is some relationship between the length of chords and their distances from the centre? Let us see if this is so.

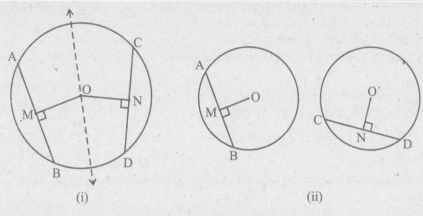

(i)                                             (ii)

**Fig. 10.22**

**Activity :** Draw a circle of any radius on a tracing paper. Draw two equal chords AB and CD of it and also the perpendiculars OM and ON on them from the centre O. Fold the figure so that D falls on B and C falls on A [see Fig.10.22 (i)]. You may observe that O lies on the crease and N falls on M. Therefore, OM = ON. Repeat the activity by drawing congruent circles with centres O and O′ and taking equal chords AB and CD one on each. Draw perpendiculars OM and O′N on them [see Fig. 10.22(ii)]. Cut one circular disc and put it on the other so that AB coincides with CD. Then you will find that O coincides with O′ and M coincides with N. In this way you verified the following:

**Theorem 10.6 :** *Equal chords of a circle (or of congruent circles) are equidistant from the centre (or centres).*

Next, it will be seen whether the converse of this theorem is true or not. For this, draw a circle with centre O. From the centre O, draw two line segments OL and OM of equal length and lying inside the circle [see Fig. 10.23(i)]. Then draw chords PQ and RS of the circle perpendicular to OL and OM respectively [see Fig 10.23(ii)]. Measure the lengths of PQ and RS. Are these different? No, both are equal. Repeat the activity for more equal line segments and drawing the chords perpendicular to

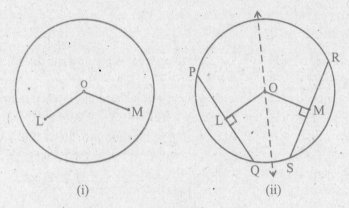

(i)                                          (ii)

**Fig. 10.23**

them. This verifies the converse of the Theorem 10.6 which is stated as follows:

**Theorem 10.7** : *Chords equidistant from the centre of a circle are equal in length.*

We now take an example to illustrate the use of the above results:

**Example 2 :** If two intersecting chords of a circle make equal angles with the diameter passing through their point of intersection, prove that the chords are equal.

**Solution :** Given that AB and CD are two chords of a circle, with centre O intersecting at a point E. PQ is a diameter through E, such that $\angle$ AEQ = $\angle$ DEQ (see Fig.10.24). You have to prove that AB = CD. Draw perpendiculars OL and OM on chords AB and CD, respectively. Now

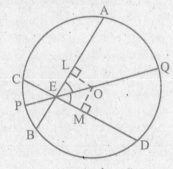

$$\angle LOE = 180° - 90° - \angle LEO = 90° - \angle LEO$$
$$\text{(Angle sum property of a triangle)}$$
$$= 90° - \angle AEQ = 90° - \angle DEQ$$
$$= 90° - \angle MEO = \angle MOE$$

**Fig. 10.24**

In triangles OLE and OME,

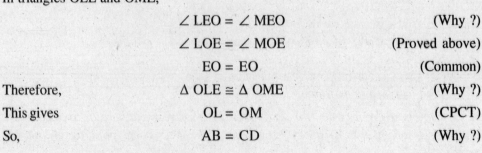

|                |                    |                   |
|----------------|--------------------|-------------------|
|                | $\angle$ LEO = $\angle$ MEO | (Why ?)           |
|                | $\angle$ LOE = $\angle$ MOE | (Proved above)    |
|                | EO = EO            | (Common)          |
| Therefore,     | $\Delta$ OLE $\cong$ $\Delta$ OME | (Why ?)           |
| This gives     | OL = OM            | (CPCT)            |
| So,            | AB = CD            | (Why ?)           |

## EXERCISE 10.4

1. Two circles of radii 5 cm and 3 cm intersect at two points and the distance between their centres is 4 cm. Find the length of the common chord.

2. If two equal chords of a circle intersect within the circle, prove that the segments of one chord are equal to corresponding segments of the other chord.

3. If two equal chords of a circle intersect within the circle, prove that the line joining the point of intersection to the centre makes equal angles with the chords.

4. If a line intersects two concentric circles (circles with the same centre) with centre O at A, B, C and D, prove that AB = CD (see Fig. 10.25).

5. Three girls Reshma, Salma and Mandip are playing a game by standing on a circle of radius 5m drawn in a park. Reshma throws a ball to Salma, Salma to Mandip, Mandip to Reshma. If the distance between Reshma and Salma and between Salma and Mandip is 6m each, what is the distance between Reshma and Mandip?

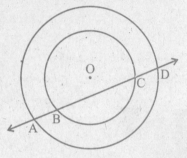

Fig. 10.25

6. A circular park of radius 20m is situated in a colony. Three boys Ankur, Syed and David are sitting at equal distance on its boundary each having a toy telephone in his hands to talk each other. Find the length of the string of each phone.

## 10.7 Angle Subtended by an Arc of a Circle

You have seen that the end points of a chord other than diameter of a circle cuts it into two arcs – one major and other minor. If you take two equal chords, what can you say about the size of arcs? Is one arc made by first chord equal to the corresponding arc made by another chord? In fact, they are more than just equal in length. They are congruent in the sense that if one arc is put on the other, without bending or twisting, one superimposes the other completely.

You can verify this fact by cutting the arc, corresponding to the chord CD from the circle along CD and put it on the corresponding arc made by equal chord AB. You will find that the arc CD superimpose the arc AB completely (see Fig. 10.26). This shows that equal chords make congruent arcs and conversely congruent arcs make equal chords of a circle. You can state it as follows:

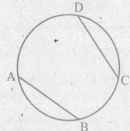

Fig. 10.26

*If two chords of a circle are equal, then their corresponding arcs are congruent and conversely, if two arcs are congruent, then their corresponding chords are equal.*

Also the angle subtended by an arc at the centre is defined to be angle subtended by the corresponding chord at the centre in the sense that the minor arc subtends the angle and the major arc subtends the reflex angle. Therefore, in Fig 10.27, the angle subtended by the minor arc PQ at O is ∠POQ and the angle subtended by the major arc PQ at O is reflex angle POQ.

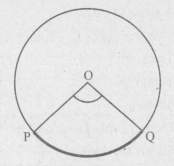

In view of the property above and Theorem 10.1, the following result is true:

**Fig. 10.27**

*Congruent arcs (or equal arcs) of a circle subtend equal angles at the centre.*

Therefore, the angle subtended by a chord of a circle at its centre is equal to the angle subtended by the corresponding (minor) arc at the centre. The following theorem gives the relationship between the angles subtended by an arc at the centre and at a point on the circle.

**Theorem 10.8 :** *The angle subtended by an arc at the centre is double the angle subtended by it at any point on the remaining part of the circle.*

**Proof :** Given an arc PQ of a circle subtending angles POQ at the centre O and PAQ at a point A on the remaining part of the circle. We need to prove that ∠ POQ = 2 ∠ PAQ.

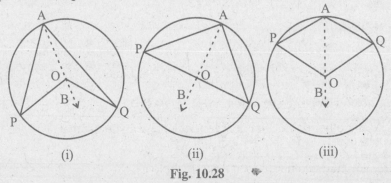

|     (i)     |     (ii)     |     (iii)     |

**Fig. 10.28**

Consider the three different cases as given in Fig. 10.28. In (i), arc PQ is minor; in (ii), arc PQ is a semicircle and in (iii), arc PQ is major.

Let us begin by joining AO and extending it to a point B.

In all the cases,

$$∠ BOQ = ∠ OAQ + ∠ AQO$$

because an exterior angle of a triangle is equal to the sum of the two interior opposite angles.

Also in Δ OAQ,

$$OA = OQ \qquad\qquad \text{(Radii of a circle)}$$

Therefore,                 $\angle OAQ = \angle OQA$                    (Theorem 7.5)

This gives                  $\angle BOQ = 2 \angle OAQ$                         (1)

Similarly,                  $\angle BOP = 2 \angle OAP$                         (2)

From (1) and (2),    $\angle BOP + \angle BOQ = 2(\angle OAP + \angle OAQ)$

This is the same as          $\angle POQ = 2 \angle PAQ$                         (3)

For the case (iii), where PQ is the major arc, (3) is replaced by

reflex angle POQ = 2 $\angle$ PAQ    ∎

**Remark** : Suppose we join points P and Q and form a chord PQ in the above figures. Then $\angle$ PAQ is also called the angle formed in the segment PAQP.

In Theorem 10.8, A can be any point on the remaining part of the circle. So if you take any other point C on the remaining part of the circle (see Fig. 10.29), you have

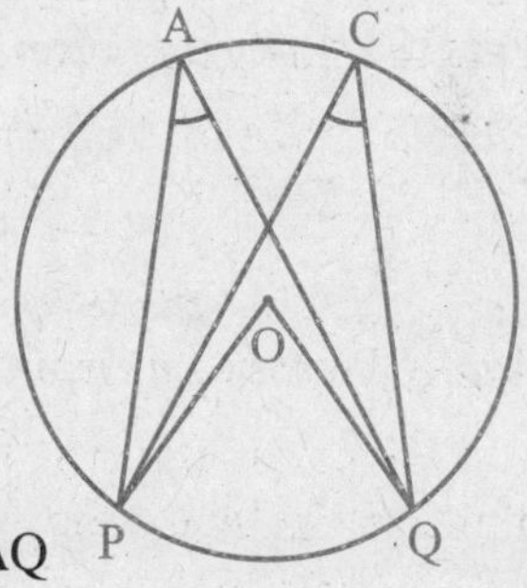

$$\angle POQ = 2 \angle PCQ = 2 \angle PAQ$$

Therefore,          $\angle PCQ = \angle PAQ.$

Fig. 10.29

This proves the following:

**Theorem 10.9** : *Angles in the same segment of a circle are equal.*

Again let us discuss the case (ii) of Theorem 10.8 separately. Here ∠PAQ is an angle in the segment, which is a semicircle. Also, $\angle PAQ = \dfrac{1}{2} \angle POQ = \dfrac{1}{2} \times 180° = 90°$.

If you take any other point C on the semicircle, again you get that

$$\angle PCQ = 90°$$

Therefore, you find another property of the circle as:

*Angle in a semicircle is a right angle.*

The converse of Theorem 10.9 is also true. It can be stated as:

**Theorem 10.10** : *If a line segment joining two points subtends equal angles at two other points lying on the same side of the line containing the line segment, the four points lie on a circle (i.e. they are concyclic).*

You can see the truth of this result as follows:

In Fig. 10.30, AB is a line segment, which subtends equal angles at two points C and D. That is

$$\angle ACB = \angle ADB$$

To show that the points A, B, C and D lie on a circle let us draw a circle through the points A, C and B. Suppose it does not pass through the point D. Then it will intersect AD (or extended AD) at a point, say E (or E').

If points A, C, E and B lie on a circle,

$$\angle ACB = \angle AEB \qquad \text{(Why?)}$$

But it is given that $\angle ACB = \angle ADB$.

Therefore,            $\angle AEB = \angle ADB$.

This is not possible unless E coincides with D. (Why?)

Similarly, E' should also coincide with D.

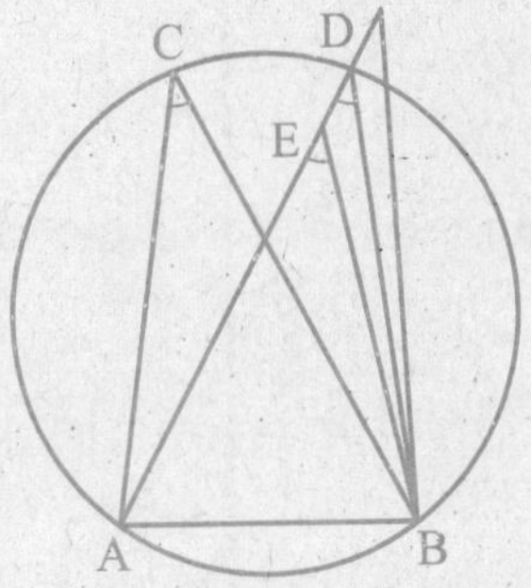

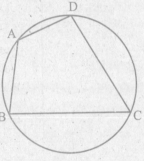

Fig. 10.30

## 10.8 Cyclic Quadrilaterals

A quadrilateral ABCD is called *cyclic* if all the four vertices of it lie on a circle (see Fig 10.31). You will find a peculiar property in such quadrilaterals. Draw several cyclic quadrilaterals of different sides and name each of these as ABCD. (This can be done by drawing several circles of different radii and taking four points on each of them.) Measure the opposite angles and write your observations in the following table.

Fig. 10.31

| S.No. of Quadrilateral | $\angle A$ | $\angle B$ | $\angle C$ | $\angle D$ | $\angle A + \angle C$ | $\angle B + \angle D$ |
|---|---|---|---|---|---|---|
| 1. | | | | | | |
| 2. | | | | | | |
| 3. | | | | | | |
| 4. | | | | | | |
| 5. | | | | | | |
| 6. | | | | | | |

What do you infer from the table?

You find that $\angle A + \angle C = 180°$ and $\angle B + \angle D = 180°$, neglecting the error in measurements. This verifies the following:

**Theorem 10.11** : *The sum of either pair of opposite angles of a cyclic quadrilateral is* 180°.

In fact, the converse of this theorem, which is stated below is also true.

**Theorem 10.12** : *If the sum of a pair of opposite angles of a quadrilateral is* 180°, *the quadrilateral is cyclic.*

You can see the truth of this theorem by following a method similar to the method adopted for Theorem 10.10.

**Example 3 :** In Fig. 10.32, AB is a diameter of the circle, CD is a chord equal to the radius of the circle. AC and BD when extended intersect at a point E. Prove that $\angle AEB = 60°$.

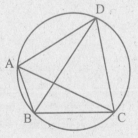

Fig. 10.32

**Solution :** Join OC, OD and BC.

Triangle ODC is equilateral                                    (Why?)

Therefore,    $\angle COD = 60°$

Now,        $\angle CBD = \dfrac{1}{2} \angle COD$    (Theorem 10.8)

This gives    $\angle CBD = 30°$

Again,        $\angle ACB = 90°$                    (Why ?)

So,            $\angle BCE = 180° - \angle ACB = 90°$

Which gives  $\angle CEB = 90° - 30° = 60°$, i.e., $\angle AEB = 60°$

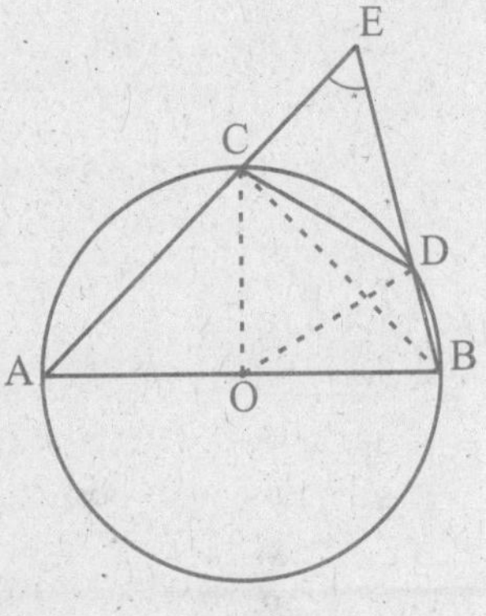

**Example 4 :** In Fig 10.33, ABCD is a cyclic quadrilateral in which AC and BD are its diagonals. If $\angle DBC = 55°$ and $\angle BAC = 45°$, find $\angle BCD$.

**Solution :**        $\angle CAD = \angle DBC = 55°$
                        (Angles in the same segment)

Therefore,        $\angle DAB = \angle CAD + \angle BAC$

                        $= 55° + 45° = 100°$

But  $\angle DAB + \angle BCD = 180°$

                (Opposite angles of a cyclic quadrilateral)

So,                    $\angle BCD = 180° - 100° = 80°$

Fig. 10.33

**Example 5 :** Two circles intersect at two points A and B. AD and AC are diameters to the two circles (see Fig.10.34). Prove that B lies on the line segment DC.

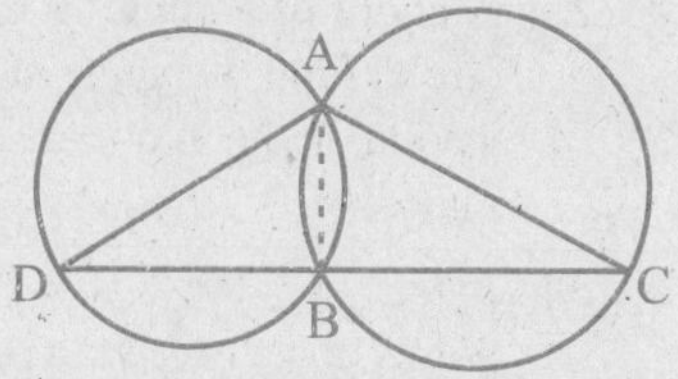

**Solution :** Join AB.

$\angle$ ABD = 90° (Angle in a semicircle)

$\angle$ ABC = 90° (Angle in a semicircle)

So, $\angle$ ABD + $\angle$ ABC = 90° + 90° = 180°

Therefore, DBC is a line. That is B lies on the line segment DC.

**Fig. 10.34**

**Example 6 :** Prove that the quadrilateral formed (if possible) by the internal angle bisectors of any quadrilateral is cyclic.

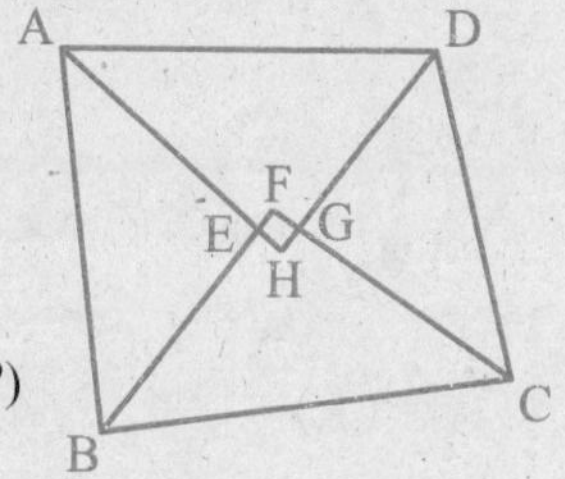

**Solution :** In Fig. 10.35, ABCD is a quadrilateral in which the angle bisectors AH, BF, CF and DH of internal angles A, B, C and D respectively form a quadrilateral EFGH.

Now, $\angle$ FEH = $\angle$ AEB = 180° – $\angle$ EAB – $\angle$ EBA (Why ?)

$$= 180° - \frac{1}{2} (\angle A + \angle B)$$

and $\angle$ FGH = $\angle$ CGD = 180° – $\angle$ GCD – $\angle$ GDC (Why ?)

$$= 180° - \frac{1}{2} (\angle C + \angle D)$$

**Fig. 10.35**

Therefore, $\angle$ FEH + $\angle$ FGH = 180° – $\frac{1}{2}$ ($\angle$ A + $\angle$ B) + 180° – $\frac{1}{2}$ ($\angle$ C + $\angle$ D)

$$= 360° - \frac{1}{2} (\angle A + \angle B + \angle C + \angle D) = 360° - \frac{1}{2} \times 360°$$

$$= 360° - 180° = 180°$$

Therefore, by Theorem 10.12, the quadrilateral EFGH is cyclic.

## EXERCISE 10.5

1.  In Fig. 10.36, A,B and C are three points on a circle with centre O such that $\angle$ BOC = 30° and $\angle$ AOB = 60°. If D is a point on the circle other than the arc ABC, find $\angle$ADC.

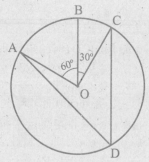

**Fig. 10.36**

2. A chord of a circle is equal to the radius of the circle. Find the angle subtended by the chord at a point on the minor arc and also at a point on the major arc.

3. In Fig. 10.37, $\angle PQR = 100°$, where P, Q and R are points on a circle with centre O. Find $\angle OPR$.

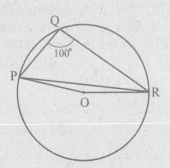

Fig. 10.37

4. In Fig. 10.38, $\angle ABC = 69°$, $\angle ACB = 31°$, find $\angle BDC$.

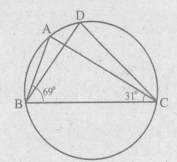

Fig. 10.38

5. In Fig. 10.39, A, B, C and D are four points on a circle. AC and BD intersect at a point E such that $\angle BEC = 130°$ and $\angle ECD = 20°$. Find $\angle BAC$.

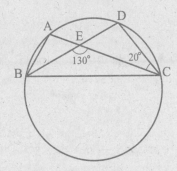

Fig. 10.39

6. ABCD is a cyclic quadrilateral whose diagonals intersect at a point E. If $\angle DBC = 70°$, $\angle BAC$ is $30°$, find $\angle BCD$. Further, if AB = BC, find $\angle ECD$.

7. If diagonals of a cyclic quadrilateral are diameters of the circle through the vertices of the quadrilateral, prove that it is a rectangle.

8. If the non-parallel sides of a trapezium are equal, prove that it is cyclic.

**9.** Two circles intersect at two points B and C. Through B, two line segments ABD and PBQ are drawn to intersect the circles at A, D and P, Q respectively (see Fig. 10.40). Prove that ∠ACP = ∠QCD.

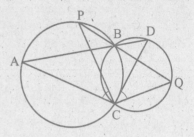

Fig. 10.40

**10.** If circles are drawn taking two sides of a triangle as diameters, prove that the point of intersection of these circles lie on the third side.

**11.** ABC and ADC are two right triangles with common hypotenuse AC. Prove that ∠CAD = ∠CBD.

**12.** Prove that a cyclic parallelogram is a rectangle.

## EXERCISE 10.6 (Optional)*

**1.** Prove that the line of centres of two intersecting circles subtends equal angles at the two points of intersection.

**2.** Two chords AB and CD of lengths 5 cm and 11 cm respectively of a circle are parallel to each other and are on opposite sides of its centre. If the distance between AB and CD is 6 cm, find the radius of the circle.

**3.** The lengths of two parallel chords of a circle are 6 cm and 8 cm. If the smaller chord is at distance 4 cm from the centre, what is the distance of the other chord from the centre?

**4.** Let the vertex of an angle ABC be located outside a circle and let the sides of the angle intersect equal chords AD and CE with the circle. Prove that ∠ABC is equal to half the difference of the angles subtended by the chords AC and DE at the centre.

**5.** Prove that the circle drawn with any side of a rhombus as diameter, passes through the point of intersection of its diagonals.

**6.** ABCD is a parallelogram. The circle through A, B and C intersect CD (produced if necessary) at E. Prove that AE = AD.

**7.** AC and BD are chords of a circle which bisect each other. Prove that (i) AC and BD are diameters, (ii) ABCD is a rectangle.

**8.** Bisectors of angles A, B and C of a triangle ABC intersect its circumcircle at D, E and F respectively. Prove that the angles of the triangle DEF are $90° - \frac{1}{2}$ A, $90° - \frac{1}{2}$ B and $90° - \frac{1}{2}$ C.

---

*These exercises are not from examination point of view.

9. Two congruent circles intersect each other at points A and B. Through A any line segment PAQ is drawn so that P, Q lie on the two circles. Prove that BP = BQ.

10. In any triangle ABC, if the angle bisector of $\angle A$ and perpendicular bisector of BC intersect, prove that they intersect on the circumcircle of the triangle ABC.

## 10.9 Summary

In this chapter, you have studied the following points:

1. A circle is the collection of all points in a plane, which are equidistant from a fixed point in the plane.

2. Equal chords of a circle (or of congruent circles) subtend equal angles at the centre.

3. If the angles subtended by two chords of a circle (or of congruent circles) at the centre (corresponding centres) are equal, the chords are equal.

4. The perpendicular from the centre of a circle to a chord bisects the chord.

5. The line drawn through the centre of a circle to bisect a chord is perpendicular to the chord.

6. There is one and only one circle passing through three non-collinear points.

7. Equal chords of a circle (or of congruent circles) are equidistant from the centre (or corresponding centres).

8. Chords equidistant from the centre (or corresponding centres) of a circle (or of congruent circles) are equal.

9. If two arcs of a circle are congruent, then their corresponding chords are equal and conversely if two chords of a circle are equal, then their corresponding arcs (minor, major) are congruent.

10. Congruent arcs of a circle subtend equal angles at the centre.

11. The angle subtended by an arc at the centre is double the angle subtended by it at any point on the remaining part of the circle.

12. Angles in the same segment of a circle are equal.

13. Angle in a semicircle is a right angle.

14. If a line segment joining two points subtends equal angles at two other points lying on the same side of the line containing the line segment, the four points lie on a circle.

15. The sum of either pair of opposite angles of a cyclic quadrilateral is $180^0$.

16. If sum of a pair of opposite angles of a quadrilateral is $180^0$, the quadrilateral is cyclic.

# CHAPTER 11

# CONSTRUCTIONS

## 11.1 Introduction

In earlier chapters, the diagrams, which were necessary to prove a theorem or solving exercises were not necessarily precise. They were drawn only to give you a feeling for the situation and as an aid for proper reasoning. However, sometimes one needs an accurate figure, for example - to draw a map of a building to be constructed, to design tools, and various parts of a machine, to draw road maps etc. To draw such figures some basic geometrical instruments are needed. You must be having a geometry box which contains the following:

(i) A graduated scale, on one side of which centimetres and millimetres are marked off and on the other side inches and their parts are marked off.

(ii) A pair of set - squares, one with angles 90°, 60° and 30° and other with angles 90°, 45° and 45°.

(iii) A pair of dividers (or a divider) with adjustments.

(iv) A pair of compasses (or a compass) with provision of fitting a pencil at one end.

(v) A protractor.

Normally, all these instruments are needed in drawing a geometrical figure, such as a triangle, a circle, a quadrilateral, a polygon, etc. with given measurements. But a geometrical construction is the process of drawing a geometrical figure using only two instruments – an *ungraduated ruler*, also called a *straight edge* and a *compass*. In construction where measurements are also required, you may use a graduated scale and protractor also. In this chapter, some basic constructions will be considered. These will then be used to construct certain kinds of triangles.

## 11.2 Basic Constructions

In Class VI, you have learnt how to construct a circle, the perpendicular bisector of a line segment, angles of 30°, 45°, 60°, 90° and 120°, and the bisector of a given angle, without giving any justification for these constructions. In this section, you will construct some of these, with reasoning behind, why these constructions are valid.

**Construction 11.1 :** *To construct the bisector of a given angle.*

Given an angle ABC, we want to construct its bisector.

**Steps of Construction :**

1. Taking B as centre and any radius, draw an arc to intersect the rays BA and BC, say at E and D respectively [see Fig.11.1(i)].

2. Next, taking D and E as centres and with the radius more than $\frac{1}{2}$ DE, draw arcs to intersect each other, say at F.

3. Draw the ray BF [see Fig.11.1(ii)]. This ray BF is the required bisector of the angle ABC.

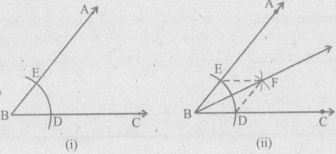

(i)                                      (ii)

**Fig. 11.1**

Let us see how this method gives us the required angle bisector.

Join DF and EF.

In triangles BEF and BDF,

$$BE = BD \quad \text{(Radii of the same arc)}$$
$$EF = DF \quad \text{(Arcs of equal radii)}$$
$$BF = BF \quad \text{(Common)}$$

Therefore,   $\triangle BEF \cong \triangle BDF$   (SSS rule)

This gives   $\angle EBF = \angle DBF$   (CPCT)

**Construction 11.2 :** *To construct the perpendicular bisector of a given line segment.*

Given a line segment AB, we want to construct its perpendicular bisector.

**Steps of Construction :**

1. Taking A and B as centres and radius more than $\frac{1}{2}$ AB, draw arcs on both sides of the line segment AB (to intersect each other).

2. Let these arcs intersect each other at P and Q. Join PQ (see Fig.11.2).

3. Let PQ intersect AB at the point M. Then line PMQ is the required perpendicular bisector of AB.

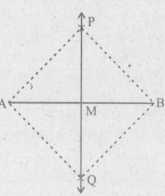

Let us see how this method gives us the perpendicular bisector of AB.

Fig. 11.2

Join A and B to both P and Q to form AP, AQ, BP and BQ.

In triangles PAQ and PBQ,

$$AP = BP \qquad \text{(Arcs of equal radii)}$$
$$AQ = BQ \qquad \text{(Arcs of equal radii)}$$
$$PQ = PQ \qquad \text{(Common)}$$

Therefore,   $\Delta$ PAQ $\cong$ $\Delta$ PBQ            (SSS rule)

So,     $\angle$ APM = $\angle$ BPM            (CPCT)

Now in triangles PMA and PMB,

$$AP = BP \qquad \text{(As before)}$$
$$PM = PM \qquad \text{(Common)}$$
$$\angle APM = \angle BPM \qquad \text{(Proved above)}$$

Therefore,   $\Delta$ PMA $\cong$ $\Delta$ PMB            (SAS rule)

So,     AM = BM and $\angle$ PMA = $\angle$ PMB            (CPCT)

As     $\angle$ PMA + $\angle$ PMB = 180°            (Linear pair axiom),

we get

$$\angle PMA = \angle PMB = 90°.$$

Therefore, PM, that is, PMQ is the perpendicular bisector of AB.

**Construction 11.3 :** *To construct an angle of 60⁰ at the initial point of a given ray.*

Let us take a ray AB with initial point A [see Fig. 11.3(i)]. We want to construct a ray AC such that $\angle$ CAB = 60°. One way of doing so is given below.

**Steps of Construction :**

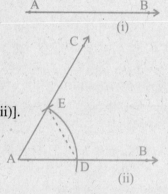

1. Taking A as centre and some radius, draw an arc of a circle, which intersects AB, say at a point D.

2. Taking D as centre and with the same radius as before, draw an arc intersecting the previously drawn arc, say at a point E.

3. Draw the ray AC passing through E [see Fig 11.3 (ii)].

   Then $\angle$ CAB is the required angle of 60°. Now, let us see how this method gives us the required angle of 60°.

   Join DE.

   Then,     AE = AD = DE     (By construction)

Fig. 11.3

Therefore, $\Delta$ EAD is an equilateral triangle and the $\angle$ EAD, which is the same as $\angle$ CAB is equal to 60°.

### EXERCISE 11.1

1. Construct an angle of 90⁰ at the initial point of a given ray and justify the construction.

2. Construct an angle of 45⁰ at the initial point of a given ray and justify the construction.

3. Construct the angles of the following measurements:

   (i)   30°                    (ii) $22\frac{1}{2}^{\circ}$                    (iii)  15°

4. Construct the following angles and verify by measuring them by a protractor:

   (i)   75°                    (ii)  105°                    (iii)  135°

5. Construct an equilateral triangle, given its side and justify the construction.

## 11.3 Some Constructions of Triangles

So far, some basic constructions have been considered. Next, some constructions of triangles will be done by using the constructions given in earlier classes and given above. Recall from the Chapter 7 that SAS, SSS, ASA and RHS rules give the congruency of two triangles. Therefore, a triangle is unique if : (i) two sides and the included angle is given, (ii) three sides are given, (iii) two angles and the included side is given and, (iv) in a right triangle, hypotenuse and one side is given. You have already learnt how to construct such triangles in Class VII. Now, let us consider some more constructions of triangles. You may have noted that at least three parts of a triangle have to be given for constructing it but not all combinations of three parts are sufficient for the purpose. For example, if two sides and an angle (not the included angle) are given, then it is not always possible to construct such a triangle uniquely.

**Construction 11.4 :** *To construct a triangle, given its base, a base angle and sum of other two sides.*

Given the base BC, a base angle, say ∠B and the sum AB + AC of the other two sides of a triangle ABC, you are required to construct it.

**Steps of Construction :**

1. Draw the base BC and at the point B make an angle, say XBC equal to the given angle.

2. Cut a line segment BD equal to AB + AC from the ray BX.

3. Join DC and make an angle DCY equal to ∠BDC.

4. Let CY intersect BX at A (see Fig. 11.4).

Then, ABC is the required triangle.

Let us see how you get the required triangle.

Base BC and ∠B are drawn as given. Next in triangle ACD,

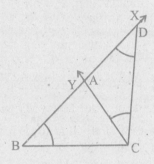

Fig. 11.4

$$\angle ACD = \angle ADC \qquad \text{(By construction)}$$

Therefore, AC = AD and then

$$AB = BD - AD = BD - AC$$

$$AB + AC = BD$$

**Alternative method :**

Follow the first two steps as above. Then draw perpendicular bisector PQ of CD to intersect BD at a point A (see Fig 11.5). Join AC. Then ABC is the required triangle. Note that A lies on the perpendicular bisector of CD, therefore AD = AC.

**Remark :** The construction of the triangle is not possible if the sum AB + AC ≤ BC.

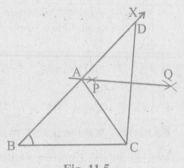

Fig. 11.5

**Construction 11.5 :** *To construct a triangle given its base, a base angle and the difference of the other two sides.*

Given the base BC, a base angle, say ∠B and the difference of other two sides AB – AC or AC – AB, you have to construct the triangle ABC. Clearly there are following two cases:

**Case (i) :** Let AB > AC that is AB – AC is given.

**Steps of Construction :**

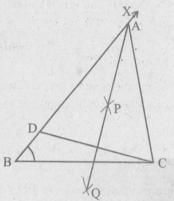

1. Draw the base BC and at point B make an angle say XBC equal to the given angle.

2. Cut the line segment BD equal to AB – AC from ray BX.

3. Join DC and draw the perpendicular bisector, say PQ of DC.

4. Let it intersect BX at a point A. Join AC (see Fig. 11.6).

Then ABC is the required triangle.

**Fig. 11.6**

Let us now see how you have obtained the required triangle ABC.

Base BC and ∠B are drawn as given. The point A lies on the perpendicular bisector of DC. Therefore,

$$AD = AC$$

So,                         $$BD = AB – AD = AB – AC.$$

**Case (ii) :** Let AB < AC that is AC – AB is given.

**Steps of Construction :**

1. Same as in case (i).

2. Cut line segment BD equal to AC – AB from the line BX extended on opposite side of line segment BC.

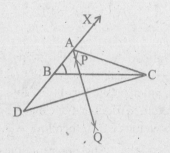

3. Join DC and draw the perpendicular bisector, say PQ of DC.

4. Let PQ intersect BX at A. Join AC (see Fig. 11.7).

Then, ABC is the required triangle.

You can justify the construction as in case (i).

**Fig. 11.7**

**Construction 11.6** : *To construct a triangle, given its perimeter and its two base angles.*

Given the base angles, say $\angle$ B and $\angle$ C and BC + CA + AB, you have to construct the triangle ABC.

**Steps of Construction :**

1. Draw a line segment, say XY equal to BC + CA + AB.

2. Make angles LXY equal to $\angle$B and MYX equal to $\angle$C.

3. Bisect $\angle$ LXY and $\angle$ MYX. Let these bisectors intersect at a point A [see Fig. 11.8(i)].

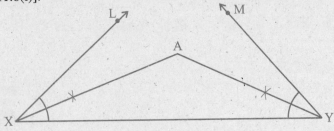

Fig. 11.8 (i)

4. Draw perpendicular bisectors PQ of AX and RS of AY.

5. Let PQ intersect XY at B and RS intersect XY at C. Join AB and AC [see Fig 11.8(ii)].

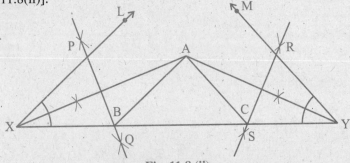

Fig. 11.8 (ii)

Then ABC is the required triangle. For the justification of the construction, you observe that, B lies on the perpendicular bisector PQ of AX.

Therefore, XB = AB and similarly, CY = AC.

This gives    BC + CA + AB = BC + XB + CY = XY.

Again                                  $\angle$BAX = $\angle$AXB (As in $\triangle$ AXB, AB = XB) and

                                         $\angle$ABC = $\angle$BAX + $\angle$AXB = 2 $\angle$AXB = $\angle$LXY

Similarly,                          $\angle$ACB = $\angle$MYX as required.

**Example 1 :** Construct a triangle ABC, in which ∠B = 60°, ∠C = 45° and AB + BC + CA = 11 cm.

**Steps of Construction :**

1. Draw a line segment PQ = 11 cm.( = AB + BC + CA).

2. At P construct an angle of 60° and at Q, an angle of 45°.

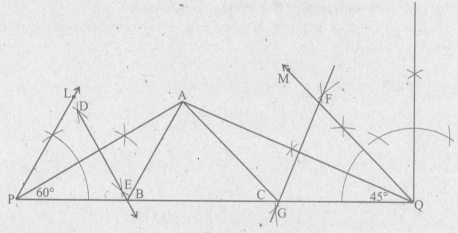

Fig. 11.9

3. Bisect these angles. Let the bisectors of these angles intersect at a point A.

4. Draw perpendicular bisectors DE of AP to intersect PQ at B and FG of AQ to intersect PQ at C.

5. Join AB and AC (see Fig. 11.9).

Then, ABC is the required triangle.

## EXERCISE 11.2

1.   Construct a triangle ABC in which BC = 7cm, ∠B = 75° and AB + AC = 13 cm.

2.   Construct a triangle ABC in which BC = 8cm, ∠B = 45° and AB – AC = 3.5 cm.

3.   Construct a triangle PQR in which QR = 6cm, ∠Q = 60° and PR – PQ = 2cm.

4.   Construct a triangle XYZ in which ∠Y = 30°, ∠Z = 90° and XY + YZ + ZX = 11 cm.

5.   Construct a right triangle whose base is 12cm and sum of its hypotenuse and other side is 18 cm.

## 11.4 Summary

In this chapter, you have done the following constructions using a ruler and a compass:

1. To bisect a given angle.
2. To draw the perpendicular bisector of a given line segment.
3. To construct an angle of 60° etc.
4. To construct a triangle given its base, a base angle and the sum of the other two sides.
5. To construct a triangle given its base, a base angle and the difference of the other two sides.
6. To construct a triangle given its perimeter and its two base angles.

# CHAPTER 12

# HERON'S FORMULA

## 12.1 Introduction

You have studied in earlier classes about figures of different shapes such as squares, rectangles, triangles and quadrilaterals. You have also calculated perimeters and the areas of some of these figures like rectangle, square etc. For instance, you can find the area and the perimeter of the floor of your classroom.

Let us take a walk around the floor along its sides once; the distance we walk is its perimeter. The size of the floor of the room is its area.

So, if your classroom is rectangular with length 10 m and width 8 m, its perimeter would be 2(10 m + 8 m) = 36 m and its area would be 10 m × 8 m, i.e., 80 m².

Unit of measurement for length or breadth is taken as metre (m) or centimetre (cm) etc.

Unit of measurement for area of any plane figure is taken as square metre (m²) or square centimetre (cm²) etc.

Suppose that you are sitting in a triangular garden. How would you find its area? From Chapter 9 and from your earlier classes, you know that:

$$\boxed{\textbf{Area of a triangle} = \frac{1}{2} \times \textbf{base} \times \textbf{height}} \qquad \text{(I)}$$

We see that when the triangle is **right angled**, we can directly apply the formula by using two sides containing the right angle as base and height. For example, suppose that the sides of a right triangle ABC are 5 cm, 12 cm and 13 cm; we take base as 12 cm and height as 5 cm (see Fig. 12.1). Then the

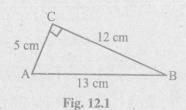

Fig. 12.1

area of Δ ABC is given by

$$\frac{1}{2} \times \text{base} \times \text{height} = \frac{1}{2} \times 12 \times 5 \text{ cm}^2, \text{ i.e., } 30 \text{ cm}^2$$

Note that we could also take 5 cm as the base and 12 cm as height.

Now suppose we want to find the area of an **equilateral triangle** PQR with side 10cm (see Fig. 12.2). To find its area we need its height. Can you find the height of this triangle?

Let us recall how we find its height when we know its sides. This is possible in an equilateral triangle. Take the mid-point of QR as M and join it to P. We know that PMQ is a right triangle. Therefore, by using Pythagoras Theorem, we can find the length PM as shown below:

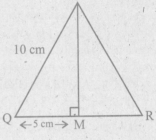

$$PQ^2 = PM^2 + QM^2$$

i.e., $(10)^2 = PM^2 + (5)^2$, since QM = MR.

Therefore, we have $PM^2 = 75$

i.e., $PM = \sqrt{75}$ cm $= 5\sqrt{3}$ cm.

Fig. 12.2

Then area of Δ PQR $= \frac{1}{2} \times \text{base} \times \text{height} = \frac{1}{2} \times 10 \times 5\sqrt{3}$ cm$^2 = 25\sqrt{3}$ cm$^2$.

Let us see now whether we can calculate the area of an **isosceles triangle** also with the help of this formula. For example, we take a triangle XYZ with two equal sides XY and XZ as 5 cm each and unequal side YZ as 8 cm (see Fig. 12.3).

In this case also, we want to know the height of the triangle. So, from X we draw a perpendicular XP to side YZ. You can see that this perpendicular XP divides the base YZ of the triangle in two equal parts.

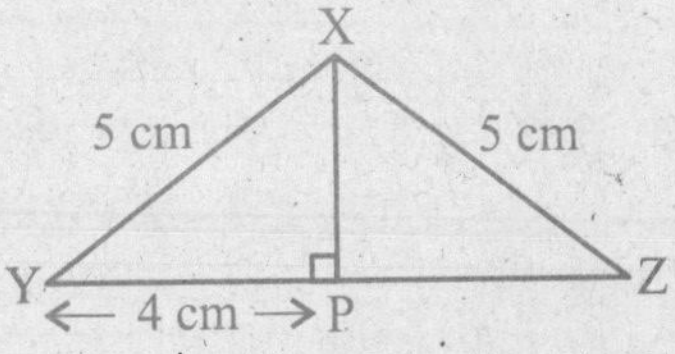

Therefore, $\quad YP = PZ = \frac{1}{2} YZ = 4$ cm

Then, by using Pythagoras theorem, we get

$$XP^2 = XY^2 - YP^2$$
$$= 5^2 - 4^2 = 25 - 16 = 9$$

So, $\quad XP = 3$ cm

Fig. 12.3

Now, area of Δ XYZ $= \frac{1}{2} \times \text{base YZ} \times \text{height XP}$

$$= \frac{1}{2} \times 8 \times 3 \text{ cm}^2 = 12 \text{ cm}^2.$$

Now suppose that we know the lengths of the sides of a scalene triangle and not the height. Can you still find its area? For instance, you have a triangular park whose sides are 40 m, 32 m, and 24 m. How will you calculate its area? Definitely if you want to apply the formula, you will have to calculate its height. But we do not have a clue to calculate the height. Try doing so. If you are not able to get it, then go to the next section.

## 12.2 Area of a Triangle — by Heron's Formula

Heron was born in about 10AD possibly in Alexandria in Egypt. He worked in applied mathematics. His works on mathematical and physical subjects are so numerous and varied that he is considered to be an encyclopedic writer in these fields. His geometrical works deal largely with problems on mensuration written in three books. Book I deals with the area of squares, rectangles, triangles, trapezoids (trapezia), various other specialised quadrilaterals, the regular polygons, circles, surfaces of cylinders, cones, spheres etc. In this book, Heron has derived the famous formula for the area of a triangle in terms of its three sides.

**Heron (10 C.E. – 75 C.E.)**

Fig. 12.4

The formula given by Heron about the area of a triangle, is also known as *Hero's formula*. It is stated as:

$$\text{Area of a triangle} = \sqrt{s(s-a)(s-b)(s-c)} \qquad \text{(II)}$$

*where a, b and c are the sides of the triangle*, and *s = semi-perimeter, i.e., half the perimeter of the triangle* = $\dfrac{a+b+c}{2}$,

This formula is helpful where it is not possible to find the height of the triangle easily. Let us apply it to calculate the area of the triangular park ABC, mentioned above (see Fig. 12.5).

Let us take $a = 40$ m, $b = 24$ m, $c = 32$ m,

so that we have $s = \dfrac{40+24+32}{2}$ m $= 48$ m.

$s - a = (48 - 40) \text{ m} = 8 \text{ m},$

$s - b = (48 - 24) \text{ m} = 24 \text{ m},$

$s - c = (48 - 32) \text{ m} = 16 \text{ m}.$

Therefore, area of the park ABC

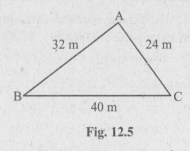

Fig. 12.5

$= \sqrt{s(s-a)(s-b)(s-c)}$

$= \sqrt{48 \times 8 \times 24 \times 16} \text{ m}^2 = 384 \text{ m}^2$

We see that $32^2 + 24^2 = 1024 + 576 = 1600 = 40^2$. Therefore, the sides of the park make a right triangle. The largest side, i.e., BC which is 40 m will be the hypotenuse and the angle between the sides AB and AC will be 90°.

By using Formula I, we can check that the area of the park is $\frac{1}{2} \times 32 \times 24$ m$^2$ $= 384$ m$^2$.

We find that the area we have got is the same as we found by using Heron's formula.

Now using Heron's formula, you verify this fact by finding the areas of other triangles discussed earlier *viz.*,

(i)  equilateral triangle with side 10 cm.

(ii) isosceles triangle with unequal side as 8 cm and each equal side as 5 cm.

You will see that

For (i), we have $s = \dfrac{10 + 10 + 10}{2}$ cm $= 15$ cm.

Area of triangle $= \sqrt{15(15 - 10)(15 - 10)(15 - 10)}$ cm$^2$

$= \sqrt{15 \times 5 \times 5 \times 5}$ cm$^2 = 25\sqrt{3}$ cm$^2$

For (ii), we have $s = \dfrac{8 + 5 + 5}{2}$ cm $= 9$ cm.

Area of triangle $= \sqrt{9(9 - 8)(9 - 5)(9 - 5)}$ cm$^2 = \sqrt{9 \times 1 \times 4 \times 4}$ cm$^2 = 12$ cm$^2$.

Let us now solve some more examples:

**Example 1 :** Find the area of a triangle, two sides of which are 8 cm and 11 cm and the perimeter is 32 cm (see Fig. 12.6).

**Solution :** Here we have perimeter of the triangle = 32 cm, $a$ = 8 cm and $b$ = 11 cm.

Third side $c$ = 32 cm – (8 + 11) cm = 13 cm

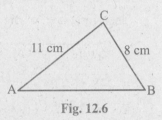

So,       $2s$ = 32, i.e., $s$ = 16 cm,

$s - a$ = (16 – 8) cm = 8 cm,

$s - b$ = (16 – 11) cm = 5 cm,

$s - c$ = (16 – 13) cm = 3 cm.

Fig. 12.6

Therefore, area of the triangle = $\sqrt{s(s-a)(s-b)(s-c)}$

$$= \sqrt{16 \times 8 \times 5 \times 3}\, \text{cm}^2 = 8\sqrt{30}\ \text{cm}^2$$

**Example 2 :** A triangular park ABC has sides 120m, 80m and 50m (see Fig. 12.7). A gardener *Dhania* has to put a fence all around it and also plant grass inside. How much area does she need to plant? Find the cost of fencing it with barbed wire at the rate of Rs 20 per metre leaving a space 3m wide for a gate on one side.

**Solution :** For finding area of the park, we have

$2s$ = 50 m + 80 m + 120 m = 250 m.

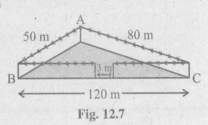

i.e.,        $s$ = 125 m

Now,    $s - a$ = (125 – 120) m = 5 m,

$s - b$ = (125 – 80) m = 45 m,

$s - c$ = (125 – 50) m = 75 m.

Fig. 12.7

Therefore, area of the park = $\sqrt{s(s-a)(s-b)(s-c)}$

$$= \sqrt{125 \times 5 \times 45 \times 75}\ \text{m}^2$$

$$= 375\sqrt{15}\ \text{m}^2$$

Also, perimeter of the park = AB + BC + CA = 250 m

Therefore, length of the wire needed for fencing = 250 m – 3 m (to be left for gate)

$$= 247\ \text{m}$$

And so the cost of fencing = Rs 20 × 247 = Rs 4940

**Example 3 :** The sides of a triangular plot are in the ratio of 3 : 5 : 7 and its perimeter is 300 m. Find its area.

**Solution :** Suppose that the sides, in metres, are $3x$, $5x$ and $7x$ (see Fig. 12.8).

Then, we know that $3x + 5x + 7x = 300$ (perimeter of the triangle)

Therefore, $15x = 300$, which gives $x = 20$.

So the sides of the triangle are $3 \times 20$ m, $5 \times 20$ m and $7 \times 20$ m

i.e., 60 m, 100 m and 140 m.

Can you now find the area [Using Heron's formula]?

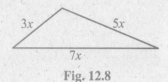

We have $s = \dfrac{60 + 100 + 140}{2}$ m $= 150$ m,

Fig. 12.8

and area will be $\sqrt{150(150- 60) \, (150 - 100) \, (150 -140)}$ m²

$$= \sqrt{150 \times 90 \times 50 \times 10} \text{ m}^2$$

$$= 1500\sqrt{3} \text{ m}^2$$

## EXERCISE 12.1

1.  A traffic signal board, indicating 'SCHOOL AHEAD', is an equilateral triangle with side '$a$'. Find the area of the signal board, using Heron's formula. If its perimeter is 180 cm, what will be the area of the signal board?

2.  The triangular side walls of a flyover have been used for advertisements. The sides of the walls are 122 m, 22 m and 120 m (see Fig. 12.9). The advertisements yield an earning of ₹ 5000 per m² per year. A company hired one of its walls for 3 months. How much rent did it pay?

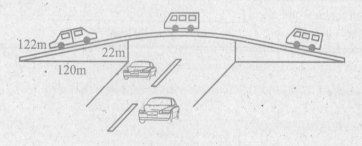

Fig. 12.9

**3.** There is a slide in a park. One of its side walls has been painted in some colour with a message "KEEP THE PARK GREEN AND CLEAN" (see Fig. 12.10 ). If the sides of the wall are 15 m, 11 m and 6 m, find the area painted in colour.

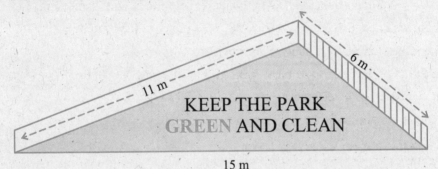

KEEP THE PARK
GREEN AND CLEAN

15 m

Fig. 12.10

**4.** Find the area of a triangle two sides of which are 18cm and 10cm and the perimeter is 42cm.

**5.** Sides of a triangle are in the ratio of 12 : 17 : 25 and its perimeter is 540cm. Find its area.

**6.** An isosceles triangle has perimeter 30 cm and each of the equal sides is 12 cm. Find the area of the triangle.

## 12.3 Application of Heron's Formula in Finding Areas of Quadrilaterals

Suppose that a farmer has a land to be cultivated and she employs some labourers for this purpose on the terms of wages calculated by area cultivated per square metre. How will she do this? Many a time, the fields are in the shape of quadrilaterals. We need to divide the quadrilateral in triangular parts and then use the formula for area of the triangle. Let us look at this problem:

**Example 4 :** Kamla has a triangular field with sides 240 m, 200 m, 360 m, where she grew wheat. In another triangular field with sides 240 m, 320 m, 400 m adjacent to the previous field, she wanted to grow potatoes and onions (see Fig. 12.11). She divided the field in two parts by joining the mid-point of the longest side to the opposite vertex and grew patatoes in one part and onions in the other part. How much area (in hectares) has been used for wheat, potatoes and onions? (1 hectare = 10000 m²)

**Solution :** Let ABC be the field where wheat is grown. Also let ACD be the field which has been divided in two parts by joining C to the mid-point E of AD. For the area of triangle ABC, we have

$$a = 200 \text{ m}, b = 240 \text{ m}, c = 360 \text{ m}$$

Therefore, $s = \dfrac{200 + 240 + 360}{2}$ m = 400 m.

So, area for growing wheat

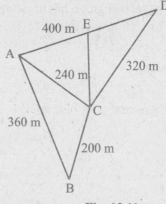

$$= \sqrt{400(400-200)\,(400-240)\,(400-360)}\ \mathrm{m}^2$$

$$= \sqrt{400 \times 200 \times 160 \times 40}\ \mathrm{m}^2$$

$$= 16000\sqrt{2}\ \mathrm{m}^2 = 1.6 \times \sqrt{2}\ \text{hectares}$$

$$= 2.26\ \text{hectares (nearly)}$$

Let us now calculate the area of triangle ACD.

Here, we have $s = \dfrac{240 + 320 + 400}{2}\ \mathrm{m} = 480\ \mathrm{m}.$

Fig. 12.11

So, area of $\triangle$ ACD $= \sqrt{480(480-240)\,(480-320)\,(480-400)}\ \mathrm{m}^2$

$$= \sqrt{480 \times 240 \times 160 \times 80}\ \mathrm{m}^2 = 38400\ \mathrm{m}^2 = 3.84\ \text{hectares}$$

We notice that the line segment joining the mid-point E of AD to C divides the triangle ACD in two parts equal in area. Can you give the reason for this? In fact, they have the bases AE and ED equal and, of course, they have the same height.

Therefore, area for growing potatoes = area for growing onions

$$= (3.84 \div 2)\ \text{hectares} = 1.92\ \text{hectares}.$$

**Example 5 :** Students of a school staged a rally for cleanliness campaign. They walked through the lanes in two groups. One group walked through the lanes AB, BC and CA; while the other through AC, CD and DA (see Fig. 12.12). Then they cleaned the area enclosed within their lanes. If AB = 9 m, BC = 40 m, CD = 15 m, DA = 28 m and $\angle$ B = 90°, which group cleaned more area and by how much? Find the total area cleaned by the students (neglecting the width of the lanes).

**Solution :** Since AB = 9 m and BC = 40 m, $\angle$ B = 90°, we have:

$$AC = \sqrt{9^2 + 40^2}\ \mathrm{m}$$

$$= \sqrt{81 + 1600}\ \mathrm{m}$$

$$= \sqrt{1681}\ \mathrm{m} = 41\mathrm{m}$$

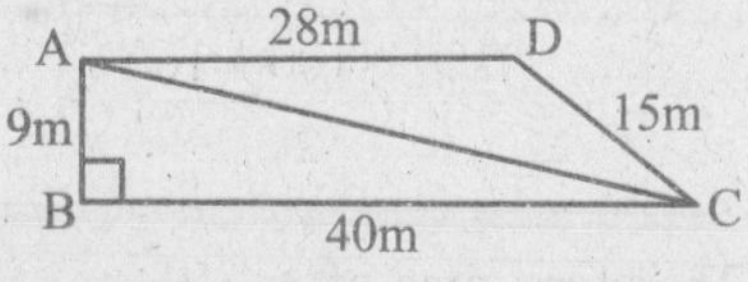

Fig. 12.12

Therefore, the first group has to clean the area of triangle ABC, which is right angled.

Area of $\triangle$ ABC $= \dfrac{1}{2} \times$ base $\times$ height

$$= \dfrac{1}{2} \times 40 \times 9\ \mathrm{m}^2 = 180\ \mathrm{m}^2$$

The second group has to clean the area of triangle ACD, which is scalene having sides 41 m, 15 m and 28 m.

Here, $$s = \frac{41 + 15 + 28}{2} \text{ m} = 42 \text{ m}$$

Therefore, area of $\triangle$ ACD $= \sqrt{s(s-a)(s-b)(s-c)}$

$$= \sqrt{42(42-41)(42-15)(42-28)} \text{ m}^2$$

$$= \sqrt{42 \times 1 \times 27 \times 14} \text{ m}^2 = 126 \text{ m}^2$$

So first group cleaned 180 m² which is $(180 - 126)$ m², i.e., 54 m² more than the area cleaned by the second group.

Total area cleaned by all the students $= (180 + 126)$ m² $= 306$ m².

**Example 6 :** Sanya has a piece of land which is in the shape of a rhombus (see Fig. 12.13). She wants her one daughter and one son to work on the land and produce different crops. She divided the land in two equal parts. If the perimeter of the land is 400 m and one of the diagonals is 160 m, how much area each of them will get for their crops?

**Solution :** Let ABCD be the field.

     Perimeter = 400 m

     So, each side = 400 m ÷ 4 = 100 m.

     i.e. AB = AD = 100 m.

Let diagonal    BD = 160 m.

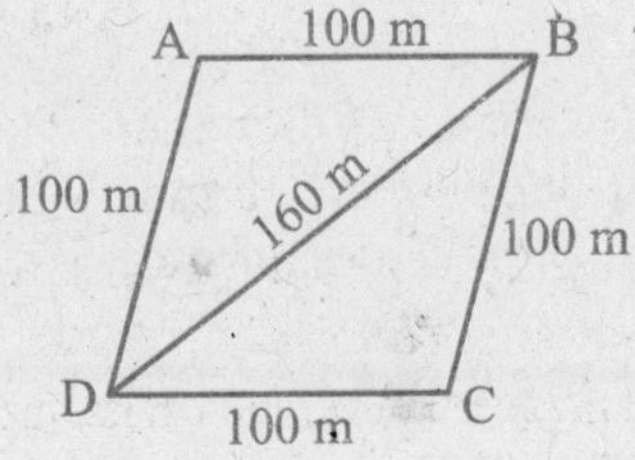

Then semi-perimeter $s$ of $\triangle$ ABD is given by

$$s = \frac{100 + 100 + 160}{2} \text{ m} = 180 \text{ m}$$

**Fig. 12.13**

Therefore, area of $\triangle$ ABD $= \sqrt{180(180-100)(180-100)(180-160)}$

$$= \sqrt{180 \times 80 \times 80 \times 20} \text{ m}^2 = 4800 \text{ m}^2$$

Therefore, each of them will get an area of 4800 m².

Alternative method :    Draw CE ⊥ BD (see Fig. 12.14).

As        BD = 160 m, we have

          DE = 160 m ÷ 2 = 80 m

And,      DE² + CE² = DC², which gives

          $CE = \sqrt{DC^2 - DE^2}$

or,       $CE = \sqrt{100^2 - 80^2}$ m = 60 m

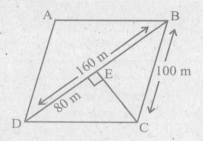

Therefore, area of Δ BCD = $\dfrac{1}{2} \times 160 \times 60$ m² = 4800 m²

**Fig. 12.14**

## EXERCISE 12.2

1.  A park, in the shape of a quadrilateral ABCD, has ∠ C = 90°, AB = 9 m, BC = 12 m, CD = 5 m and AD = 8 m. How much area does it occupy?

2.  Find the area of a quadrilateral ABCD in which AB = 3 cm, BC = 4 cm, CD = 4 cm, DA = 5 cm and AC = 5 cm.

3.  Radha made a picture of an aeroplane with coloured paper as shown in Fig 12.15. Find the total area of the paper used.

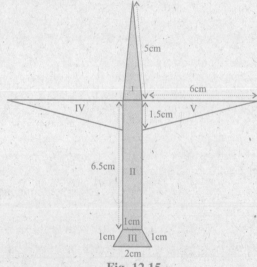

**Fig. 12.15**

4.  A triangle and a parallelogram have the same base and the same area. If the sides of the triangle are 26 cm, 28 cm and 30 cm, and the parallelogram stands on the base 28 cm, find the height of the parallelogram.

5. A rhombus shaped field has green grass for 18 cows to graze. If each side of the rhombus is 30 m and its longer diagonal is 48 m, how much area of grass field will each cow be getting?

6. An umbrella is made by stitching 10 triangular pieces of cloth of two different colours (see Fig. 12.16), each piece measuring 20 cm, 50 cm and 50 cm. How much cloth of each colour is required for the umbrella?

7. A kite in the shape of a square with a diagonal 32 cm and an isosceles triangle of base 8 cm and sides 6 cm each is to be made of three different shades as shown in Fig. 12.17. How much paper of each shade has been used in it?

Fig. 12.16

Fig. 12.17

8. A floral design on a floor is made up of 16 tiles which are triangular, the sides of the triangle being 9 cm, 28 cm and 35 cm (see Fig. 12.18). Find the cost of polishing the tiles at the rate of 50p per cm². 

9. A field is in the shape of a trapezium whose parallel sides are 25 m and 10 m. The non-parallel sides are 14 m and 13 m. Find the area of the field.

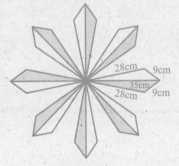

Fig. 12.18

## 12.4 Summary

In this chapter, you have studied the following points :

1. Area of a triangle with its sides as *a*, *b* and *c* is calculated by using Heron's formula, stated as

$$\text{Area of triangle} = \sqrt{s(s-a)(s-b)(s-c)}$$

where $$s = \frac{a+b+c}{2}$$

2. Area of a quadrilateral whose sides and one diagonal are given, can be calculated by dividing the quadrilateral into two triangles and using the Heron's formula.

# CHAPTER 13

# SURFACE AREAS AND VOLUMES

## 13.1 Introduction

Wherever we look, usually we see solids. So far, in all our study, we have been dealing with figures that can be easily drawn on our notebooks or blackboards. These are called *plane figures*. We have understood what rectangles, squares and circles are, what we mean by their perimeters and areas, and how we can find them. We have learnt these in earlier classes. It would be interesting to see what happens if we cut out many of these plane figures of the same shape and size from cardboard sheet and stack them up in a vertical pile. By this process, we shall obtain some *solid figures* (briefly called *solids*) such as a cuboid, a cylinder, etc. In the earlier classes, you have also learnt to find the surface areas and volumes of cuboids, cubes and cylinders. We shall now learn to find the surface areas and volumes of cuboids and cylinders in details and extend this study to some other solids such as cones and spheres.

## 13.2 Surface Area of a Cuboid and a Cube

Have you looked at a bundle of many sheets of paper? How does it look? Does it look like what you see in Fig. 13.1?

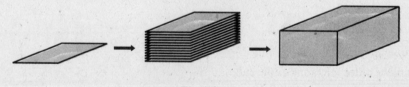

Fig. 13.1

That makes up a cuboid. How much of brown paper would you need, if you want to cover this cuboid? Let us see:

First we would need a rectangular piece to cover the bottom of the bundle. That would be as shown in Fig. 13.2 (a)

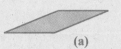
(a)

Then we would need two long rectangular pieces to cover the two side ends. Now, it would look like Fig. 13.2 (b).

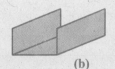
(b)

Now to cover the front and back ends, we would need two more rectangular pieces of a different size. With them, we would now have a figure as shown in Fig. 13.2(c).

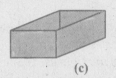
(c)

This figure, when opened out, would look like Fig. 13.2 (d).

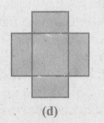
(d)

Finally, to cover the top of the bundle, we would require another rectangular piece exactly like the one at the bottom, which if we attach on the right side, it would look like Fig. 13.2(e).

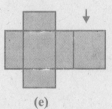
(e)

So we have used six rectangular pieces to cover the complete outer surface of the cuboid.

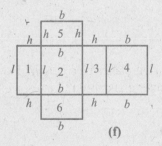
(f)

Fig. 13.2

This shows us that the outer surface of a cuboid is made up of six rectangles (in fact, rectangular regions, called the faces of the cuboid), whose areas can be found by multiplying length by breadth for each of them separately and then adding the six areas together.

Now, if we take the length of the cuboid as $l$, breadth as $b$ and the height as $h$, then the figure with these dimensions would be like the shape you see in Fig. 13.2(f).

So, the sum of the areas of the six rectangles is:

Area of rectangle 1 ($= l \times h$)

+

Area of rectangle 2 ($= l \times b$)

+

Area of rectangle 3 ($= l \times h$)

+

Area of rectangle 4 ($= l \times b$)

+

Area of rectangle 5 ($= b \times h$)

+

Area of rectangle 6 ($= b \times h$)

$$= 2(l \times b) + 2(b \times h) + 2(l \times h)$$
$$= 2(lb + bh + hl)$$

This gives us:

$$\boxed{\text{Surface Area of a Cuboid} = 2(lb + bh + hl)}$$

where $l$, $b$ and $h$ are respectively the three edges of the cuboid.

Note : The unit of area is taken as the square unit, because we measure the magnitude of a region by filling it with squares of side of unit length.

For example, if we have a cuboid whose length, breadth and height are 15 cm, 10 cm and 20 cm respectively, then its surface area would be:

$$2[(15 \times 10) + (10 \times 20) + (20 \times 15)] \text{ cm}^2$$
$$= 2(150 + 200 + 300) \text{ cm}^2$$
$$= 2 \times 650 \text{ cm}^2$$
$$= 1300 \text{ cm}^2$$

Recall that a cuboid, whose length, breadth and height are all equal, is called a *cube*. If each edge of the cube is $a$, then the surface area of this cube would be

$2(a \times a + a \times a + a \times a)$, i.e., $6a^2$ (see Fig. 13.3), giving us

$$\boxed{\textbf{Surface Area of a Cube} = \textbf{6}a^2}$$

where $a$ is the edge of the cube.

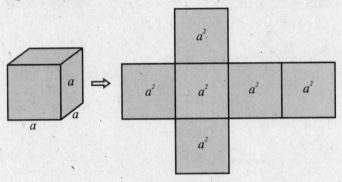

Fig. 13.3

Suppose, out of the six faces of a cuboid, we only find the area of the four faces, leaving the bottom and top faces. In such a case, the area of these four faces is called the **lateral surface area** of the cuboid. So, *lateral surface area of a cuboid of length l, breadth b and height h is equal to 2lh + 2bh or 2(l + b)h. Similarly, lateral surface area of a cube of side a is equal to 4a²*.

Keeping in view of the above, the surface area of a cuboid (or a cube) is sometimes also referred to as the **total surface area**. Let us now solve some examples.

**Example 1 :** Mary wants to decorate her Christmas tree. She wants to place the tree on a wooden box covered with coloured paper with picture of Santa Claus on it (see Fig. 13.4). She must know the exact quantity of paper to buy for this purpose. If the box has length, breadth and height as 80 cm, 40 cm and 20 cm respectively how many square sheets of paper of side 40 cm would she require?

Fig. 13.4

**Solution :** Since Mary wants to paste the paper on the outer surface of the box; the quantity of paper required would be equal to the surface area of the box which is of the shape of a cuboid. The dimensions of the box are:

Length =80 cm, Breadth = 40 cm, Height = 20 cm.

The surface area of the box = $2(lb + bh + hl)$

$$= 2[(80 \times 40) + (40 \times 20) + (20 \times 80)] \text{ cm}^2$$

$$= 2[3200 + 800 + 1600] \text{ cm}^2$$

$$= 2 \times 5600 \text{ cm}^2 = 11200 \text{ cm}^2$$

The area of each sheet of the paper = $40 \times 40$ cm²

$$= 1600 \text{ cm}^2$$

Therefore, number of sheets required $= \dfrac{\text{surface area of box}}{\text{area of one sheet of paper}}$

$$= \dfrac{11200}{1600} = 7$$

So, she would require 7 sheets.

**Example 2 :** Hameed has built a cubical water tank with lid for his house, with each outer edge 1.5 m long. He gets the outer surface of the tank excluding the base, covered with square tiles of side 25 cm (see Fig. 13.5). Find how much he would spend for the tiles, if the cost of the tiles is ₹ 360 per dozen.

**Solution :** Since Hameed is getting the five outer faces of the tank covered with tiles, he would need to know the surface area of the tank, to decide on the number of tiles required.

Edge of the cubical tank = 1.5 m = 150 cm (= $a$)

So,                surface area of the tank = $5 \times 150 \times 150$ cm²

Area of each square tile = side × side = $25 \times 25$ cm²

So, the number of tiles required $= \dfrac{\text{surface area of the tank}}{\text{area of each tile}}$

$$= \dfrac{5 \times 150 \times 150}{25 \times 25} = 180$$

Fig. 13.5

Cost of 1 dozen tiles, i.e., cost of 12 tiles = ₹ 360

Therefore, cost of one tile = ₹ $\dfrac{360}{12}$ = ₹ 30

So, the cost of 180 tiles = 180 × ₹ 30 = ₹ 5400

## EXERCISE 13.1

1. A plastic box 1.5 m long, 1.25 m wide and 65 cm deep is to be made. It is opened at the top. Ignoring the thickness of the plastic sheet, determine:

   (i) The area of the sheet required for making the box.

   (ii) The cost of sheet for it, if a sheet measuring 1m² costs Rs 20.

2. The length, breadth and height of a room are 5 m, 4 m and 3 m respectively. Find the cost of white washing the walls of the room and the ceiling at the rate of ₹ 7.50 per m².

3. The floor of a rectangular hall has a perimeter 250 m. If the cost of painting the four walls at the rate of ₹ 10 per m² is ₹ 15000, find the height of the hall.
   [**Hint :** Area of the four walls = Lateral surface area.]

4. The paint in a certain container is sufficient to paint an area equal to 9.375 m². How many bricks of dimensions 22.5 cm × 10 cm × 7.5 cm can be painted out of this container?

5. A cubical box has each edge 10 cm and another cuboidal box is 12.5 cm long, 10 cm wide and 8 cm high.

   (i) Which box has the greater lateral surface area and by how much?

   (ii) Which box has the smaller total surface area and by how much?

6. A small indoor greenhouse (herbarium) is made entirely of glass panes (including base) held together with tape. It is 30 cm long, 25 cm wide and 25 cm high.

   (i) What is the area of the glass?

   (ii) How much of tape is needed for all the 12 edges?

7. Shanti Sweets Stall was placing an order for making cardboard boxes for packing their sweets. Two sizes of boxes were required. The bigger of dimensions 25 cm × 20 cm × 5 cm and the smaller of dimensions 15 cm × 12 cm × 5 cm. For all the overlaps, 5% of the total surface area is required extra. If the cost of the cardboard is ₹ 4 for 1000 cm², find the cost of cardboard required for supplying 250 boxes of each kind.

8. Parveen wanted to make a temporary shelter for her car, by making a box-like structure with tarpaulin that covers all the four sides and the top of the car (with the front face as a flap which can be rolled up). Assuming that the stitching margins are very small, and therefore negligible, how much tarpaulin would be required to make the shelter of height 2.5 m, with base dimensions 4 m × 3 m?

## 13.3 Surface Area of a Right Circular Cylinder

If we take a number of circular sheets of paper and stack them up as we stacked up rectangular sheets earlier, what would we get (see Fig. 13.6)?

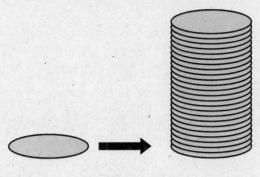

Fig. 13.6

Here, if the stack is kept vertically up, we get what is called a *right circular cylinder*, since it has been kept at right angles to the base, and the base is circular. Let us see what kind of cylinder is *not* a right circular cylinder.

In Fig 13.7 (a), you see a cylinder, which is certainly circular, but it is not at right angles to the base. So, we can *not* say this a *right circular cylinder*.

Of course, if we have a cylinder with a non circular base, as you see in Fig. 13.7 (b), then we also cannot call it a right circular cylinder.

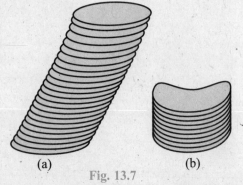

(a)                                          (b)

Fig. 13.7

**Remark :** Here, we will be dealing with only right circular cylinders. So, unless stated otherwise, the word cylinder would mean a right circular cylinder.

Now, if a cylinder is to be covered with coloured paper, how will we do it with the minimum amount of paper? First take a rectangular sheet of paper, whose length is just enough to go round the cylinder and whose breadth is equal to the height of the cylinder as shown in Fig. 13.8.

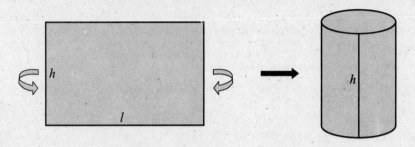

Fig. 13.8

The area of the sheet gives us the curved surface area of the cylinder. Note that the length of the sheet is equal to the circumference of the circular base which is equal to $2\pi r$.

So, curved surface area of the cylinder

$$= \text{area of the rectangular sheet} = \text{length} \times \text{breadth}$$

$$= \text{perimeter of the base of the cylinder} \times h$$

$$= 2\pi r \times h$$

Therefore, | **Curved Surface Area of a Cylinder** = $2\pi rh$ |

where $r$ is the radius of the base of the cylinder and $h$ is the height of the cylinder.

**Remark :** In the case of a cylinder, unless stated otherwise, 'radius of a cylinder' shall mean' base radius of the cylinder'.

If the top and the bottom of the cylinder are also to be covered, then we need two circles (infact, circular regions) to do that, each of radius $r$, and thus having an area of $\pi r^2$ each (see Fig. 13.9), giving us the total surface area as $2\pi rh + 2\pi r^2 = 2\pi r(r + h)$.

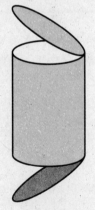

So, | **Total Surface Area of a Cylinder** = $2\pi r(r + h)$ |

where $h$ is the height of the cylinder and $r$ its radius.

Fig. 13.9

**Remark :** You may recall from Chapter 1 that $\pi$ is an irrational number. So, the value of $\pi$ is a non-terminating, non-repeating decimal. But when we use its value in our calculations, we usually take its value as approximately equal to $\dfrac{22}{7}$ or 3.14.

**Example 3 :** Savitri had to make a model of a cylindrical kaleidoscope for her science project. She wanted to use chart paper to make the curved surface of the kaleidoscope. (see Fig 13.10). What would be the area of chart paper required by her, if she wanted to make a kaleidoscope of length 25 cm with a 3.5 cm radius? You may take $\pi = \dfrac{22}{7}$.

**Solution :** Radius of the base of the cylindrical kaleidoscope $(r) = 3.5$ cm.

Height (length) of kaleidoscope $(h) = 25$ cm.

Area of chart paper required = curved surface area of the kaleidoscope

$$= 2\pi rh$$

$$= 2 \times \dfrac{22}{7} \times 3.5 \times 25 \text{ cm}^2$$

$$= 550 \text{ cm}^2$$

Fig. 13.10

## EXERCISE 13.2

Assume $\pi = \dfrac{22}{7}$, unless stated otherwise.

1.  The curved surface area of a right circular cylinder of height 14 cm is 88 cm². Find the diameter of the base of the cylinder.

2.  It is required to make a closed cylindrical tank of height 1 m and base diameter 140 cm from a metal sheet. How many square metres of the sheet are required for the same?

3.  A metal pipe is 77 cm long. The inner diameter of a cross section is 4 cm, the outer diameter being 4.4 cm (see Fig. 13.11). Find its

    (i)   inner curved surface area,

    (ii)  outer curved surface area,

    (iii) total surface area.

Fig. 13.11

4.  The diameter of a roller is 84 cm and its length is 120 cm. It takes 500 complete revolutions to move once over to level a playground. Find the area of the playground in m².

5.  A cylindrical pillar is 50 cm in diameter and 3.5 m in height. Find the cost of painting the curved surface of the pillar at the rate of ₹ 12.50 per m².

6.  Curved surface area of a right circular cylinder is 4.4 m². If the radius of the base of the cylinder is 0.7 m, find its height.

7.  The inner diameter of a circular well is 3.5 m. It is 10 m deep. Find

    (i)   its inner curved surface area,

    (ii)  the cost of plastering this curved surface at the rate of ₹ 40 per m².

8.  In a hot water heating system, there is a cylindrical pipe of length 28 m and diameter 5 cm. Find the total radiating surface in the system.

9.  Find

    (i)   the lateral or curved surface area of a closed cylindrical petrol storage tank that is 4.2 m in diameter and 4.5 m high.

    (ii)  how much steel was actually used, if $\dfrac{1}{12}$ of the steel actually used was wasted in making the tank.

10. In Fig. 13.12, you see the frame of a lampshade. It is to be covered with a decorative cloth. The frame has a base diameter of 20 cm and height of 30 cm. A margin of 2.5 cm is to be given for folding it over the top and bottom of the frame. Find how much cloth is required for covering the lampshade.

Fig. 13.12

11. The students of a Vidyalaya were asked to participate in a competition for making and decorating penholders in the shape of a cylinder with a base, using cardboard. Each penholder was to be of radius 3 cm and height 10.5 cm. The Vidyalaya was to supply the competitors with cardboard. If there were 35 competitors, how much cardboard was required to be bought for the competition?

## 13.4 Surface Area of a Right Circular Cone

So far, we have been generating solids by stacking up congruent figures. Incidentally, such figures are called *prisms*. Now let us look at another kind of solid which is not a prism (These kinds of solids are called *pyramids*.). Let us see how we can generate them.

**Activity :** Cut out a right-angled triangle ABC right angled at B. Paste a long thick string along one of the perpendicular sides say AB of the triangle [see Fig. 13.13(a)]. Hold the string with your hands on either sides of the triangle and rotate the triangle about the string a number of times. What happens? Do you recognize the shape that the triangle is forming as it rotates around the string [see Fig. 13.13(b)]? Does it remind you of the time you had eaten an ice-cream heaped into a container of that shape [see Fig. 13.13 (c) and (d)]?

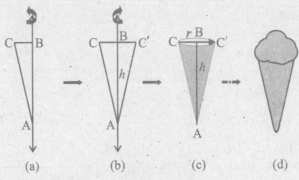

(a)        (b)        (c)        (d)

**Fig. 13.13**

This is called a *right circular cone*. In Fig. 13.13(c) of the right circular cone, the point A is called the vertex, AB is called the height, BC is called the *radius* and AC is called the slant height of the cone. Here B will be the centre of circular base of the cone. The height, radius and slant height of the cone are usually denoted by $h$, $r$ and $l$ respectively. Once again, let us see what kind of cone we can *not* call a right circular cone. Here, you are (see Fig. 13.14)! What you see in these figures are not right circular cones; because in (a), the line joining its vertex to the centre of its base is not at right angle to the base, and in (b) the base is not circular.

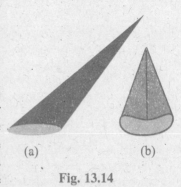

(a)                          (b)

**Fig. 13.14**

As in the case of cylinder, since we will be studying only about right circular cones, remember that by 'cone' in this chapter, we shall mean a 'right circular cone.'

**Activity :** (i) Cut out a neatly made paper cone that does not have any overlapped paper, straight along its side, and opening it out, to see the shape of paper that forms the surface of the cone. (The line along which you cut the cone is the *slant height* of the cone which is represented by *l*). It looks like a part of a round cake.

(ii)  If you now bring the sides marked A and B at the tips together, you can see that the curved portion of Fig. 13.15 (c) will form the circular base of the cone.

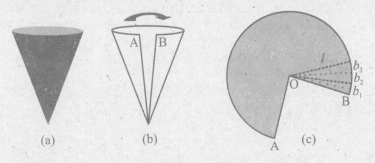

(a)                    (b)                                        (c)

Fig. 13.15

(iii) If the paper like the one in Fig. 13.15 (c) is now cut into hundreds of little pieces, along the lines drawn from the point O, each cut portion is almost a small triangle, whose height is the slant height $l$ of the cone.

(iv) Now the area of each triangle = $\dfrac{1}{2}$ × base of each triangle × $l$.

So, area of the entire piece of paper

$$= \text{sum of the areas of all the triangles}$$

$$= \frac{1}{2}b_1 l + \frac{1}{2}b_2 l + \frac{1}{2}b_3 l + \cdots = \frac{1}{2}l\,(b_1 + b_2 + b_3 + \cdots)$$

$$= \frac{1}{2} \times l \times \text{length of entire curved boundary of Fig. 13.15(c)}$$

(as $b_1 + b_2 + b_3 + \ldots$ makes up the curved portion of the figure)

But the curved portion of the figure makes up the perimeter of the base of the cone and the circumference of the base of the cone = $2\pi r$, where $r$ is the base radius of the cone.

So, | **Curved Surface Area of a Cone** = $\dfrac{1}{2} \times l \times 2\pi r = \pi r l$ |

where $r$ is its base radius and $l$ its slant height.

Note that $l^2 = r^2 + h^2$ (as can be seen from Fig. 13.16), by applying Pythagoras Theorem. Here $h$ is the *height* of the cone.

Fig. 13.16

Therefore, $l = \sqrt{r^2 + h^2}$

Now if the base of the cone is to be closed, then a circular piece of paper of radius $r$ is also required whose area is $\pi r^2$.

So, | **Total Surface Area of a Cone = $\pi r l + \pi r^2 = \pi r(l + r)$** |

**Example 4 :** Find the curved surface area of a right circular cone whose slant height is 10 cm and base radius is 7 cm.

**Solution :** Curved surface area $= \pi r l$

$$= \frac{22}{7} \times 7 \times 10 \text{ cm}^2$$

$$= 220 \text{ cm}^2$$

**Example 5 :** The height of a cone is 16 cm and its base radius is 12 cm. Find the curved surface area and the total surface area of the cone (Use $\pi = 3.14$).

**Solution :** Here, $h = 16$ cm and $r = 12$ cm.

So, from $l^2 = h^2 + r^2$, we have

$$l = \sqrt{16^2 + 12^2} \text{ cm} = 20 \text{ cm}$$

So, curved surface area $= \pi r l$

$$= 3.14 \times 12 \times 20 \text{ cm}^2$$

$$= 753.6 \text{ cm}^2$$

Further, total surface area $= \pi r l + \pi r^2$

$$= (753.6 + 3.14 \times 12 \times 12) \text{ cm}^2$$

$$= (753.6 + 452.16) \text{ cm}^2$$

$$= 1205.76 \text{ cm}^2$$

**Example 6 :** A corn cob (see Fig. 13.17), shaped somewhat like a cone, has the radius of its broadest end as 2.1 cm and length (height) as 20 cm. If each 1 cm$^2$ of the surface of the cob carries an average of four grains, find how many grains you would find on the entire cob.

**Fig. 13.17**

**Solution :** Since the grains of corn are found only on the curved surface of the corn cob, we would need to know the curved surface area of the corn cob to find the total number of grains on it. In this question, we are given the height of the cone, so we need to find its slant height.

Here,     $l = \sqrt{r^2 + h^2} = \sqrt{(2.1)^2 + 20^2}$ cm

$\qquad = \sqrt{404.41}$ cm = 20.11 cm

Therefore, the curved surface area of the corn cob = $\pi r l$

$\qquad = \dfrac{22}{7} \times 2.1 \times 20.11$ cm$^2$ = 132.726 cm$^2$ = 132.73 cm$^2$ (approx.)

Number of grains of corn on 1 cm$^2$ of the surface of the corn cob = 4

Therefore, number of grains on the entire curved surface of the cob

$\qquad = 132.73 \times 4 = 530.92 = 531$ (approx.)

So, there would be approximately 531 grains of corn on the cob.

## EXERCISE 13.3

Assume $\pi = \dfrac{22}{7}$, unless stated otherwise.

1. Diameter of the base of a cone is 10.5 cm and its slant height is 10 cm. Find its curved surface area.

2. Find the total surface area of a cone, if its slant height is 21 m and diameter of its base is 24 m.

3. Curved surface area of a cone is 308 cm$^2$ and its slant height is 14 cm. Find (i) radius of the base and (ii) total surface area of the cone.

4. A conical tent is 10 m high and the radius of its base is 24 m. Find

   (i) slant height of the tent.

   (ii) cost of the canvas required to make the tent, if the cost of 1 m$^2$ canvas is ₹ 70.

5. What length of tarpaulin 3 m wide will be required to make conical tent of height 8 m and base radius 6 m? Assume that the extra length of material that will be required for stitching margins and wastage in cutting is approximately 20 cm (Use $\pi = 3.14$).

6. The slant height and base diameter of a conical tomb are 25 m and 14 m respectively. Find the cost of white-washing its curved surface at the rate of ₹ 210 per 100 m$^2$.

7. A joker's cap is in the form of a right circular cone of base radius 7 cm and height 24 cm. Find the area of the sheet required to make 10 such caps.

8. A bus stop is barricaded from the remaining part of the road, by using 50 hollow cones made of recycled cardboard. Each cone has a base diameter of 40 cm and height 1 m. If the outer side of each of the cones is to be painted and the cost of painting is ₹ 12 per m$^2$, what will be the cost of painting all these cones? (Use $\pi = 3.14$ and take $\sqrt{1.04} = 1.02$)

## 13.5 Surface Area of a Sphere

What is a sphere? Is it the same as a circle? Can you draw a circle on a paper? Yes, you can, because a circle is a plane closed figure whose every point lies at a constant distance (called **radius**) from a fixed point, which is called the **centre** of the circle. Now if you paste a string along a diameter of a circular disc and rotate it as you had rotated the triangle in the previous section, you see a new solid (see Fig 13.18). What does it resemble? A ball? Yes. It is called a **sphere**.

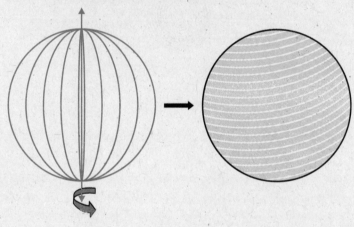

Fig. 13.18

Can you guess what happens to the centre of the circle, when it forms a sphere on rotation? Of course, it becomes the centre of the sphere. So, *a sphere is a three dimensional figure (solid figure), which is made up of all points in the space, which lie at a constant distance called the radius, from a fixed point called the centre of the sphere.*

Note : A sphere is like the surface of a ball. The word *solid sphere* is used for the solid whose surface is a sphere.

Activity : Have you ever played with a top or have you at least watched someone play with one? You must be aware of how a string is wound around it. Now, let us take a rubber ball and drive a nail into it. Taking support of the nail, let us wind a string around the ball. When you have reached the 'fullest' part of the ball, use pins to keep the string in place, and continue to wind the string around the remaining part of the ball, till you have completely covered the ball [see Fig. 13.19(a)]. Mark the starting and finishing points on the string, and slowly unwind the string from the surface of the ball.

Now, ask your teacher to help you in measuring the diameter of the ball, from which you easily get its radius. Then on a sheet of paper, draw four circles with radius equal to the radius of the ball. Start filling the circles one by one, with the string you had wound around the ball [see Fig. 13.19(b)].

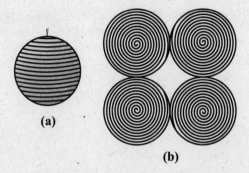

(a)

(b)

Fig. 13.19

What have you achieved in all this?

The string, which had completely covered the surface area of the sphere, has been used to completely fill the regions of four circles, all of the same radius as of the sphere.

So, what does that mean? This suggests that the surface area of a sphere of radius $r$

$$= 4 \text{ times the area of a circle of radius } r = 4 \times (\pi r^2).$$

So,

$$\boxed{\textbf{Surface Area of a Sphere} = 4\,\pi\,r^2}$$

where $r$ is the radius of the sphere.

How many faces do you see in the surface of a sphere? There is only one, which is curved.

Now, let us take a solid sphere, and slice it exactly 'through the middle' with a plane that passes through its centre. What happens to the sphere?

Yes, it gets divided into two equal parts (see Fig. 13.20)! What will each half be called? It is called a **hemisphere**. (Because 'hemi' also means 'half')

Fig. 13.20

And what about the surface of a hemisphere? How many faces does it have?

Two! There is a curved face and a flat face (base).

The curved surface area of a hemisphere is half the surface area of the sphere, which is $\dfrac{1}{2}$ of $4\pi r^2$.

Therefore, | **Curved Surface Area of a Hemisphere = $2\pi r^2$** |

where $r$ is the radius of the sphere of which the hemisphere is a part.

Now taking the two faces of a hemisphere, its surface area $2\pi r^2 + \pi r^2$

So, | **Total Surface Area of a Hemisphere = $3\pi r^2$** |

**Example 7 :** Find the surface area of a sphere of radius 7 cm.

**Solution :** The surface area of a sphere of radius 7 cm would be

$$4\pi r^2 = 4 \times \frac{22}{7} \times 7 \times 7 \ cm^2 = 616 \ cm^2$$

**Example 8 :** Find (i) the curved surface area and (ii) the total surface area of a hemisphere of radius 21 cm.

**Solution :** The curved surface area of a hemisphere of radius 21 cm would be

$$= 2\pi r^2 = 2 \times \frac{22}{7} \times 21 \times 21 \ cm^2 = 2772 \ cm^2$$

(ii) the total surface area of the hemisphere would be

$$3\pi r^2 = 3 \times \frac{22}{7} \times 21 \times 21 \ cm^2 = 4158 \ cm^2$$

**Example 9 :** The hollow sphere, in which the circus motorcyclist performs his stunts, has a diameter of 7 m. Find the area available to the motorcyclist for riding.

**Solution :** Diameter of the sphere = 7 m. Therefore, radius is 3.5 m. So, the riding space available for the motorcyclist is the surface area of the 'sphere' which is given by

$$4\pi r^2 = 4 \times \frac{22}{7} \times 3.5 \times 3.5 \ m^2$$

$$= 154 \ m^2$$

**Example 10 :** A hemispherical dome of a building needs to be painted (see Fig. 13.21). If the circumference of the base of the dome is 17.6 m, find the cost of painting it, given the cost of painting is ₹ 5 per 100 cm$^2$.

**Solution :** Since only the rounded surface of the dome is to be painted, we would need to find the curved surface area of the hemisphere to know the extent of painting that needs to be done. Now, circumference of the dome = 17.6 m. Therefore, $17.6 = 2\pi r$.

So, the radius of the dome = $17.6 \times \dfrac{7}{2 \times 22}$ m = 2.8 m

The curved surface area of the dome = $2\pi r^2$

$$= 2 \times \frac{22}{7} \times 2.8 \times 2.8 \text{ m}^2$$

$$= 49.28 \text{ m}^2$$

Now, cost of painting 100 cm² is ₹ 5.

So, cost of painting 1 m² = ₹ 500

Therefore, cost of painting the whole dome

$$= ₹ 500 \times 49.28$$

$$= ₹ 24640$$

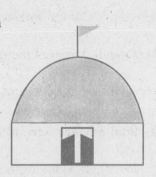

Fig. 13.21

## EXERCISE 13.4

Assume $\pi = \dfrac{22}{7}$, unless stated otherwise.

1. Find the surface area of a sphere of radius:
   (i) 10.5 cm          (ii) 5.6 cm          (iii) 14 cm

2. Find the surface area of a sphere of diameter:
   (i) 14 cm          (ii) 21 cm          (iii) 3.5 m

3. Find the total surface area of a hemisphere of radius 10 cm. (Use $\pi = 3.14$)

4. The radius of a spherical balloon increases from 7 cm to 14 cm as air is being pumped into it. Find the ratio of surface areas of the balloon in the two cases.

5. A hemispherical bowl made of brass has inner diameter 10.5 cm. Find the cost of tin-plating it on the inside at the rate of ₹ 16 per 100 cm².

6. Find the radius of a sphere whose surface area is 154 cm².

7. The diameter of the moon is approximately one fourth of the diameter of the earth. Find the ratio of their surface areas.

8. A hemispherical bowl is made of steel, 0.25 cm thick. The inner radius of the bowl is 5 cm. Find the outer curved surface area of the bowl.

9. A right circular cylinder just encloses a sphere of radius $r$ (see Fig. 13.22). Find

   (i) surface area of the sphere,

   (ii) curved surface area of the cylinder,

   (iii) ratio of the areas obtained in (i) and (ii).

Fig. 13.22

## 13.6 Volume of a Cuboid

You have already learnt about volumes of certain figures (objects) in earlier classes. Recall that solid objects occupy space. The measure of this occupied space is called the **Volume** of the object.

Note : If an object is solid, then the space occupied by such an object is measured, and is termed the **Volume** of the object. On the other hand, if the object is hollow, then interior is empty, and can be filled with air, or some liquid that will take the shape of its container. In this case, the volume of the substance that can fill the interior is called the **capacity of the container**. In short, the volume of an object is the measure of the space it occupies, and the capacity of an object is the volume of substance its interior can accommodate. Hence, the unit of measurement of either of the two is cubic unit.

So, if we were to talk of the volume of a cuboid, we would be considering the measure of the space occupied by the cuboid.

Further, the area or the volume is measured as the magnitude of a region. So, correctly speaking, we should be finding the area of a circular region, or volume of a cuboidal region, or volume of a spherical region, etc. But for the sake of simplicity, we say, find the area of a circle, volume of a cuboid or a sphere even though these mean only their boundaries.

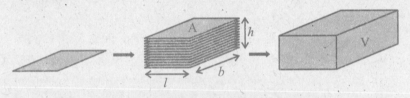

Fig. 13.23

Observe Fig. 13.23. Suppose we say that the area of each rectangle is A, the height up to which the rectangles are stacked is $h$ and the volume of the cuboid is V. Can you tell what would be the relationship between V, A and $h$?

The area of the plane region occupied by each rectangle × height

= Measure of the space occupied by the cuboid

So, we get    $A \times h = V$

That is,    | **Volume of a Cuboid = base area × height = length × breadth × height**

or $l \times b \times h$, where $l$, $b$ and $h$ are respectively the length, breadth and height of the cuboid.

Note : When we measure the magnitude of the region of a space, that is, the space occupied by a solid, we do so by counting the number of cubes of edge of unit length that can fit into it exactly. Therefore, the unit of measurement of volume is cubic unit.

Again | **Volume of a Cube = edge × edge × edge = $a^3$**

where *a* is the edge of the cube (see Fig. 13.24).

So, if a cube has edge of 12 cm,

then volume of the cube = 12 × 12 × 12 cm³

$\qquad\qquad\qquad$ = 1728 cm³.

Recall that you have learnt these formulae in earlier classes. Now let us take some examples to illustrate the use of these formulae:

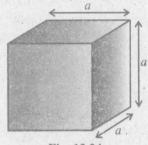

Fig. 13.24

**Example 11 :** A wall of length 10 m was to be built across an open ground. The height of the wall is 4 m and thickness of the wall is 24 cm. If this wall is to be built up with bricks whose dimensions are 24 cm × 12 cm × 8 cm, how many bricks would be required?

**Solution :** Since the wall with all its bricks makes up the space occupied by it, we need to find the volume of the wall, which is nothing but a cuboid.

Here,$\qquad\qquad\qquad\qquad$ Length = 10 m = 1000 cm

$\qquad\qquad\qquad\qquad\qquad$ Thickness = 24 cm

$\qquad\qquad\qquad\qquad\qquad$ Height = 4 m = 400 cm

Therefore,$\qquad\qquad$ Volume of the wall = length × thickness × height

$\qquad\qquad\qquad\qquad\qquad\qquad$ = 1000 × 24 × 400 cm³

Now, each brick is a cuboid with length = 24 cm, breadth = 12 cm and height = 8 cm

So, volume of each brick = length × breadth × height

$\qquad\qquad\qquad\qquad\qquad$ = 24 × 12 × 8 cm³

So, number of bricks required $= \dfrac{\text{volume of the wall}}{\text{volume of each brick}}$

$\qquad\qquad\qquad\qquad = \dfrac{1000 \times 24 \times 400}{24 \times 12 \times 8}$

$\qquad\qquad\qquad\qquad$ = 4166.6

So, the wall requires 4167 bricks.

**Example 12 :** A child playing with building blocks, which are of the shape of cubes, has built a structure as shown in Fig. 13.25. If the edge of each cube is 3 cm, find the volume of the structure built by the child.

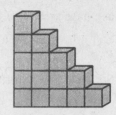

**Solution :** Volume of each cube = edge × edge × edge

$$= 3 \times 3 \times 3 \text{ cm}^3 = 27 \text{ cm}^3$$

**Fig. 13.25**

Number of cubes in the structure = 15

Therefore, volume of the structure = 27 × 15 cm³

$$= 405 \text{ cm}^3$$

### EXERCISE 13.5

1. A matchbox measures 4 cm × 2.5 cm × 1.5 cm. What will be the volume of a packet containing 12 such boxes?

2. A cuboidal water tank is 6 m long, 5 m wide and 4.5 m deep. How many litres of water can it hold? ($1 \text{ m}^3 = 1000 \, l$)

3. A cuboidal vessel is 10 m long and 8 m wide. How high must it be made to hold 380 cubic metres of a liquid?

4. Find the cost of digging a cuboidal pit 8 m long, 6 m broad and 3 m deep at the rate of ₹ 30 per m³.

5. The capacity of a cuboidal tank is 50000 litres of water. Find the breadth of the tank, if its length and depth are respectively 2.5 m and 10 m.

6. A village, having a population of 4000, requires 150 litres of water per head per day. It has a tank measuring 20 m × 15 m × 6 m. For how many days will the water of this tank last?

7. A godown measures 40 m × 25 m × 15 m. Find the maximum number of wooden crates each measuring 1.5 m × 1.25 m × 0.5 m that can be stored in the godown.

8. A solid cube of side 12 cm is cut into eight cubes of equal volume. What will be the side of the new cube? Also, find the ratio between their surface areas.

9. A river 3 m deep and 40 m wide is flowing at the rate of 2 km per hour. How much water will fall into the sea in a minute?

## 13.7 Volume of a Cylinder

Just as a cuboid is built up with rectangles of the same size, we have seen that a right circular cylinder can be built up using circles of the same size. So, using the same argument as for a cuboid, we can see that the volume of a cylinder can be obtained

as : base area × height

$= $ area of circular base × height $= \pi r^2 h$

So,     | **Volume of a Cylinder = $\pi r^2 h$** |

where $r$ is the base radius and $h$ is the height of the cylinder.

**Example 13 :** The pillars of a temple are cylindrically shaped (see Fig. 13.26). If each pillar has a circular base of radius 20 cm and height 10 m, how much concrete mixture would be required to build 14 such pillars?

**Solution :** Since the concrete mixture that is to be used to build up the pillars is going to occupy the entire space of the pillar, what we need to find here is the volume of the cylinders.

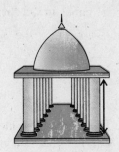

Fig. 13.26

Radius of base of a cylinder = 20 cm

Height of the cylindrical pillar = 10 m = 1000 cm

So,     volume of each cylinder $= \pi r^2 h$

$$= \frac{22}{7} \times 20 \times 20 \times 1000 \text{ cm}^3$$

$$= \frac{8800000}{7} \text{ cm}^3$$

$$= \frac{8.8}{7} \text{ m}^3 \text{ (Since } 1000000 \text{ cm}^3 = 1\text{m}^3)$$

Therefore, volume of 14 pillars = volume of each cylinder × 14

$$= \frac{8.8}{7} \times 14 \text{ m}^3$$

$$= 17.6 \text{ m}^3$$

So, 14 pillars would need 17.6 m³ of concrete mixture.

**Example 14 :** At a Ramzan Mela, a stall keeper in one of the food stalls has a large cylindrical vessel of base radius 15 cm filled up to a height of 32 cm with orange juice. The juice is filled in small cylindrical glasses (see Fig. 13.27) of radius 3 cm up to a height of 8 cm, and sold for ₹ 3 each. How much money does the stall keeper receive by selling the juice completely?

Fig. 13.27

**Solution :** The volume of juice in the vessel

$$= \text{volume of the cylindrical vessel}$$
$$= \pi R^2 H$$

(where R and H are taken as the radius and height respectively of the vessel)

$$= \pi \times 15 \times 15 \times 32 \text{ cm}^3$$

Similarly, the volume of juice each glass can hold $= \pi r^2 h$

(where $r$ and $h$ are taken as the radius and height respectively of each glass)

$$= \pi \times 3 \times 3 \times 8 \text{ cm}^3$$

So, number of glasses of juice that are sold

$$= \frac{\text{volume of the vessel}}{\text{volume of each glass}}$$

$$= \frac{\pi \times 15 \times 15 \times 32}{\pi \times 3 \times 3 \times 8}$$

$$= 100$$

Therefore, amount received by the stall keeper $= ₹\, 3 \times 100$

$$= ₹\, 300$$

## EXERCISE 13.6

Assume $\pi = \dfrac{22}{7}$, unless stated otherwise.

1. The circumference of the base of a cylindrical vessel is 132 cm and its height is 25 cm. How many litres of water can it hold? ($1000 \text{ cm}^3 = 1l$)

2. The inner diameter of a cylindrical wooden pipe is 24 cm and its outer diameter is 28 cm. The length of the pipe is 35 cm. Find the mass of the pipe, if 1 cm³ of wood has a mass of 0.6 g.

3. A soft drink is available in two packs – (i) a tin can with a rectangular base of length 5 cm and width 4 cm, having a height of 15 cm and (ii) a plastic cylinder with circular base of diameter 7 cm and height 10 cm. Which container has greater capacity and by how much?

4. If the lateral surface of a cylinder is 94.2 cm² and its height is 5 cm, then find
(i) radius of its base       (ii) its volume. (Use $\pi = 3.14$)

5. It costs ₹ 2200 to paint the inner curved surface of a cylindrical vessel 10 m deep. If the cost of painting is at the rate of ₹ 20 per m², find

(i) inner curved surface area of the vessel,

(ii) radius of the base,

(iii) capacity of the vessel.

6. The capacity of a closed cylindrical vessel of height 1 m is 15.4 litres. How many square metres of metal sheet would be needed to make it?

7. A lead pencil consists of a cylinder of wood with a solid cylinder of graphite filled in the interior. The diameter of the pencil is 7 mm and the diameter of the graphite is 1 mm. If the length of the pencil is 14 cm, find the volume of the wood and that of the graphite.

8. A patient in a hospital is given soup daily in a cylindrical bowl of diameter 7 cm. If the bowl is filled with soup to a height of 4 cm, how much soup the hospital has to prepare daily to serve 250 patients?

## 13.8 Volume of a Right Circular Cone

In Fig 13.28, can you see that there is a right circular cylinder and a right circular cone of the same base radius and the same height?

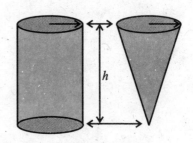

Fig. 13.28

Activity : Try to make a hollow cylinder and a hollow cone like this with the same base radius and the same height (see Fig. 13.28). Then, we can try out an experiment that will help us, to see practically what the volume of a right circular cone would be!

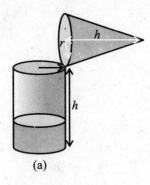
(a)

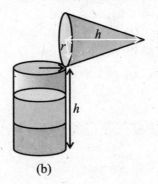
(b)

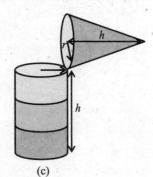
(c)

Fig. 13.29

So, let us start like this.

Fill the cone up to the brim with sand once, and empty it into the cylinder. We find that it fills up only a part of the cylinder [see Fig. 13.29(a)].

When we fill up the cone again to the brim, and empty it into the cylinder, we see that the cylinder is still not full [see Fig. 13.29(b)].

When the cone is filled up for the third time, and emptied into the cylinder, it can be seen that the cylinder is also full to the brim [see Fig. 13.29(c)].

With this, we can safely come to the conclusion that three times the volume of a cone, makes up the volume of a cylinder, which has the same base radius and the same height as the cone, which means that the volume of the cone is one-third the volume of the cylinder.

So,

$$\text{Volume of a Cone} = \frac{1}{3}\pi r^2 h$$

where $r$ is the base radius and $h$ is the height of the cone.

**Example 15 :** The height and the slant height of a cone are 21 cm and 28 cm respectively. Find the volume of the cone.

**Solution :** From $l^2 = r^2 + h^2$, we have

$$r = \sqrt{l^2 - h^2} = \sqrt{28^2 - 21^2} \text{ cm} = 7\sqrt{7} \text{ cm}$$

So, volume of the cone $= \frac{1}{3}\pi r^2 h = \frac{1}{3} \times \frac{22}{7} \times 7\sqrt{7} \times 7\sqrt{7} \times 21 \text{ cm}^3$

$$= 7546 \text{ cm}^3$$

**Example 16 :** Monica has a piece of canvas whose area is 551 m². She uses it to have a conical tent made, with a base radius of 7 m. Assuming that all the stitching margins and the wastage incurred while cutting, amounts to approximately 1 m², find the volume of the tent that can be made with it.

**Solution :** Since the area of the canvas = 551 m² and area of the canvas lost in wastage is 1 m², therefore the area of canvas available for making the tent is (551 – 1) m² = 550 m².

Now, the surface area of the tent = 550 m² and the required base radius of the conical tent = 7 m

Note that a tent has only a curved surface (the floor of a tent is not covered by canvas!!).

Therefore, curved surface area of tent = 550 m².

That is,                                        $\pi r l = 550$

or,                                        $\dfrac{22}{7} \times 7 \times l = 550$

or,                                        $l = 3\dfrac{550}{22} \text{ m} = 25 \text{ m}$

Now,                                        $l^2 = r^2 + h^2$

Therefore,        $h = \sqrt{l^2 - r^2} = \sqrt{25^2 - 7^2} \text{ m} = \sqrt{625 - 49} \text{ m} = \sqrt{576} \text{ m}$

$$= 24 \text{ m}$$

So, the volume of the conical tent $= \dfrac{1}{3}\pi r^2 h = \dfrac{1}{3} \times \dfrac{22}{7} \times 7 \times 7 \times 24 \text{ m}^3 = 1232 \text{ m}^3$.

## EXERCISE 13.7

Assume $\pi = \dfrac{22}{7}$, unless stated otherwise.

1.  Find the volume of the right circular cone with
    (i) radius 6 cm, height 7 cm           (ii) radius 3.5 cm, height 12 cm

2.  Find the capacity in litres of a conical vessel with
    (i) radius 7 cm, slant height 25 cm    (ii) height 12 cm, slant height 13 cm

3.  The height of a cone is 15 cm. If its volume is 1570 cm³, find the radius of the base. (Use $\pi = 3.14$)

4.  If the volume of a right circular cone of height 9 cm is $48\,\pi$ cm³, find the diameter of its base.

5.  A conical pit of top diameter 3.5 m is 12 m deep. What is its capacity in kilolitres?

6.  The volume of a right circular cone is 9856 cm³. If the diameter of the base is 28 cm, find
    (i) height of the cone                 (ii) slant height of the cone
    (iii) curved surface area of the cone

7.  A right triangle ABC with sides 5 cm, 12 cm and 13 cm is revolved about the side 12 cm. Find the volume of the solid so obtained.

8.  If the triangle ABC in the Question 7 above is revolved about the side 5 cm, then find the volume of the solid so obtained. Find also the ratio of the volumes of the two solids obtained in Questions 7 and 8.

9.  A heap of wheat is in the form of a cone whose diameter is 10.5 m and height is 3 m. Find its volume. The heap is to be covered by canvas to protect it from rain. Find the area of the canvas required.

## 13.9 Volume of a Sphere

Now, let us see how to go about measuring the volume of a sphere. First, take two or three spheres of different radii, and a container big enough to be able to put each of the spheres into it, one at a time. Also, take a large trough in which you can place the container. Then, fill the container up to the brim with water [see Fig. 13.30(a)].

Now, carefully place one of the spheres in the container. Some of the water from the container will over flow into the trough in which it is kept [see Fig. 13.30(b)]. Carefully pour out the water from the trough into a measuring cylinder (i.e., a graduated cylindrical jar) and measure the water over flowed [see Fig. 13.30(c)]. Suppose the radius of the immersed sphere is $r$ (you can find the radius by measuring the diameter of the sphere). Then evaluate $\dfrac{4}{3}\pi r^3$. Do you find this value almost equal to the measure of the volume over flowed?

 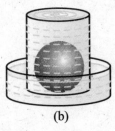 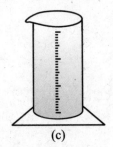

(a)                              (b)                              (c)

Fig. 13.30

Once again repeat the procedure done just now, with a different size of sphere. Find the radius R of this sphere and then calculate the value of $\dfrac{4}{3}\pi R^3$. Once again this value is nearly equal to the measure of the volume of the water displaced (over flowed) by the sphere. What does this tell us? We know that the volume of the sphere is the same as the measure of the volume of the water displaced by it. By doing this experiment repeatedly with spheres of varying radii, we are getting the same result, namely, the volume of a sphere is equal to $\dfrac{4}{3}\pi$ times the cube of its radius. This gives us the idea that

$$\textbf{Volume of a Sphere} = \frac{4}{3}\pi r^3$$

where $r$ is the radius of the sphere.

Later, in higher classes it can be proved also. But at this stage, we will just take it as true.

Since a hemisphere is half of a sphere, can you guess what the volume of a

hemisphere will be? Yes, it is $\dfrac{1}{2}$ of $\dfrac{4}{3}\pi r^3 = \dfrac{2}{3}\pi r^3$.

So, | **Volume of a Hemisphere** $= \dfrac{2}{3}\pi r^3$ |

where $r$ is the radius of the hemisphere.

Let us take some examples to illustrate the use of these formulae.

**Example 17** : Find the volume of a sphere of radius 11.2 cm.

**Solution** : Required volume $= \dfrac{4}{3}\pi r^3$

$$= \dfrac{4}{3}\times\dfrac{22}{7}\times11.2\times11.2\times11.2 \text{ cm}^3 = 5887.32 \text{ cm}^3$$

**Example 18** : A shot-putt is a metallic sphere of radius 4.9 cm. If the density of the metal is 7.8 g per cm³, find the mass of the shot-putt.

**Solution** : Since the shot-putt is a solid sphere made of metal and its mass is equal to the product of its volume and density, we need to find the volume of the sphere.

Now, volume of the sphere $= \dfrac{4}{3}\pi r^3$

$$= \dfrac{4}{3}\times\dfrac{22}{7}\times4.9\times4.9\times4.9 \text{ cm}^3$$

$$= 493 \text{ cm}^3 \text{ (nearly)}$$

Further, mass of 1 cm³ of metal is 7.8 g.

Therefore, mass of the shot-putt $= 7.8 \times 493$ g

$$= 3845.44 \text{ g} = 3.85 \text{ kg (nearly)}$$

**Example 19** : A hemispherical bowl has a radius of 3.5 cm. What would be the volume of water it would contain?

**Solution** : The volume of water the bowl can contain

$$= \dfrac{2}{3}\pi r^3$$

$$= \dfrac{2}{3}\times\dfrac{22}{7}\times3.5\times3.5\times3.5 \text{ cm}^3 = 89.8 \text{ cm}^3$$

## EXERCISE 13.8

Assume $\pi = \dfrac{22}{7}$, unless stated otherwise.

1. Find the volume of a sphere whose radius is
   (i) 7 cm                       (ii) 0.63 m

2. Find the amount of water displaced by a solid spherical ball of diameter
   (i) 28 cm                 (ii) 0.21 m

3. The diameter of a metallic ball is 4.2 cm. What is the mass of the ball, if the density of the metal is 8.9 g per $cm^3$?

4. The diameter of the moon is approximately one-fourth of the diameter of the earth. What fraction of the volume of the earth is the volume of the moon?

5. How many litres of milk can a hemispherical bowl of diameter 10.5 cm hold?

6. A hemispherical tank is made up of an iron sheet 1 cm thick. If the inner radius is 1 m, then find the volume of the iron used to make the tank.

7. Find the volume of a sphere whose surface area is 154 $cm^2$.

8. A dome of a building is in the form of a hemisphere. From inside, it was white-washed at the cost of ₹ 498.96. If the cost of white-washing is ₹ 2.00 per square metre, find the
   (i) inside surface area of the dome,     (ii) volume of the air inside the dome.

9. Twenty seven solid iron spheres, each of radius $r$ and surface area S are melted to form a sphere with surface area S′. Find the
   (i) radius $r′$ of the new sphere,        (ii) ratio of S and S′.

10. A capsule of medicine is in the shape of a sphere of diameter 3.5 mm. How much medicine (in $mm^3$) is needed to fill this capsule?

## EXERCISE 13.9 (Optional)*

1. A wooden bookshelf has external dimensions as follows: Height = 110 cm, Depth = 25 cm, Breadth = 85 cm (see Fig. 13.31). The thickness of the plank is 5 cm everywhere. The external faces are to be polished and the inner faces are to be painted. If the rate of polishing is 20 paise per $cm^2$ and the rate of painting is 10 paise per $cm^2$, find the total expenses required for polishing and painting the surface of the bookshelf.

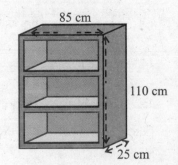

Fig. 13.31

*These exercises are not from examination point of view.

**2.** The front compound wall of a house is decorated by wooden spheres of diameter 21 cm, placed on small supports as shown in Fig 13.32. Eight such spheres are used for this purpose, and are to be painted silver. Each support is a cylinder of radius 1.5 cm and height 7 cm and is to be painted black. Find the cost of paint required if silver paint costs 25 paise per cm² and black paint costs 5 paise per cm².

**Fig. 13.32**

**3.** The diameter of a sphere is decreased by 25%. By what per cent does its curved surface area decrease?

## 13.10 Summary

In this chapter, you have studied the following points:

1. **Surface area of a cuboid = 2 (lb + bh + hl)**

2. **Surface area of a cube = 6a²**

3. **Curved surface area of a cylinder = 2πrh**

4. **Total surface area of a cylinder = 2πr(r + h)**

5. **Curved surface area of a cone = πrl**

6. **Total surface area of a right circular cone = πrl + πr², i.e., πr (l + r)**

7. **Surface area of a sphere of radius r = 4 π r²**

8. **Curved surface area of a hemisphere = 2πr²**

9. **Total surface area of a hemisphere = 3πr²**

10. **Volume of a cuboid = l × b × h**

11. **Volume of a cube = a³**

12. **Volume of a cylinder = πr²h**

13. **Volume of a cone = $\dfrac{1}{3}$ πr²h**

14. **Volume of a sphere of radius r = $\dfrac{4}{3}$ π r³**

15. **Volume of a hemisphere = $\dfrac{2}{3}$ π r³**

[Here, letters *l, b, h, a, r*, etc. have been used in their usual meaning, depending on the context.]

# CHAPTER 14

# STATISTICS

## 14.1 Introduction

Everyday we come across a lot of information in the form of facts, numerical figures, tables, graphs, etc. These are provided by newspapers, televisions, magazines and other means of communication. These may relate to cricket batting or bowling averages, profits of a company, temperatures of cities, expenditures in various sectors of a five year plan, polling results, and so on. These facts or figures, which are numerical or otherwise, collected with a definite purpose are called *data*. Data is the plural form of the Latin word *datum*. Of course, the word 'data' is not new for you. You have studied about data and data handling in earlier classes.

Our world is becoming more and more information oriented. Every part of our lives utilises data in one form or the other. So, it becomes essential for us to know how to extract meaningful information from such data. This extraction of meaningful information is studied in a branch of mathematics called *Statistics*.

The word 'statistics' appears to have been derived from the Latin word 'status' meaning 'a (political) state'. In its origin, statistics was simply the collection of data on different aspects of the life of people, useful to the State. Over the period of time, however, its scope broadened and statistics began to concern itself not only with the collection and presentation of data but also with the interpretation and drawing of inferences from the data. Statistics deals with collection, organisation, analysis and interpretation of data. The word 'statistics' has different meanings in different contexts. Let us observe the following sentences:

1. May I have the latest copy of 'Educational Statistics of India'.

2. I like to study 'Statistics' because it is used in day-to-day life.

In the first sentence, statistics is used in a plural sense, meaning numerical data. These may include a number of educational institutions of India, literacy rates of various states, etc. In the second sentence, the word 'statistics' is used as a singular noun, meaning the subject which deals with the collection, presentation, analysis of data as well as drawing of meaningful conclusions from the data.

In this chapter, we shall briefly discuss all these aspects regarding data.

## 14.2 Collection of Data

Let us begin with an exercise on gathering data by performing the following activity.

**Activity 1 :** Divide the students of your class into four groups. Allot each group the work of collecting one of the following kinds of data:

(i) Heights of 20 students of your class.

(ii) Number of absentees in each day in your class for a month.

(iii) Number of members in the families of your classmates.

(iv) Heights of 15 plants in or around your school.

Let us move to the results students have gathered. How did they collect their data in each group?

(i) Did they collect the information from each and every student, house or person concerned for obtaining the information?

(ii) Did they get the information from some source like available school records?

In the first case, when the information was collected by the investigator herself or himself with a definite objective in her or his mind, the data obtained is called *primary data*.

In the second case, when the information was gathered from a source which already had the information stored, the data obtained is called *secondary data*. Such data, which has been collected by someone else in another context, needs to be used with great care ensuring that the source is reliable.

By now, you must have understood how to collect data and distinguish between primary and secondary data.

## EXERCISE 14.1

1. Give five examples of data that you can collect from your day-to-day life.

2. Classify the data in Q.1 above as primary or secondary data.

## 14.3 Presentation of Data

As soon as the work related to collection of data is over, the investigator has to find out ways to present them in a form which is meaningful, easily understood and gives its main features at a glance. Let us now recall the various ways of presenting the data through some examples.

**Example 1** : Consider the marks obtained by 10 students in a mathematics test as given below:

| 55 | 36 | 95 | 73 | 60 | 42 | 25 | 78 | 75 | 62 |

The data in this form is called *raw data*.

By looking at it in this form, can you find the highest and the lowest marks?

Did it take you some time to search for the maximum and minimum scores? Wouldn't it be less time consuming if these scores were arranged in ascending or descending order? So let us arrange the marks in ascending order as

| 25 | 36 | 42 | 55 | 60 | 62 | 73 | 75 | 78 | 95 |

Now, we can clearly see that the lowest marks are 25 and the highest marks are 95.

The difference of the highest and the lowest values in the data is called the *range* of the data. So, the range in this case is $95 - 25 = 70$.

Presentation of data in ascending or descending order can be quite time consuming, particularly when the number of observations in an experiment is large, as in the case of the next example.

**Example 2** : Consider the marks obtained (out of 100 marks) by 30 students of Class IX of a school:

| 10 | 20 | 36 | 92 | 95 | 40 | 50 | 56 | 60 | 70 |
| 92 | 88 | 80 | 70 | 72 | 70 | 36 | 40 | 36 | 40 |
| 92 | 40 | 50 | 50 | 56 | 60 | 70 | 60 | 60 | 88 |

Recall that the number of students who have obtained a certain number of marks is called the *frequency* of those marks. For instance, 4 students got 70 marks. So the frequency of 70 marks is 4. To make the data more easily understandable, we write it in a table, as given below:

Table 14.1

| Marks | Number of students (i.e., the frequency) |
|:-----:|:-----:|
| 10 | 1 |
| 20 | 1 |
| 36 | 3 |
| 40 | 4 |
| 50 | 3 |
| 56 | 2 |
| 60 | 4 |
| 70 | 4 |
| 72 | 1 |
| 80 | 1 |
| 88 | 2 |
| 92 | 3 |
| 95 | 1 |
| **Total** | 30 |

Table 14.1 is called *an ungrouped frequency distribution table,* or simply a *frequency distribution table*. Note that you can use also *tally marks* in preparing these tables, as in the next example.

**Example 3 :** 100 plants each were planted in 100 schools during Van Mahotsava. After one month, the number of plants that survived were recorded as :

| | | | | | | | | | |
|---|---|---|---|---|---|---|---|---|---|
| 95 | 67 | 28 | 32 | 65 | 65 | 69 | 33 | 98 | 96 |
| 76 | 42 | 32 | 38 | 42 | 40 | 40 | 69 | 95 | 92 |
| 75 | 83 | 76 | 83 | 85 | 62 | 37 | 65 | 63 | 42 |
| 89 | 65 | 73 | 81 | 49 | 52 | 64 | 76 | 83 | 92 |
| 93 | 68 | 52 | 79 | 81 | 83 | 59 | 82 | 75 | 82 |
| 86 | 90 | 44 | 62 | 31 | 36 | 38 | 42 | 39 | 83 |
| 87 | 56 | 58 | 23 | 35 | 76 | 83 | 85 | 30 | 68 |
| 69 | 83 | 86 | 43 | 45 | 39 | 83 | 75 | 66 | 83 |
| 92 | 75 | 89 | 66 | 91 | 27 | 88 | 89 | 93 | 42 |
| 53 | 69 | 90 | 55 | 66 | 49 | 52 | 83 | 34 | 36 |

To present such a large amount of data so that a reader can make sense of it easily, we condense it into groups like 20-29, 30-39, . . ., 90-99 (since our data is from 23 to 98). These groupings are called 'classes' or 'class-intervals', and their size is called the *class-size* or *class width*, which is 10 in this case. In each of these classes, the least number is called the *lower class limit* and the greatest number is called the *upper class limit,* e.g., in 20-29, 20 is the 'lower class limit' and 29 is the 'upper class limit'.

Also, recall that using tally marks, the data above can be condensed in tabular form as follows:

Table 14.2

| Number of plants survived | Tally Marks | Number of schools (frequency) |
|:---:|:---|:---:|
| 20 - 29 | III | 3 |
| 30 - 39 | NI NI IIII | 14 |
| 40 - 49 | NI NI II | 12 |
| 50 - 59 | NI III | 8 |
| 60 - 69 | NI NI NI III | 18 |
| 70 - 79 | NI NI | 10 |
| 80 - 89 | NI NI NI NI III | 23 |
| 90 - 99 | NI NI II | 12 |
| **Total** | | 100 |

Presenting data in this form simplifies and condenses data and enables us to observe certain important features at a glance. This is called *a grouped frequency distribution table*. Here we can easily observe that 50% or more plants survived in 8 + 18 + 10 + 23 + 12 = 71 schools.

We observe that the classes in the table above are non-overlapping. Note that we could have made more classes of shorter size, or fewer classes of larger size also. For instance, the intervals could have been 22-26, 27-31, and so on. So, there is no hard and fast rule about this except that the classes should not overlap.

**Example 4 :** Let us now consider the following frequency distribution table which gives the weights of 38 students of a class:

Table 14.3

| Weights (in kg) | Number of students |
|---|---|
| 31 - 35 | 9 |
| 36 - 40 | 5 |
| 41 - 45 | 14 |
| 46 - 50 | 3 |
| 51 - 55 | 1 |
| 56 - 60 | 2 |
| 61 - 65 | 2 |
| 66 - 70 | 1 |
| 71 - 75 | 1 |
| **Total** | 38 |

Now, if two new students of weights 35.5 kg and 40.5 kg are admitted in this class, then in which interval will we include them? We cannot add them in the ones ending with 35 or 40, nor to the following ones. This is because there are gaps in between the upper and lower limits of two consecutive classes. So, we need to divide the intervals so that the upper and lower limits of consecutive intervals are the same. For this, we find the difference between the upper limit of a class and the lower limit of its succeeding class. We then add half of this difference to each of the upper limits and subtract the same from each of the lower limits.

For example, consider the classes 31 - 35 and 36 - 40.

The lower limit of 36 - 40 = 36

The upper limit of 31 - 35 = 35

The difference = 36 – 35 = 1

So,    half the difference = $\dfrac{1}{2} = 0.5$

So the new class interval formed from 31 - 35 is (31 – 0.5) - (35 + 0.5), i.e., 30.5 - 35.5.

Similarly, the new class formed from the class 36 - 40 is (36 – 0.5) - (40 + 0.5), i.e., 35.5 - 40.5.

Continuing in the same manner, the continuous classes formed are:

30.5-35.5, 35.5-40.5, 40.5-45.5, 45.5-50.5, 50.5-55.5, 55.5-60.5, 60.5 - 65.5, 65.5 - 70.5, 70.5 - 75.5.

Now it is possible for us to include the weights of the new students in these classes. But, another problem crops up because 35.5 appears in both the classes 30.5 - 35.5 and 35.5 - 40.5. In which class do you think this weight should be considered?

If it is considered in both classes, it will be counted twice.

*By convention*, we consider 35.5 in the class 35.5 - 40.5 and not in 30.5 - 35.5. Similarly, 40.5 is considered in 40.5 - 45.5 and not in 35.5 - 40.5.

So, the new weights 35.5 kg and 40.5 kg would be included in 35.5 - 40.5 and 40.5 - 45.5, respectively. Now, with these assumptions, the new frequency distribution table will be as shown below:

Table 14.4

| Weights (in kg) | Number of students |
|:---:|:---:|
| 30.5-35.5 | 9 |
| 35.5-40.5 | 6 |
| 40.5-45.5 | 15 |
| 45.5-50.5 | 3 |
| 50.5-55.5 | 1 |
| 55.5-60.5 | 2 |
| 60.5-65.5 | 2 |
| 65.5-70.5 | 1 |
| 70.5-75.5 | 1 |
| **Total** | 40 |

Now, let us move to the data collected by you in Activity 1. This time we ask you to present these as frequency distribution tables.

**Activity 2 :** Continuing with the same four groups, change your data to frequency distribution tables. Choose convenient classes with suitable class-sizes, keeping in mind the range of the data and the type of data.

## EXERCISE 14.2

1.  The blood groups of 30 students of Class VIII are recorded as follows:

    A, B, O, O, AB, O, A, O, B, A, O, B, A, O, O,

    A, AB, O, A, A, O, O, AB, B, A, O, B, A, B, O.

    Represent this data in the form of a frequency distribution table. Which is the most common, and which is the rarest, blood group among these students?

2.  The distance (in km) of 40 engineers from their residence to their place of work were found as follows:

    | 5 | 3 | 10 | 20 | 25 | 11 | 13 | 7 | 12 | 31 |
    |---|---|----|----|----|----|----|---|----|----|
    | 19 | 10 | 12 | 17 | 18 | 11 | 32 | 17 | 16 | 2 |
    | 7 | 9 | 7 | 8 | 3 | 5 | 12 | 15 | 18 | 3 |
    | 12 | 14 | 2 | 9 | 6 | 15 | 15 | 7 | 6 | 12 |

    Construct a grouped frequency distribution table with class size 5 for the data given above taking the first interval as 0-5 (5 not included). What main features do you observe from this tabular representation?

3.  The relative humidity (in %) of a certain city for a month of 30 days was as follows:

    | 98.1 | 98.6 | 99.2 | 90.3 | 86.5 | 95.3 | 92.9 | 96.3 | 94.2 | 95.1 |
    |------|------|------|------|------|------|------|------|------|------|
    | 89.2 | 92.3 | 97.1 | 93.5 | 92.7 | 95.1 | 97.2 | 93.3 | 95.2 | 97.3 |
    | 96.2 | 92.1 | 84.9 | 90.2 | 95.7 | 98.3 | 97.3 | 96.1 | 92.1 | 89 |

    (i) Construct a grouped frequency distribution table with classes 84 - 86, 86 - 88, etc.

    (ii) Which month or season do you think this data is about?

    (iii) What is the range of this data?

4.  The heights of 50 students, measured to the nearest centimetres, have been found to be as follows:

    | 161 | 150 | 154 | 165 | 168 | 161 | 154 | 162 | 150 | 151 |
    |-----|-----|-----|-----|-----|-----|-----|-----|-----|-----|
    | 162 | 164 | 171 | 165 | 158 | 154 | 156 | 172 | 160 | 170 |
    | 153 | 159 | 161 | 170 | 162 | 165 | 166 | 168 | 165 | 164 |
    | 154 | 152 | 153 | 156 | 158 | 162 | 160 | 161 | 173 | 166 |
    | 161 | 159 | 162 | 167 | 168 | 159 | 158 | 153 | 154 | 159 |

    (i) Represent the data given above by a grouped frequency distribution table, taking the class intervals as 160 - 165, 165 - 170, etc.

    (ii) What can you conclude about their heights from the table?

5.  A study was conducted to find out the concentration of sulphur dioxide in the air in

parts per million (ppm) of a certain city. The data obtained for 30 days is as follows:

| | | | | | |
|---|---|---|---|---|---|
| 0.03 | 0.08 | 0.08 | 0.09 | 0.04 | 0.17 |
| 0.16 | 0.05 | 0.02 | 0.06 | 0.18 | 0.20 |
| 0.11 | 0.08 | 0.12 | 0.13 | 0.22 | 0.07 |
| 0.08 | 0.01 | 0.10 | 0.06 | 0.09 | 0.18 |
| 0.11 | 0.07 | 0.05 | 0.07 | 0.01 | 0.04 |

(i) Make a grouped frequency distribution table for this data with class intervals as 0.00 - 0.04, 0.04 - 0.08, and so on.

(ii) For how many days, was the concentration of sulphur dioxide more than 0.11 parts per million?

6. Three coins were tossed 30 times simultaneously. Each time the number of heads occurring was noted down as follows:

| | | | | | | | | | |
|---|---|---|---|---|---|---|---|---|---|
| 0 | 1 | 2 | 2 | 1 | 2 | 3 | 1 | 3 | 0 |
| 1 | 3 | 1 | 1 | 2 | 2 | 0 | 1 | 2 | 1 |
| 3 | 0 | 0 | 1 | 1 | 2 | 3 | 2 | 2 | 0 |

Prepare a frequency distribution table for the data given above.

7. The value of $\pi$ upto 50 decimal places is given below:

3.14159265358979323846264338327950288419716939937510

(i) Make a frequency distribution of the digits from 0 to 9 after the decimal point.

(ii) What are the most and the least frequently occurring digits?

8. Thirty children were asked about the number of hours they watched TV programmes in the previous week. The results were found as follows:

| | | | | | | | | | |
|---|---|---|---|---|---|---|---|---|---|
| 1 | 6 | 2 | 3 | 5 | 12 | 5 | 8 | 4 | 8 |
| 10 | 3 | 4 | 12 | 2 | 8 | 15 | 1 | 17 | 6 |
| 3 | 2 | 8 | 5 | 9 | 6 | 8 | 7 | 14 | 12 |

(i) Make a grouped frequency distribution table for this data, taking class width 5 and one of the class intervals as 5 - 10.

(ii) How many children watched television for 15 or more hours a week?

9. A company manufactures car batteries of a particular type. The lives (in years) of 40 such batteries were recorded as follows:

| | | | | | | | |
|---|---|---|---|---|---|---|---|
| 2.6 | 3.0 | 3.7 | 3.2 | 2.2 | 4.1 | 3.5 | 4.5 |
| 3.5 | 2.3 | 3.2 | 3.4 | 3.8 | 3.2 | 4.6 | 3.7 |
| 2.5 | 4.4 | 3.4 | 3.3 | 2.9 | 3.0 | 4.3 | 2.8 |
| 3.5 | 3.2 | 3.9 | 3.2 | 3.2 | 3.1 | 3.7 | 3.4 |
| 4.6 | 3.8 | 3.2 | 2.6 | 3.5 | 4.2 | 2.9 | 3.6 |

Construct a grouped frequency distribution table for this data, using class intervals of size 0.5 starting from the interval 2 - 2.5.

## 14.4 Graphical Representation of Data

The representation of data by tables has already been discussed. Now let us turn our attention to another representation of data, i.e., the graphical representation. It is well said that one picture is better than a thousand words. Usually comparisons among the individual items are best shown by means of graphs. The representation then becomes easier to understand than the actual data. We shall study the following graphical representations in this section.

(A) Bar graphs

(B) Histograms of uniform width, and of varying widths

(C) Frequency polygons

### (A) Bar Graphs

In earlier classes, you have already studied and constructed bar graphs. Here we shall discuss them through a more formal approach. Recall that a bar graph is a pictorial representation of data in which usually bars of uniform width are drawn with equal spacing between them on one axis (say, the $x$-axis), depicting the variable. The values of the variable are shown on the other axis (say, the $y$-axis) and the heights of the bars depend on the values of the variable.

**Example 5 :** In a particular section of Class IX, 40 students were asked about the months of their birth and the following graph was prepared for the data so obtained:

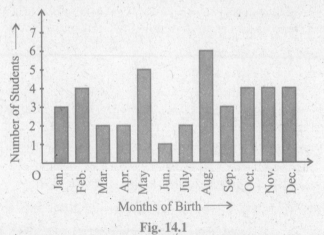

Fig. 14.1

Observe the bar graph given above and answer the following questions:

(i)    How many students were born in the month of November?

(ii)    In which month were the maximum number of students born?

**Solution :** Note that the variable here is the 'month of birth', and the value of the variable is the 'Number of students born'.

(i) 4 students were born in the month of November.

(ii) The Maximum number of students were born in the month of August.

Let us now recall how a bar graph is constructed by considering the following example.

**Example 6 :** A family with a monthly income of Rs 20,000 had planned the following expenditures per month under various heads:

Table 14.5

| Heads | Expenditure (in thousand rupees) |
|---|---|
| Grocery | 4 |
| Rent | 5 |
| Education of children | 5 |
| Medicine | 2 |
| Fuel | 2 |
| Entertainment | 1 |
| Miscellaneous | 1 |

Draw a bar graph for the data above.

**Solution :** We draw the bar graph of this data in the following steps. Note that the unit in the second column is thousand rupees. So, '4' against 'grocery' means Rs 4000.

1. We represent the Heads (variable) on the horizontal axis choosing any scale, since the width of the bar is not important. But for clarity, we take equal widths for all bars and maintain equal gaps in between. Let one Head be represented by one unit.

2. We represent the expenditure (value) on the vertical axis. Since the maximum expenditure is Rs 5000, we can choose the scale as 1 unit = Rs 1000.

3. To represent our first Head, i.e., grocery, we draw a rectangular bar with width 1 unit and height 4 units.

4. Similarly, other Heads are represented leaving a gap of 1 unit in between two consecutive bars.

   The bar graph is drawn in Fig. 14.2.

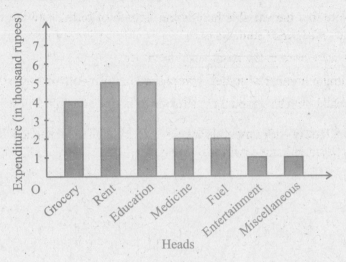

Fig. 14.2

Here, you can easily visualise the relative characteristics of the data at a glance, e.g., the expenditure on education is more than double that of medical expenses. Therefore, in some ways it serves as a better representation of data than the tabular form.

**Activity 3 :** Continuing with the same four groups of Activity 1, represent the data by suitable bar graphs.

Let us now see how a frequency distribution table for *continuous* class intervals can be represented graphically.

## (B) Histogram

This is a form of representation like the bar graph, but it is used for continuous class intervals. For instance, consider the frequency distribution Table 14.6, representing the weights of 36 students of a class:

Table 14.6

| Weights (in kg) | Number of students |
|---|---|
| 30.5 - 35.5 | 9 |
| 35.5 - 40.5 | 6 |
| 40.5 - 45.5 | 15 |
| 45.5 - 50.5 | 3 |
| 50.5 - 55.5 | 1 |
| 55.5 - 60.5 | 2 |
| **Total** | 36 |

Let us represent the data given above graphically as follows:

(i)   We represent the weights on the horizontal axis on a suitable scale. We can choose
      the scale as 1 cm = 5 kg. Also, since the first class interval is starting from 30.5
      and not zero, we show it on the graph by marking a *kink* or a break on the axis.

(ii)  We represent the number of students (frequency) on the vertical axis on a suitable
      scale. Since the maximum frequency is 15, we need to choose the scale to
      accomodate this maximum frequency.

(iii) We now draw rectangles (or rectangular bars) of width equal to the class-size
      and lengths according to the frequencies of the corresponding class intervals. For
      example, the rectangle for the class interval 30.5 - 35.5 will be of width 1 cm and
      length 4.5 cm.

(iv)  In this way, we obtain the graph as shown in Fig. 14.3:

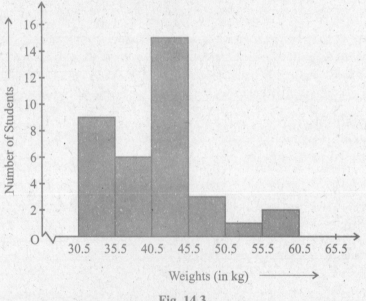

Fig. 14.3

Observe that since there are no gaps in between consecutive rectangles, the resultant
graph appears like a solid figure. This is called a *histogram*, which is a graphical
representation of a grouped frequency distribution with continuous classes. Also, unlike
a bar graph, the width of the bar plays a significant role in its construction.

Here, in fact, areas of the rectangles erected are proportional to the corresponding
frequencies. However, since the widths of the rectangles are all equal, the lengths of
the rectangles are proportional to the frequencies. That is why, we draw the lengths
according to (iii) above.

Now, consider a situation different from the one above.

**Example 7 :** A teacher wanted to analyse the performance of two sections of students in a mathematics test of 100 marks. Looking at their performances, she found that a few students got under 20 marks and a few got 70 marks or above. So she decided to group them into intervals of varying sizes as follows: 0 - 20, 20 - 30, . . ., 60 - 70, 70 - 100. Then she formed the following table:

Table 14.7

| Marks | Number of students |
|:---:|:---:|
| 0 - 20 | 7 |
| 20 - 30 | 10 |
| 30 - 40 | 10 |
| 40 - 50 | 20 |
| 50 - 60 | 20 |
| 60 - 70 | 15 |
| 70 - above | 8 |
| **Total** | **90** |

A histogram for this table was prepared by a student as shown in Fig. 14.4.

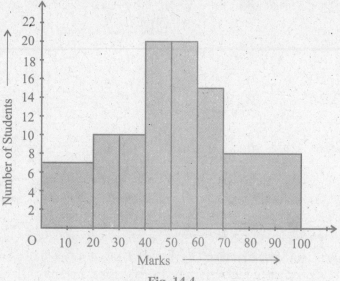

Fig. 14.4

Carefully examine this graphical representation. Do you think that it correctly represents the data? No, the graph is giving us a misleading picture. As we have mentioned earlier, the areas of the rectangles are proportional to the frequencies in a histogram. Earlier this problem did not arise, because the widths of all the rectangles were equal. But here, since the widths of the rectangles are varying, the histogram above does not give a correct picture. For example, it shows a greater frequency in the interval 70 - 100, than in 60 - 70, which is not the case.

So, we need to make certain modifications in the lengths of the rectangles so that the areas are again proportional to the frequencies.

The steps to be followed are as given below:

1. Select a class interval with the minimum class size. In the example above, the minimum class-size is 10.

2. The lengths of the rectangles are then modified to be proportionate to the class-size 10.

For instance, when the class-size is 20, the length of the rectangle is 7. So when the class-size is 10, the length of the rectangle will be $\dfrac{7}{20}$ $10 = 3.5$.

Similarly, proceeding in this manner, we get the following table:

Table 14.8

| Marks | Frequency | Width of the class | Length of the rectangle |
|-------|-----------|--------------------|-------------------------|
| 0 - 20 | 7 | 20 | $\dfrac{7}{20}$ $10 = 3.5$ |
| 20 - 30 | 10 | 10 | $\dfrac{10}{10}$ $10 = 10$ |
| 30 - 40 | 10 | 10 | $\dfrac{10}{10}$ $10 = 10$ |
| 40 - 50 | 20 | 10 | $\dfrac{20}{10}$ $10 = 20$ |
| 50 - 60 | 20 | 10 | $\dfrac{20}{10}$ $10 = 20$ |
| 60 - 70 | 15 | 10 | $\dfrac{15}{10}$ $10 = 15$ |
| 70 - 100 | 8 | 30 | $\dfrac{8}{30}$ $10 = 2.67$ |

Since we have calculated these lengths for an interval of 10 marks in each case, we may call these lengths as "proportion of students per 10 marks interval".

So, the correct histogram with varying width is given in Fig. 14.5.

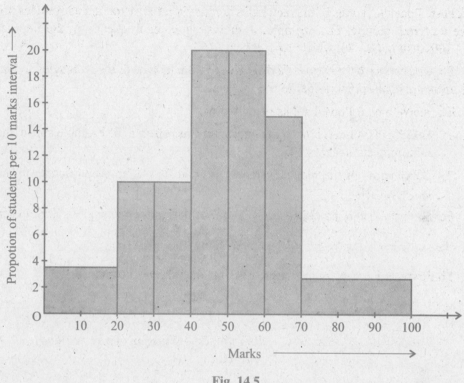

**Fig. 14.5**

## (C) Frequency Polygon

There is yet another visual way of representing quantitative data and its frequencies. This is a polygon. To see what we mean, consider the histogram represented by Fig. 14.3. Let us join the mid-points of the upper sides of the adjacent rectangles of this histogram by means of line segments. Let us call these mid-points B, C, D, E, F and G. When joined by line segments, we obtain the figure BCDEFG (see Fig. 14.6). To complete the polygon, we assume that there is a class interval with frequency zero before 30.5 - 35.5, and one after 55.5 - 60.5, and their mid-points are A and H, respectively. ABCDEFGH is the frequency polygon corresponding to the data shown in Fig. 14.3. We have shown this in Fig. 14.6.

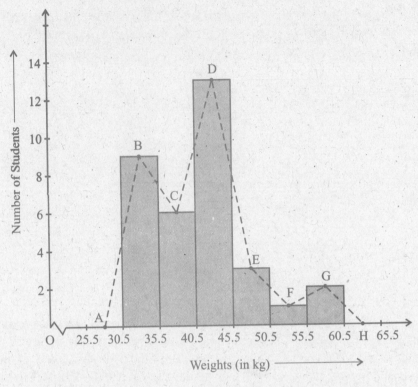

Fig. 14.6

Although, there exists no class preceding the lowest class and no class succeeding the highest class, addition of the two class intervals with zero frequency enables us to make the area of the frequency polygon the same as the area of the histogram. Why is this so? (**Hint :** Use the properties of congruent triangles.)

Now, the question arises: how do we complete the polygon when there is no class preceding the first class? Let us consider such a situation.

**Example 8 :** Consider the marks, out of 100, obtained by 51 students of a class in a test, given in Table 14.9.

Table 14.9

| Marks | Number of students |
|---|---|
| 0 - 10 | 5 |
| 10 - 20 | 10 |
| 20 - 30 | 4 |
| 30 - 40 | 6 |
| 40 - 50 | 7 |
| 50 - 60 | 3 |
| 60 - 70 | 2 |
| 70 - 80 | 2 |
| 80 - 90 | 3 |
| 90 - 100 | 9 |
| **Total** | 51 |

Draw a frequency polygon corresponding to this frequency distribution table.

**Solution :** Let us first draw a histogram for this data and mark the mid-points of the tops of the rectangles as B, C, D, E, F, G, H, I, J, K, respectively. Here, the first class is 0-10. So, to find the class preceeding 0-10, we extend the horizontal axis in the negative direction and find the mid-point of the imaginary class-interval (–10) - 0. The first end point, i.e., B is joined to this mid-point with zero frequency on the negative direction of the horizontal axis. The point where this line segment meets the vertical axis is marked as A. Let L be the mid-point of the class succeeding the last class of the given data. Then OABCDEFGHIJKL is the frequency polygon, which is shown in Fig. 14.7.

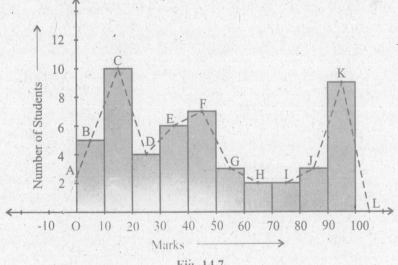

Fig. 14.7

*Frequency polygons can also be drawn independently without drawing histograms.* For this, we require the mid-points of the class-intervals used in the data. These mid-points of the class-intervals are called **class-marks**.

To find the class-mark of a class interval, we find the sum of the upper limit and lower limit of a class and divide it by 2. Thus,

$$\text{Class-mark} = \frac{\textbf{Upper limit} + \textbf{Lower limit}}{2}$$

Let us consider an example.

**Example 9 :** In a city, the weekly observations made in a study on the cost of living index are given in the following table:

Table 14.10

| Cost of living index | Number of weeks |
|:---:|:---:|
| 140 - 150 | 5 |
| 150 - 160 | 10 |
| 160 - 170 | 20 |
| 170 - 180 | 9 |
| 180 - 190 | 6 |
| 190 - 200 | 2 |
| **Total** | 52 |

Draw a frequency polygon for the data above (without constructing a histogram).

**Solution :** Since we want to draw a frequency polygon without a histogram, let us find the class-marks of the classes given above, that is of 140 - 150, 150 - 160,....

For 140 - 150, the upper limit = 150, and the lower limit = 140

So, the class-mark $= \dfrac{150 + 140}{2} = \dfrac{290}{2} = 145.$

Continuing in the same manner, we find the class-marks of the other classes as well.

So, the new table obtained is as shown in the following table:

Table 14.11

| Classes | Class-marks | Frequency |
|---------|-------------|-----------|
| 140 - 150 | 145 | 5 |
| 150 - 160 | 155 | 10 |
| 160 - 170 | 165 | 20 |
| 170 - 180 | 175 | 9 |
| 180 - 190 | 185 | 6 |
| 190 - 200 | 195 | 2 |
| **Total** | | 52 |

We can now draw a frequency polygon by plotting the class-marks along the horizontal axis, the frequencies along the vertical-axis, and then plotting and joining the points B(145, 5), C(155, 10), D(165, 20), E(175, 9), F(185, 6) and G(195, 2) by line segments. We should not forget to plot the point corresponding to the class-mark of the class 130 - 140 (just before the lowest class 140 - 150) with zero frequency, that is, A(135, 0), and the point H (205, 0) occurs immediately after G(195, 2). So, the resultant frequency polygon will be ABCDEFGH (see Fig. 14.8).

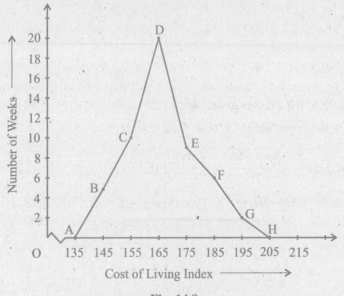

Fig. 14.8

Frequency polygons are used when the data is continuous and very large. It is very useful for comparing two different sets of data of the same nature, for example, comparing the performance of two different sections of the same class.

## EXERCISE 14.3

1. A survey conducted by an organisation for the cause of illness and death among the women between the ages 15 - 44 (in years) worldwide, found the following figures (in %):

| S.No. | Causes | Female fatality rate (%) |
|---|---|---|
| 1. | Reproductive health conditions | 31.8 |
| 2. | Neuropsychiatric conditions | 25.4 |
| 3. | Injuries | 12.4 |
| 4. | Cardiovascular conditions | 4.3 |
| 5. | Respiratory conditions | 4.1 |
| 6. | Other causes | 22.0 |

   (i)   Represent the information given above graphically.

   (ii)  Which condition is the major cause of women's ill health and death worldwide?

   (iii) Try to find out, with the help of your teacher, any two factors which play a major role in the cause in (ii) above being the major cause.

2. The following data on the number of girls (to the nearest ten) per thousand boys in different sections of Indian society is given below.

| Section | Number of girls per thousand boys |
|---|---|
| Scheduled Caste (SC) | 940 |
| Scheduled Tribe (ST) | 970 |
| Non SC/ST | 920 |
| Backward districts | 950 |
| Non-backward districts | 920 |
| Rural | 930 |
| Urban | 910 |

(i) Represent the information above by a bar graph.

(ii) In the classroom discuss what conclusions can be arrived at from the graph.

3. Given below are the seats won by different political parties in the polling outcome of a state assembly elections:

| Political Party | A | B | C | D | E | F |
|---|---|---|---|---|---|---|
| Seats Won | 75 | 55 | 37 | 29 | 10 | 37 |

(i) Draw a bar graph to represent the polling results.

(ii) Which political party won the maximum number of seats?

4. The length of 40 leaves of a plant are measured correct to one millimetre, and the obtained data is represented in the following table:

| Length (in mm) | Number of leaves |
|---|---|
| 118 - 126 | 3 |
| 127 - 135 | 5 |
| 136 - 144 | 9 |
| 145 - 153 | 12 |
| 154 - 162 | 5 |
| 163 - 171 | 4 |
| 172 - 180 | 2 |

(i) Draw a histogram to represent the given data. [Hint: First make the class intervals continuous]

(ii) Is there any other suitable graphical representation for the same data?

(iii) Is it correct to conclude that the maximum number of leaves are 153 mm long? Why?

5. The following table gives the life times of 400 neon lamps:

| Life time (in hours) | Number of lamps |
|---|---|
| 300 - 400 | 14 |
| 400 - 500 | 56 |
| 500 - 600 | 60 |
| 600 - 700 | 86 |
| 700 - 800 | 74 |
| 800 - 900 | 62 |
| 900 - 1000 | 48 |

(i) Represent the given information with the help of a histogram.

(ii) How many lamps have a life time of more than 700 hours?

6. The following table gives the distribution of students of two sections according to the marks obtained by them:

| Section A | | Section B | |
|---|---|---|---|
| Marks | Frequency | Marks | Frequency |
| 0 - 10 | 3 | 0 - 10 | 5 |
| 10 - 20 | 9 | 10 - 20 | 19 |
| 20 - 30 | 17 | 20 - 30 | 15 |
| 30 - 40 | 12 | 30 - 40 | 10 |
| 40 - 50 | 9 | 40 - 50 | 1 |

Represent the marks of the students of both the sections on the same graph by two frequency polygons. From the two polygons compare the performance of the two sections.

7. The runs scored by two teams A and B on the first 60 balls in a cricket match are given below:

| Number of balls | Team A | Team B |
|---|---|---|
| 1 - 6 | 2 | 5 |
| 7 - 12 | 1 | 6 |
| 13 - 18 | 8 | 2 |
| 19 - 24 | 9 | 10 |
| 25 - 30 | 4 | 5 |
| 31 - 36 | 5 | 6 |
| 37 - 42 | 6 | 3 |
| 43 - 48 | 10 | 4 |
| 49 - 54 | 6 | 8 |
| 55 - 60 | 2 | 10 |

Represent the data of both the teams on the same graph by frequency polygons.

[**Hint :** First make the class intervals continuous.]

8. A random survey of the number of children of various age groups playing in a park was found as follows:

| Age (in years) | Number of children |
|---|---|
| 1 - 2 | 5 |
| 2 - 3 | 3 |
| 3 - 5 | 6 |
| 5 - 7 | 12 |
| 7 - 10 | 9 |
| 10 - 15 | 10 |
| 15 - 17 | 4 |

Draw a histogram to represent the data above.

9. 100 surnames were randomly picked up from a local telephone directory and a frequency distribution of the number of letters in the English alphabet in the surnames was found as follows:

| Number of letters | Number of surnames |
|---|---|
| 1 - 4 | 6 |
| 4 - 6 | 30 |
| 6 - 8 | 44 |
| 8 - 12 | 16 |
| 12 - 20 | 4 |

(i) Draw a histogram to depict the given information.

(ii) Write the class interval in which the maximum number of surnames lie.

## 14.5 Measures of Central Tendency

Earlier in this chapter, we represented the data in various forms through frequency distribution tables, bar graphs, histograms and frequency polygons. Now, the question arises if we always need to study all the data to 'make sense' of it, or if we can make out some important features of it by considering only certain representatives of the data. This is possible, by using measures of central tendency or averages.

Consider a situation when two students Mary and Hari received their test copies. The test had five questions, each carrying ten marks. Their scores were as follows:

| Question Numbers | 1 | 2 | 3 | 4 | 5 |
|---|---|---|---|---|---|
| Mary's score | 10 | 8 | 9 | 8 | 7 |
| Hari's score | 4 | 7 | 10 | 10 | 10 |

Upon getting the test copies, both of them found their average scores as follows:

$$\text{Mary's average score} = \frac{42}{5} = 8.4$$

$$\text{Hari's average score} = \frac{41}{5} = 8.2$$

Since Mary's average score was more than Hari's, Mary claimed to have performed better than Hari, but Hari did not agree. He arranged both their scores in ascending order and found out the middle score as given below:

| Mary's Score | 7 | 8 | ⑧ | 9 | 10 |
|---|---|---|---|---|---|
| Hari's Score | 4 | 7 | ⑩ | 10 | 10 |

Hari said that since his middle-most score was 10, which was higher than Mary's middle-most score, that is 8, his performance should be rated better.

But Mary was not convinced. To convince Mary, Hari tried out another strategy. He said he had scored 10 marks more often (3 times) as compared to Mary who scored 10 marks only once. So, his performance was better.

Now, to settle the dispute between Hari and Mary, let us see the three measures they adopted to make their point.

The average score that Mary found in the first case is the *mean*. The 'middle' score that Hari was using for his argument is the *median*. The most often scored mark that Hari used in his second strategy is the *mode*.

Now, let us first look at the mean in detail.

The **mean** (or **average**) of a number of observations is the sum of the values of all the observations divided by the total number of observations.

It is denoted by the symbol $\overline{x}$, read as '**x bar**'.

Let us consider an example.

**Example 10 :** 5 people were asked about the time in a week they spend in doing social work in their community. They said 10, 7, 13, 20 and 15 hours, respectively.

Find the mean (or average) time in a week devoted by them for social work.

**Solution :** We have already studied in our earlier classes that the mean of a certain number of observations is equal to $\dfrac{\text{Sum of all the observations}}{\text{Total number of observations}}$. To simplify our working of finding the mean, let us use a variable $x_i$ to denote the $i$th observation. In this case, $i$ can take the values from 1 to 5. So our first observation is $x_1$, second observation is $x_2$, and so on till $x_5$.

Also $x_1 = 10$ means that the value of the first observation, denoted by $x_1$, is 10. Similarly, $x_2 = 7, x_3 = 13, x_4 = 20$ and $x_5 = 15$.

Therefore, the mean $\bar{x} = \dfrac{\text{Sum of all the observations}}{\text{Total number of observations}}$

$$= \frac{x_1 + x_2 + x_3 + x_4 + x_5}{5}$$

$$= \frac{10 + 7 + 13 + 20 + 15}{5} = \frac{65}{5} = 13$$

So, the mean time spent by these 5 people in doing social work is 13 hours in a week.

Now, in case we are finding the mean time spent by 30 people in doing social work, writing $x_1 + x_2 + x_3 + \ldots + x_{30}$ would be a tedious job. We use the Greek symbol $\Sigma$ (for the letter Sigma) for *summation*. Instead of writing $x_1 + x_2 + x_3 + \ldots + x_{30}$, we write $\displaystyle\sum_{i=1}^{30} x_i$, which is read as 'the sum of $x_i$ as $i$ varies from 1 to 30'.

So, $$\bar{x} = \frac{\displaystyle\sum_{i=1}^{30} x_i}{30}$$

Similarly, for $n$ observations $\quad \bar{x} = \dfrac{\displaystyle\sum_{i=1}^{n} x_i}{n}$

**Example 11 :** Find the mean of the marks obtained by 30 students of Class IX of a school, given in Example 2.

**Solution :** Now, $\quad \bar{x} = \dfrac{x_1 + x_2 + \cdots + x_{30}}{30}$

$$\sum_{i=1}^{30} x_i = 10 + 20 + 36 + 92 + 95 + 40 + 50 + 56 + 60 + 70 + 92 + 88$$
$$80 + 70 + 72 + 70 + 36 + 40 + 36 + 40 + 92 + 40 + 50 + 50$$
$$56 + 60 + 70 + 60 + 60 + 88 = 1779$$

So, $$\bar{x} = \frac{1779}{30} = 59.3$$

Is the process not time consuming? Can we simplify it? Note that we have formed a frequency table for this data (see Table 14.1).

The table shows that 1 student obtained 10 marks, 1 student obtained 20 marks, 3 students obtained 36 marks, 4 students obtained 40 marks, 3 students obtained 50 marks, 2 students obtained 56 marks, 4 students obtained 60 marks, 4 students obtained 70 marks, 1 student obtained 72 marks, 1 student obtained 80 marks, 2 students obtained 88 marks, 3 students obtained 92 marks and 1 student obtained 95 marks.

So, the total marks obtained $= (1 \times 10) + (1 \times 20) + (3 \times 36) + (4 \times 40) + (3 \times 50)$
$+ (2 \times 56) + (4 \times 60) + (4 \times 70) + (1 \times 72) + (1 \times 80)$
$+ (2 \times 88) + (3 \times 92) + (1 \times 95)$

$= f_1 x_1 + \ldots + f_{13} x_{13}$, where $f_i$ is the frequency of the $i$th entry inTable 14.1.

In brief, we write this as $\sum_{i=1}^{13} f_i x_i$ .

So, the total marks obtained $= \sum_{i=1}^{13} f_i x_i$

$= 10 + 20 + 108 + 160 + 150 + 112 + 240 + 280 + 72 + 80$
$+ 176 + 276 + 95$

$= 1779$

Now, the total number of observations

$$= \sum_{i=1}^{13} f_i$$

$= f_1 + f_2 + \ldots + f_{13}$
$= 1 + 1 + 3 + 4 + 3 + 2 + 4 + 4 + 1 + 1 + 2 + 3 + 1$
$= 30$

So,           the mean $\bar{x} = \dfrac{\text{Sum of all the observations}}{\text{Total number of observations}} = \left( \dfrac{\sum_{i=1}^{13} f_i x_i}{\sum_{i=1}^{13} f_i} \right)$

$= \dfrac{1779}{30} = 59.3$

This process can be displayed in the following table, which is a modified form of Table 14.1.

## Table 14.12

| Marks ($x_i$) | Number of students ($f_i$) | $f_i x_i$ |
|:---:|:---:|:---:|
| 10 | 1 | 10 |
| 20 | 1 | 20 |
| 36 | 3 | 108 |
| 40 | 4 | 160 |
| 50 | 3 | 150 |
| 56 | 2 | 112 |
| 60 | 4 | 240 |
| 70 | 4 | 280 |
| 72 | 1 | 72 |
| 80 | 1 | 80 |
| 88 | 2 | 176 |
| 92 | 3 | 276 |
| 95 | 1 | 95 |
| $\sum_{i=1}^{13} f_i = 30$ | | $\sum_{i=1}^{13} f_i x_i = 1779$ |

Thus, in the case of an ungrouped frequency distribution, you can use the formula

$$\overline{x} = \frac{\sum\limits_{i=1}^{n} f_i x_i}{\sum\limits_{i=1}^{n} f_i}$$

for calculating the mean.

Let us now move back to the situation of the argument between Hari and Mary, and consider the second case where Hari found his performance better by finding the middle-most score. As already stated, this measure of central tendency is called the *median*.

The **median** is that value of the given number of observations, which divides it into exactly two parts. So, when the data is arranged in ascending (or descending) order the median of ungrouped data is calculated as follows:

(i) When the number of observations (n) is odd, the median is the value of the $\left(\dfrac{n+1}{2}\right)^{th}$ observation. For example, if $n = 13$, the value of the $\left(\dfrac{13+1}{2}\right)^{th}$, i.e., the 7th observation will be the median [see Fig. 14.9 (i)].

(ii) When the number of observations (n) is even, the median is the mean of the $\left(\dfrac{n}{2}\right)^{th}$ and the $\left(\dfrac{n}{2}+1\right)^{th}$ observations. For example, if $n = 16$, the mean of the values of the $\left(\dfrac{16}{2}\right)^{th}$ and the $\left(\dfrac{16}{2}+1\right)^{th}$ observations, i.e., the mean of the values of the 8th and 9th observations will be the median [see Fig. 14.9 (ii)].

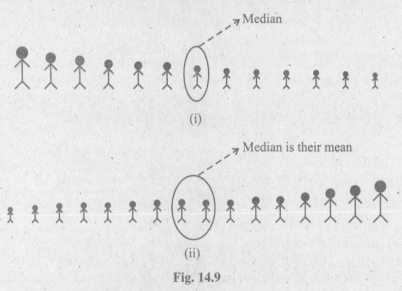

(i)

(ii)

Fig. 14.9

Let us illustrate this with the help of some examples.

**Example 12 :** The heights (in cm) of 9 students of a class are as follows:

     155    160    145    149    150    147    152    144    148

Find the median of this data.

**Solution :** First of all we arrange the data in ascending order, as follows:

     144   145   147   148   149   150   152   155   160

Since the number of students is 9, an odd number, we find out the median by finding the height of the $\left(\dfrac{n+1}{2}\right)$th $=\left(\dfrac{9+1}{2}\right)$th $=$ the 5th student, which is 149 cm.

So, the median, i.e., the medial height is 149 cm.

Example 13 : The points scored by a Kabaddi team in a series of matches are as follows:

17, 2, 7, 27, 15, 5, 14, 8, 10, 24, 48, 10, 8, 7, 18, 28

Find the median of the points scored by the team.

Solution : Arranging the points scored by the team in ascending order, we get

2, 5, 7, 7, 8, 8, 10, 10, 14, 15, 17, 18, 24, 27, 28, 48.

There are 16 terms. So there are two middle terms, i.e. the $\dfrac{16}{2}$th and $\left(\dfrac{16}{2}+1\right)$th, i.e., the 8th and 9th terms.

So, the median is the mean of the values of the 8th and 9th terms.

i.e, the median $=\dfrac{10+14}{2}=12$

So, the medial point scored by the Kabaddi team is 12.

Let us again go back to the unsorted dispute of Hari and Mary.

The third measure used by Hari to find the average was the *mode*.

The **mode** is that value of the observation which occurs most frequently, i.e., an observation with the maximum frequency is called the mode.

The readymade garment and shoe industries make great use of this measure of central tendency. Using the knowledge of mode, these industries decide which size of the product should be produced in large numbers.

Let us illustrate this with the help of an example.

Example 14 : Find the mode of the following marks (out of 10) obtained by 20 students:

4, 6, 5, 9, 3, 2, 7, 7, 6, 5, 4, 9, 10, 10, 3, 4, 7, 6, 9, 9

Solution : We arrange this data in the following form :

2, 3, 3, 4, 4, 4, 5, 5, 6, 6, 6, 7, 7, 7, 9, 9, 9, 9, 10, 10

Here 9 occurs most frequently, i.e., four times. So, the mode is 9.

**Example 15 :** Consider a small unit of a factory where there are 5 employees : a supervisor and four labourers. The labourers draw a salary of ₹ 5,000 per month each while the supervisor gets ₹ 15,000 per month. Calculate the mean, median and mode of the salaries of this unit of the factory.

**Solution : Mean** $= \dfrac{5000 + 5000 + 5000 + 5000 + 15000}{5} = \dfrac{35000}{5} = 7000$

So, the mean salary is ₹ 7000 per month.

To obtain the median, we arrange the salaries in ascending order:

$$5000, \quad 5000, \quad 5000, \quad 5000, \quad 15000$$

Since the number of employees in the factory is 5, the median is given by the $\left(\dfrac{5+1}{2}\right)$ th $= \dfrac{6}{2}$ th = 3rd observation. Therefore, the median is ₹ 5000 per month.

To find the mode of the salaries, i.e., the modal salary, we see that 5000 occurs the maximum number of times in the data 5000, 5000, 5000, 5000, 15000. So, the modal salary is ₹ 5000 per month.

Now compare the three measures of central tendency for the given data in the example above. You can see that the mean salary of ₹ 7000 does not give even an approximate estimate of any one of their wages, while the medial and modal salaries of ₹ 5000 represents the data more effectively.

Extreme values in the data affect the mean. This is one of the weaknesses of the mean. So, if the data has a few points which are very far from most of the other points, (like 1,7,8,9,9) then the mean is not a good representative of this data. Since the median and mode are not affected by extreme values present in the data, they give a better estimate of the average in such a situation.

Again let us go back to the situation of Hari and Mary, and compare the three measures of central tendency.

| Measures of central tendency | Hari | Mary |
|---|---|---|
| Mean | 8.2 | 8.4 |
| Median | 10 | 8 |
| Mode | 10 | 8 |

This comparison helps us in stating that these measures of central tendency are not sufficient for concluding which student is better. We require some more information to conclude this, which you will study about in the higher classes.

## EXERCISE 14.4

1. The following number of goals were scored by a team in a series of 10 matches:

   2,  3,  4,  5,  0,  1,  3,  3,  4,  3

   Find the mean, median and mode of these scores.

2. In a mathematics test given to 15 students, the following marks (out of 100) are recorded:

   41,  39,  48,  52,  46,  62,  54,  40,  96,  52,  98,  40,  42,  52,  60

   Find the mean, median and mode of this data.

3. The following observations have been arranged in ascending order. If the median of the data is 63, find the value of $x$.

   29,   32,   48,   50,   $x$,   $x+2$,   72,   78,   84,   95

4. Find the mode of 14, 25, 14, 28, 18, 17, 18, 14, 23, 22, 14, 18.

5. Find the mean salary of 60 workers of a factory from the following table:

| Salary (in ₹) | Number of workers |
|:---:|:---:|
| 3000 | 16 |
| 4000 | 12 |
| 5000 | 10 |
| 6000 | 8 |
| 7000 | 6 |
| 8000 | 4 |
| 9000 | 3 |
| 10000 | 1 |
| **Total** | 60 |

6. Give one example of a situation in which

   (i)   the mean is an appropriate measure of central tendency.

   (ii)  the mean is not an appropriate measure of central tendency but the median is an appropriate measure of central tendency.

## 14.6 Summary

In this chapter, you have studied the following points:

1. Facts or figures, collected with a definite purpose, are called data.

2. Statistics is the area of study dealing with the presentation, analysis and interpretation of data.

3. How data can be presented graphically in the form of bar graphs, histograms and frequency polygons.

4. The three measures of central tendency for **ungrouped data** are:

   (i) Mean : It is found by adding all the values of the observations and dividing it by the total number of observations. It is denoted by $\bar{x}$ .

   So, $\bar{x} = \dfrac{\displaystyle\sum_{i=1}^{n} x_i}{n}$ . For an ungrouped frequency distribution, it is $\bar{x} = \dfrac{\displaystyle\sum_{i=1}^{n} f_i x_i}{\displaystyle\sum_{i=1}^{n} f_i}$ .

   (ii) Median : It is the value of the middle-most observation (s).

   If $n$ is an odd number, the median = value of the $\left(\dfrac{n+1}{2}\right)^{\text{th}}$ observation.

   If $n$ is an even number, median = Mean of the values of the $\left(\dfrac{n}{2}\right)^{\text{th}}$ and $\left(\dfrac{n}{2}+1\right)^{\text{th}}$ observations.

   (iii) Mode : The mode is the most frequently occurring observation.

# CHAPTER 15

# PROBABILITY

*It is remarkable that a science, which began with the consideration of games of chance, should be elevated to the rank of the most important subject of human knowledge.* —**Pierre Simon Laplace**

## 15.1 Introduction

In everyday life, we come across statements such as

(1) It will **probably** rain today.

(2) I **doubt** that he will pass the test.

(3) **Most probably**, Kavita will stand first in the annual examination.

(4) **Chances** are high that the prices of diesel will go up.

(5) There is a 50-50 **chance** of India winning a toss in today's match.

The words 'probably', 'doubt', 'most probably', 'chances', etc., used in the statements above involve an element of uncertainty. For example, in (1), 'probably rain' will mean it may rain or may not rain today. We are predicting rain today based on our past experience when it rained under similar conditions. Similar predictions are also made in other cases listed in (2) to (5).

The uncertainty of 'probably' etc can be measured numerically by means of 'probability' in many cases.

Though probability started with gambling, it has been used extensively in the fields of Physical Sciences, Commerce, Biological Sciences, Medical Sciences, Weather Forecasting, etc.

## 15.2 Probability – an Experimental Approach

In earlier classes, you have had a glimpse of probability when you performed experiments like tossing of coins, throwing of dice, etc., and observed their *outcomes*. You will now learn to measure the chance of occurrence of a particular *outcome* in an experiment.

**Blaise Pascal (1623–1662)**
Fig. 15.1

The concept of probability developed in a very strange manner. In 1654, a gambler Chevalier de Mere, approached the well-known 17th century French philosopher and mathematician Blaise Pascal regarding certain dice problems. Pascal became interested in these problems, studied them and discussed them with another French mathematician, Pierre de Fermat. Both Pascal and Fermat solved the problems independently. This work was the beginning of Probability Theory.

**Pierre de Fermat (1601–1665)**
Fig. 15.2

The first book on the subject was written by the Italian mathematician, J.Cardan (1501–1576). The title of the book was 'Book on Games of Chance' (Liber de Ludo Aleae), published in 1663. Notable contributions were also made by mathematicians J. Bernoulli (1654–1705), P. Laplace (1749–1827), A.A. Markov (1856–1922) and A.N. Kolmogorov (born 1903).

**Activity 1 :** (i) Take any coin, toss it ten times and note down the number of times a head and a tail come up. Record your observations in the form of the following table

Table 15.1

| Number of times the coin is tossed | Number of times head comes up | Number of times tail comes up |
|:---:|:---:|:---:|
| 10 | — | — |

Write down the values of the following fractions:

$$\frac{\text{Number of times a head comes up}}{\text{Total number of times the coin is tossed}}$$

and

$$\frac{\text{Number of times a tail comes up}}{\text{Total number of times the coin is tossed}}$$

(ii) Toss the coin twenty times and in the same way record your observations as above. Again find the values of the fractions given above for this collection of observations.

(iii) Repeat the same experiment by increasing the number of tosses and record the number of heads and tails. Then find the values of the corresponding fractions.

You will find that as the number of tosses gets larger, the values of the fractions come closer to 0.5. To record what happens in more and more tosses, the following group activity can also be performed:

**Acitivity 2 :** Divide the class into groups of 2 or 3 students. Let a student in each group toss a coin 15 times. Another student in each group should record the observations regarding heads and tails. [Note that coins of the same denomination should be used in all the groups. It will be treated as if only one coin has been tossed by all the groups.]

Now, on the blackboard, make a table like Table 15.2. First, Group 1 can write down its observations and calculate the resulting fractions. Then Group 2 can write down its observations, but will calculate the fractions for the combined data of Groups 1 and 2, and so on. (We may call these fractions as *cumulative fractions*.) We have noted the first three rows based on the observations given by one class of students.

**Table 15.2**

| Group | Number of heads | Number of tails | Cumulative number of heads | Cumulative number of tails |
|:---:|:---:|:---:|:---:|:---:|
| | | | Total number of times the coin is tossed | Total number of times the coin is tossed |
| (1) | (2) | (3) | (4) | (5) |
| 1 | 3 | 12 | $\dfrac{3}{15}$ | $\dfrac{12}{15}$ |
| 2 | 7 | 8 | $\dfrac{7+3}{15+15} = \dfrac{10}{30}$ | $\dfrac{8+12}{15+15} = \dfrac{20}{30}$ |
| 3 | 7 | 8 | $\dfrac{7+10}{15+30} = \dfrac{17}{45}$ | $\dfrac{8+20}{15+30} = \dfrac{28}{45}$ |
| 4 | $\vdots$ | $\vdots$ | $\vdots$ | $\vdots$ |

What do you observe in the table? You will find that as the total number of tosses of the coin increases, the values of the fractions in Columns (4) and (5) come nearer and nearer to 0.5.

**Activity 3 :** (i) Throw a die[*] 20 times and note down the number of times the numbers

---

[*]A die is a well balanced cube with its six faces marked with numbers from 1 to 6, one number on one face. Sometimes dots appear in place of numbers.

1, 2, 3, 4, 5, 6 come up. Record your observations in the form of a table, as in Table 15.3:

Table 15.3

| Number of times a die is thrown | Number of times these scores turn up | | | | | |
|---|---|---|---|---|---|---|
| | 1 | 2 | 3 | 4 | 5 | 6 |
| 20 | | | | | | |

Find the values of the following fractions:

$$\frac{\text{Number of times 1 turned up}}{\text{Total number of times the die is thrown}}$$

$$\frac{\text{Number of times 2 turned up}}{\text{Total number of times the die is thrown}}$$

$$\vdots$$

$$\frac{\text{Number of times 6 turned up}}{\text{Total number of times the die is thrown}}$$

(ii) Now throw the die 40 times, record the observations and calculate the fractions as done in (i).

As the number of throws of the die increases, you will find that the value of each fraction calculated in (i) and (ii) comes closer and closer to $\frac{1}{6}$.

To see this, you could perform a group activity, as done in Activity 2. Divide the students in your class, into small groups. One student in each group should throw a die ten times. Observations should be noted and cumulative fractions should be calculated.

The values of the fractions for the number 1 can be recorded in Table 15.4. This table can be extended to write down fractions for the other numbers also or other tables of the same kind can be created for the other numbers.

Table 15.4

| Group (1) | Total number of times a die is thrown in a group (2) | Cumulative number of times 1 turned up / Total number of times the die is thrown (3) |
|---|---|---|
| 1 | — | — |
| 2 | — | — |
| 3 | — | — |
| 4 | — | — |

The dice used in all the groups should be almost the same in size and appearence. Then all the throws will be treated as throws of the same die.

What do you observe in these tables?

You will find that as the total number of throws gets larger, the fractions in Column (3) move closer and closer to $\frac{1}{6}$.

Activity 4 : (i) Toss two coins simultaneously ten times and record your observations in the form of a table as given below:

Table 15.5

| Number of times the two coins are tossed | Number of times no head comes up | Number of times one head comes up | Number of times two heads come up |
|---|---|---|---|
| 10 | — | — | — |

Write down the fractions:

$$A = \frac{\text{Number of times no head comes up}}{\text{Total number of times two coins are tossed}}$$

$$B = \frac{\text{Number of times one head comes up}}{\text{Total number of times two coins are tossed}}$$

$$C = \frac{\text{Number of times two heads come up}}{\text{Total number of times two coins are tossed}}$$

Calculate the values of these fractions.

Now increase the number of tosses (as in Activitiy 2). You will find that the more the number of tosses, the closer are the values of A, B and C to 0.25, 0.5 and 0.25, respectively.

In Activity 1, each toss of a coin is called a *trial*. Similarly in Activity 3, each throw of a die is a *trial*, and each simultaneous toss of two coins in Activity 4 is also a *trial*.

So, *a trial is an action which results in one or several outcomes*. The possible outcomes in Activity 1 were Head and Tail; whereas in Activity 3, the possible outcomes were 1, 2, 3, 4, 5 and 6.

In Activity 1, the getting of a head in a particular throw is an *event with outcome 'head'*. Similarly, *getting a tail is an event with outcome 'tail'*. In Activity 2, the getting of a particular number, say 1, is an *event* with outcome 1.

If our experiment was to throw the die for getting an even number, then the event would consist of three outcomes, namely, 2, 4 and 6.

So, an *event* for an experiment is the collection of some outcomes of the experiment. In Class X, you will study a more formal definition of an event.

So, can you now tell what the events are in Activity 4?

With this background, let us now see what probability is. Based on what we directly observe as the outcomes of our trials, we find the *experimental* or *empirical* probability.

Let $n$ be the total number of trials. The *empirical probability* P(E) of an event E happening, is given by

$$P(E) = \frac{\text{Number of trials in which the event happened}}{\text{The total number of trials}}$$

In this chapter, we shall be finding the empirical probability, though we will write 'probability' for convenience.

Let us consider some examples.

To start with let us go back to Activity 2, and Table 15.2. In Column (4) of this table, what is the fraction that you calculated? Nothing, but it is the empirical probability of getting a head. Note that this probability kept changing depending on the number of trials and the number of heads obtained in these trials. Similarly, the empirical probability of getting a tail is obtained in Column (5) of Table 15.2. This is $\frac{12}{15}$ to start with, then it is $\frac{2}{3}$, then $\frac{28}{45}$, and so on.

So, the empirical probability depends on the number of trials undertaken, and the number of times the outcomes you are looking for coming up in these trials.

Activity 5 : Before going further, look at the tables you drew up while doing Activity 3. Find the probabilities of getting a 3 when throwing a die a certain number of times. Also, show how it changes as the number of trials increases.

Now let us consider some other examples.

Example 1 : A coin is tossed 1000 times with the following frequencies:

Head : 455,  Tail : 545

Compute the probability for each event.

Solution : Since the coin is tossed 1000 times, the total number of trials is 1000. Let us call the events of getting a head and of getting a tail as E and F, respectively. Then, the number of times E happens, i.e., the number of times a head come up, is 455.

So,        the probability of E $= \dfrac{\text{Number of heads}}{\text{Total number of trials}}$

i.e.,                     $P(E) = \dfrac{455}{1000} = 0.455$

Similarly, the probability of the event of getting a tail $= \dfrac{\text{Number of tails}}{\text{Total number of trials}}$

i.e.,                        $P(F) = \dfrac{545}{1000} = 0.545$

Note that in the example above, $P(E) + P(F) = 0.455 + 0.545 = 1$, and E and F are the only two possible outcomes of each trial.

Example 2 : Two coins are tossed simultaneously 500 times, and we get

Two heads : 105 times

One head : 275 times

No head : 120 times

Find the probability of occurrence of each of these events.

Solution : Let us denote the events of getting two heads, one head and no head by $E_1$, $E_2$ and $E_3$, respectively. So,

$$P(E_1) = \dfrac{105}{500} = 0.21$$

$$P(E_2) = \dfrac{275}{500} = 0.55$$

$$P(E_3) = \dfrac{120}{500} = 0.24$$

Observe that $P(E_1) + P(E_2) + P(E_3) = 1$. Also $E_1$, $E_2$ and $E_3$ cover all the outcomes of a trial.

**Example 3 :** A die is thrown 1000 times with the frequencies for the outcomes 1, 2, 3, 4, 5 and 6 as given in the following table :

Table 15.6

| Outcome | 1 | 2 | 3 | 4 | 5 | 6 |
|---------|-----|-----|-----|-----|-----|-----|
| Frequency | 179 | 150 | 157 | 149 | 175 | 190 |

Find the probability of getting each outcome.

**Solution :** Let $E_i$ denote the event of getting the outcome $i$, where $i = 1, 2, 3, 4, 5, 6$. Then

Probability of the outcome $1 =$ $P(E_1)$ $= \dfrac{\text{Frequency of 1}}{\text{Total number of times the die is thrown}}$

$$= \frac{179}{1000} = 0.179$$

Similarly, $P(E_2) = \dfrac{150}{1000} = 0.15$, $P(E_3) = \dfrac{157}{1000} = 0.157$,

$P(E_4) = \dfrac{149}{1000} = 0.149$, $P(E_5) = \dfrac{175}{1000} = 0.175$

and $P(E_6) = \dfrac{190}{1000} = 0.19$.

Note that $P(E_1) + P(E_2) + P(E_3) + P(E_4) + P(E_5) + P(E_6) = 1$

Also note that:

(i)  The probability of each event lies between 0 and 1.

(ii) The sum of all the probabilities is 1.

(iii) $E_1$, $E_2$, . . ., $E_6$ cover all the possible outcomes of a trial.

**Example 4 :** On one page of a telephone directory, there were 200 telephone numbers. The frequency distribution of their unit place digit (for example, in the number 25828573, the unit place digit is 3) is given in Table 15.7 :

Table 15.7

| Digit | 0 | 1 | 2 | 3 | 4 | 5 | 6 | 7 | 8 | 9 |
|---|---|---|---|---|---|---|---|---|---|---|
| Frequency | 22 | 26 | 22 | 22 | 20 | 10 | 14 | 28 | 16 | 20 |

Without looking at the page, the pencil is placed on one of these numbers, i.e., the number is chosen at *random*. What is the probability that the digit in its unit place is 6?

Solution : The probability of digit 6 being in the unit place.

$$= \frac{\text{Frequency of 6}}{\text{Total number of selected telephone numbers}}$$

$$= \frac{14}{200} = 0.07$$

You can similarly obtain the empirical probabilities of the occurrence of the numbers having the other digits in the unit place.

Example 5 : The record of a weather station shows that out of the past 250 consecutive days, its weather forecasts were correct 175 times.

(i)   What is the probability that on a given day it was correct?

(ii)  What is the probability that it was not correct on a given day?

Solution : The total number of days for which the record is available = 250

(i)   P(the forecast was correct on a given day)

$$= \frac{\text{Number of days when the forecast was correct}}{\text{Total number of days for which the record is available}}$$

$$= \frac{175}{250} = 0.7$$

(ii)  The number of days when the forecast was not correct = 250 – 175 = 75

So, P(the forecast was not correct on a given day) $= \dfrac{75}{250} = 0.3$

Notice that:

P(forecast was correct on a given day) + P(forecast was not correct on a given day)

$$= 0.7 + 0.3 = 1$$

**Example 6 :** A tyre manufacturing company kept a record of the distance covered before a tyre needed to be replaced. The table shows the results of 1000 cases.

Table 15.8

| Distance (in km) | less than 4000 | 4000 to 9000 | 9001 to 14000 | more than 14000 |
|---|---|---|---|---|
| Frequency | 20 | 210 | 325 | 445 |

If you buy a tyre of this company, what is the probability that :

(i)   it will need to be replaced before it has covered 4000 km?

(ii)  it will last more than 9000 km?

(iii) it will need to be replaced after it has covered somewhere between 4000 km and 14000 km?

**Solution :** (i) The total number of trials = 1000.

The frequency of a tyre that needs to be replaced before it covers 4000 km is 20.

So, P(tyre to be replaced before it covers 4000 km) = $\dfrac{20}{1000}$ = 0.02

(ii) The frequency of a tyre that will last more than 9000 km is 325 + 445 = 770

So, P(tyre will last more than 9000 km) = $\dfrac{770}{1000}$ = 0.77

(iii) The frequency of a tyre that requires replacement between 4000 km and 14000 km is 210 + 325 = 535.

So, P(tyre requiring replacement between 4000 km and 14000 km) = $\dfrac{535}{1000}$ = 0.535

**Example 7 :** The percentage of marks obtained by a student in the monthly unit tests are given below:

Table 15.9

| Unit test | I | II | III | IV | V |
|---|---|---|---|---|---|
| Percentage of marks obtained | 69 | 71 | 73 | 68 | 74 |

Based on this data, find the probability that the student gets more than 70% marks in a unit test.

**Solution :** The total number of unit tests held is 5.
The number of unit tests in which the student obtained more than 70% marks is 3.

So, P(scoring more than 70% marks) = $\dfrac{3}{5}$ = 0.6

**Example 8 :** An insurance company selected 2000 drivers at random (i.e., without any preference of one driver over another) in a particular city to find a relationship between age and accidents. The data obtained are given in the following table:

Table 15.10

| Age of drivers (in years) | Accidents in one year | | | | |
|---|---|---|---|---|---|
| | **0** | **1** | **2** | **3** | **over 3** |
| 18 - 29 | 440 | 160 | 110 | 61 | 35 |
| 30 - 50 | 505 | 125 | 60 | 22 | 18 |
| Above 50 | 360 | 45 | 35 | 15 | 9 |

Find the probabilities of the following events for a driver chosen at random from the city:

(i) being 18-29 years of age *and* having exactly 3 accidents in one year.

(ii) being 30-50 years of age *and* having one or more accidents in a year.

(iii) having no accidents in one year.

**Solution :** Total number of drivers = 2000.

(i) The number of drivers who are 18-29 years old and have exactly 3 accidents in one year is 61.

So, P (driver is 18-29 years old with exactly 3 accidents) = $\dfrac{61}{2000}$

$$= 0.0305 \approx 0.031$$

(ii) The number of drivers 30-50 years of age and having one or more accidents in one year = 125 + 60 + 22 + 18 = 225

So, P(driver is 30-50 years of age and having one or more accidents)

$$= \dfrac{225}{2000} = 0.1125 \approx 0.113$$

(iii) The number of drivers having no accidents in one year = 440 + 505 + 360

$$= 1305$$

Therefore, P(drivers with no accident) $= \dfrac{1305}{2000} = 0.653$

**Example 9 :** Consider the frequency distribution table (Table 14.3, Example 4, Chapter 14), which gives the weights of 38 students of a class.

(i)  Find the probability that the weight of a student in the class lies in the interval 46-50 kg.

(ii) Give two events in this context, one having probability 0 and the other having probability 1.

**Solution :** (i) The total number of students is 38, and the number of students with weight in the interval 46 - 50 kg is 3.

So, P(weight of a student is in the interval 46 - 50 kg) $= \dfrac{3}{38} = 0.079$

(ii) For instance, consider the event that a student weighs 30 kg. Since no student has this weight, the probability of occurrence of this event is 0. Similarly, the probability of a student weighing more than 30 kg is $\dfrac{38}{38} = 1$.

**Example 10 :** Fifty seeds were selected at random from each of 5 bags of seeds, and were kept under standardised conditions favourable to germination. After 20 days, the number of seeds which had germinated in each collection were counted and recorded as follows:

Table 15.11

| Bag | 1 | 2 | 3 | 4 | 5 |
|---|---|---|---|---|---|
| Number of seeds germinated | 40 | 48 | 42 | 39 | 41 |

What is the probability of germination of

(i)   more than 40 seeds in a bag?

(ii)  49 seeds in a bag?

(iii) more that 35 seeds in a bag?

**Solution :** Total number of bags is 5.

(i)   Number of bags in which more than 40 seeds germinated out of 50 seeds is 3.

P(germination of more than 40 seeds in a bag) $= \dfrac{3}{5} = 0.6$

(ii) Number of bags in which 49 seeds germinated = 0.

P(germination of 49 seeds in a bag) = $\dfrac{0}{5}$ = 0.

(iii) Number of bags in which more than 35 seeds germinated = 5.

So, the required probability = $\dfrac{5}{5}$ = 1.

**Remark** : In all the examples above, you would have noted that the probability of an event can be any fraction from 0 to 1.

## EXERCISE 15.1

1. In a cricket match, a batswoman hits a boundary 6 times out of 30 balls she plays. Find the probability that she did not hit a boundary.

2. 1500 families with 2 children were selected randomly, and the following data were recorded:

| Number of girls in a family | 2 | 1 | 0 |
|---|---|---|---|
| Number of families | 475 | 814 | 211 |

Compute the probability of a family, chosen at random, having

(i) 2 girls          (ii) 1 girl          (iii) No girl

Also check whether the sum of these probabilities is 1.

3. Refer to Example 5, Section 14.4, Chapter 14. Find the probability that a student of the class was born in August.

4. Three coins are tossed simultaneously 200 times with the following frequencies of different outcomes:

| Outcome | 3 heads | 2 heads | 1 head | No head |
|---|---|---|---|---|
| Frequency | 23 | 72 | 77 | 28 |

If the three coins are simultaneously tossed again, compute the probability of 2 heads coming up.

5. An organisation selected 2400 families at random and surveyed them to determine a relationship between income level and the number of vehicles in a family. The

information gathered is listed in the table below:

| Monthly income | Vehicles per family | | | |
|---|---|---|---|---|
| (in ₹) | 0 | 1 | 2 | Above 2 |
| Less than 7000 | 10 | 160 | 25 | 0 |
| 7000 – 10000 | 0 | 305 | 27 | 2 |
| 10000 – 13000 | 1 | 535 | 29 | 1 |
| 13000 – 16000 | 2 | 469 | 59 | 25 |
| 16000 or more | 1 | 579 | 82 | 88 |

Suppose a family is chosen. Find the probability that the family chosen is

(i)    earning ₹ 10000 – 13000 per month and owning exactly 2 vehicles.

(ii)   earning ₹ 16000 or more per month and owning exactly 1 vehicle.

(iii)  earning less than ₹ 7000 per month and does not own any  vehicle.

(iv)   earning ₹ 13000 – 16000 per month and owning more than 2  vehicles.

(v)    owning not more than 1 vehicle.

**6.** Refer to Table 14.7, Chapter 14.

(i)    Find the probability that a student obtained less than 20% in the mathematics test.

(ii)   Find the probability that a student obtained marks 60 or above.

**7.** To know the opinion of the students about the subject *statistics*, a survey of 200 students was conducted. The data is recorded in the following table.

| Opinion | Number of students |
|---|---|
| like | 135 |
| dislike | 65 |

Find the probability that a student chosen at random

(i)    likes statistics,                          (ii)  does not like it.

**8.** Refer to Q.2, Exercise 14.2. What is the empirical probability that an engineer lives:

(i)    less than 7 km from her place of work?

(ii)   more than or equal to 7 km from her place of work?

(iii)  within $\dfrac{1}{2}$ km from her place of work?

9. **Activity :** Note the frequency of two-wheelers, three-wheelers and four-wheelers going past during a time interval, in front of your school gate. Find the probability that any one vehicle out of the total vehicles you have observed is a two-wheeler.

10. **Activity :** Ask all the students in your class to write a 3-digit number. Choose any student from the room at random. What is the probability that the number written by her/him is divisible by 3? Remember that a number is divisible by 3, if the sum of its digits is divisible by 3.

11. Eleven bags of wheat flour, each marked 5 kg, actually contained the following weights of flour (in kg):

    4.97   5.05   5.08   5.03   5.00   5.06   5.08   4.98   5.04   5.07   5.00

    Find the probability that any of these bags chosen at random contains more than 5 kg of flour.

12. In Q.5, Exercise 14.2, you were asked to prepare a frequency distribution table, regarding the concentration of sulphur dioxide in the air in parts per million of a certain city for 30 days. Using this table, find the probability of the concentration of sulphur dioxide in the interval 0.12 - 0.16 on any of these days.

13. In Q.1, Exercise 14.2, you were asked to prepare a frequency distribution table regarding the blood groups of 30 students of a class. Use this table to determine the probability that a student of this class, selected at random, has blood group AB.

## 15.3 Summary

In this chapter, you have studied the following points:

1. An event for an experiment is the collection of some outcomes of the experiment.

2. The empirical (or experimental) probability P(E) of an event E is given by

$$P(E) = \frac{\text{Number of trials in which E has happened}}{\text{Total number of trials}}$$

3. The Probability of an event lies between 0 and 1 (0 and 1 inclusive).

# PROOFS IN MATHEMATICS

## A1.1 Introduction

Suppose your family owns a plot of land and there is no fencing around it. Your neighbour decides one day to fence off his land. After he has fenced his land, you discover that a part of your family's land has been enclosed by his fence. How will you prove to your neighbour that he has tried to encroach on your land? Your first step may be to seek the help of the village elders to sort out the difference in boundaries. But, suppose opinion 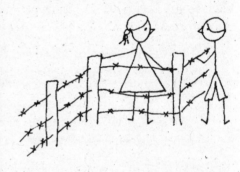 is divided among the elders. Some feel you are right and others feel your neighbour is right. What can you do? Your only option is to find a way of establishing your claim for the boundaries of your land that is acceptable to all. For example, a government approved survey map of your village can be used, if necessary in a court of law, to prove (claim) that you are correct and your neighbour is wrong.

Let us look at another situation. Suppose your mother has paid the electricity bill of your house for the month of August, 2005. The bill for September, 2005, however, claims that the bill for August has not been paid. How will you disprove the claim made by the electricity department? You will have to produce a receipt proving that your August bill has been paid.

You have just seen some examples that show that in our daily life we are often called upon to prove that a certain statement or claim is true or false. However, we also accept many statements without bothering to prove them. But, in mathematics we only accept a statement as true or false (except for some axioms) if it has been proved to be so, according to the logic of mathematics.

In fact, proofs in mathematics have been in existence for thousands of years, and they are central to any branch of mathematics. The first known proof is believed to have been given by the Greek philosopher and mathematician Thales. While mathematics was central to many ancient civilisations like Mesopotamia, Egypt, China and India, there is no clear evidence that they used proofs the way we do today.

In this chapter, we will look at what a statement is, what kind of reasoning is involved in mathematics, and what a mathematical proof consists of.

## A1.2 Mathematically Acceptable Statements

In this section, we shall try to explain the meaning of a mathematically acceptable statement. A 'statement' is a sentence which is not an order or an exclamatory sentence. And, of course, a statement is not a question! For example,

"What is the colour of your hair?" is not a statement, it is a question.

"Please go and bring me some water." is a request or an order, not a statement.

"What a marvellous sunset!" is an exclamatory remark, not a statement.

However, "The colour of your hair is black" is a statement.

In general, statements can be one of the following:

• *always true*

• *always false*

• *ambiguous*

The word 'ambiguous' needs some explanation. There are two situations which make a statement ambiguous. The first situation is when we cannot decide if the statement is always true or always false. For example, "Tomorrow is Thursday" is ambiguous, since enough of a context is not given to us to decide if the statement is true or false.

The second situation leading to ambiguity is when the statement is subjective, that is, it is true for some people and not true for others. For example, "Dogs are intelligent" is ambiguous because some people believe this is true and others do not.

**Example 1 :** State whether the following statements are always true, always false or ambiguous. Justify your answers.

(i)     There are 8 days in a week.

(ii)    It is raining here.

(iii)   The sun sets in the west.

(iv)   Gauri is a kind girl.

(v)    The product of two odd integers is even.

(vi)   The product of two even natural numbers is even.

**Solution :**

(i)    This statement is always false, since there are 7 days in a week.

(ii)   This statement is ambiguous, since it is not clear where 'here' is.

(iii)  This statement is always true. The sun sets in the west no matter where we live.

(iv)   This statement is ambiguous, since it is subjective–Gauri may be kind to some and not to others.

(v)    This statement is always false. The product of two odd integers is always odd.

(vi)   This statement is always true. However, to justify that it is true we need to do some work. It will be proved in Section A1.4.

As mentioned before, in our daily life, we are not so careful about the validity of statements. For example, suppose your friend tells you that in July it rains everyday in Manantavadi, Kerala. In all probability, you will believe her, even though it may not have rained for a day or two in July. Unless you are a lawyer, you will not argue with her!

As another example, consider statements we often make to each other like "it is very hot today". We easily accept such statements because we know the context even though these statements are ambiguous. 'It is very hot today' can mean different things to different people because what is very hot for a person from Kumaon may not be hot for a person from Chennai.

But a mathematical statement cannot be ambiguous. *In mathematics, a statement is only acceptable or valid, if it is either true or false.* We say that a statement is true, if it is always true otherwise it is called a false statement.

For example, $5 + 2 = 7$ is always true, so '$5 + 2 = 7$' is a true statement and $5 + 3 = 7$ is a false statement.

**Example 2 :** State whether the following statements are true or false:

(i) The sum of the interior angles of a triangle is 180°.

(ii) Every odd number greater than 1 is prime.

(iii) For any real number $x$, $4x + x = 5x$.

(iv) For every real number $x$, $2x > x$.

(v) For every real number $x$, $x^2 \geq x$.

(vi) If a quadrilateral has all its sides equal, then it is a square.

**Solution :**

(i) This statement is true. You have already proved this in Chapter 6.

(ii) This statement is false; for example, 9 is not a prime number.

(iii) This statement is true.

(iv) This statement is false; for example, $2 \times (-1) = -2$, and $-2$ is not greater than $-1$.

(v) This statement is false; for example, $\left(\dfrac{1}{2}\right)^2 = \dfrac{1}{4}$, and $\dfrac{1}{4}$ is not greater than $\dfrac{1}{2}$.

(vi) This statement is false, since a rhombus has equal sides but need not be a square.

You might have noticed that to establish that a statement is not true according to mathematics, all we need to do is to find one case or example where it breaks down. So in (ii), since 9 is not a prime, it is an example that shows that the statement "Every odd number greater than 1 is prime" is not true. Such an example, that counters a statement, is called a *counter-example*. We shall discuss counter-examples in greater detail in Section A1.5.

You might have also noticed that while Statements (iv), (v) and (vi) are false, they can be restated with some conditions in order to make them true.

**Example 3 :** Restate the following statements with appropriate conditions, so that they become true statements.

(i) For every real number $x$, $2x > x$.

(ii) For every real number $x$, $x^2 \geq x$.

(iii) If you divide a number by itself, you will always get 1.

(iv) The angle subtended by a chord of a circle at a point on the circle is 90°.

(v) If a quadrilateral has all its sides equal, then it is a square.

**Solution :**

(i)  If $x > 0$, then $2x > x$.

(ii) If $x \le 0$ or $x \ge 1$, then $x^2 \ge x$.

(iii) If you divide a number except zero by itself, you will always get 1.

(iv) The angle subtended by a diameter of a circle at a point on the circle is 90°.

(v) If a quadrilateral has all its sides and interior angles equal, then it is a square.

## EXERCISE A1.1

1.  State whether the following statements are always true, always false or ambiguous. Justify your answers.

    (i)   There are 13 months in a year.

    (ii)  Diwali falls on a Friday.

    (iii) The temperature in Magadi is $26^0$ C.

    (iv)  The earth has one moon.

    (v)   Dogs can fly.

    (vi)  February has only 28 days.

2.  State whether the following statements are true or false. Give reasons for your answers.

    (i)   The sum of the interior angles of a quadrilateral is 350°.

    (ii)  For any real number $x$, $x^2 \ge 0$.

    (iii) A rhombus is a parallelogram.

    (iv)  The sum of two even numbers is even.

    (v)   The sum of two odd numbers is odd.

3.  Restate the following statements with appropriate conditions, so that they become true statements.

    (i)   All prime numbers are odd.

    (ii)  Two times a real number is always even.

    (iii) For any $x$, $3x +1 > 4$.

    (iv)  For any $x$, $x^3 \ge 0$.

    (v)   In every triangle, a median is also an angle bisector.

## A1.3 Deductive Reasoning

The main logical tool used in establishing the truth of an **unambiguous** statement is *deductive reasoning*. To understand what deductive reasoning is all about, let us begin with a puzzle for you to solve.

You are given four cards. Each card has a number printed on one side and a letter on the other side.

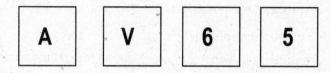

Suppose you are told that these cards follow the rule:

"If a card has an even number on one side, then it has a vowel on the other side."

What is the **smallest number** of cards you need to turn over to check if the rule is true?

Of course, you have the option of turning over all the cards and checking. But can you manage with turning over a fewer number of cards?

Notice that the statement mentions that a card with an even number on one side has a vowel on the other. It does not state that a card with a vowel on one side must have an even number on the other side. That may or may not be so. The rule also does not state that a card with an odd number on one side must have a consonant on the other side. It may or may not.

So, do we need to turn over 'A'? No! Whether there is an even number or an odd number on the other side, the rule still holds.

What about '5'? Again we do not need to turn it over, because whether there is a vowel or a consonant on the other side, the rule still holds.

But you do need to turn over V and 6. If V has an even number on the other side, then the rule has been broken. Similarly, if 6 has a consonant on the other side, then the rule has been broken.

The kind of reasoning we have used to solve this puzzle is called **deductive reasoning**. It is called 'deductive' because we arrive at (i.e., deduce or infer) a result or a statement from a previously established statement using logic. For example, in the puzzle above, by a series of logical arguments we deduced that we need to turn over only V and 6.

Deductive reasoning also helps us to conclude that a particular statement is true, because it is a special case of a more general statement that is known to be true. For example, once we prove that the product of two odd numbers is always odd, we can immediately conclude (without computation) that $70001 \times 134563$ is odd simply because 70001 and 134563 are odd.

Deductive reasoning has been a part of human thinking for centuries, and is used all the time in our daily life. For example, suppose the statements "The flower Solaris blooms, only if the maximum temperature is above 28° C on the previous day" and "Solaris bloomed in Imaginary Valley on 15th September, 2005" are true. Then using deductive reasoning, we can conclude that the maximum temperature in Imaginary Valley on 14th September, 2005 was more than 28° C.

Unfortunately we do not always use correct reasoning in our daily life! We often come to many conclusions based on faulty reasoning. For example, if your friend does not smile at you one day, then you may conclude that she is angry with you. While it may be true that "if she is angry with me, she will not smile at me", it may also be true that "if she has a bad headache, she will not smile at me". Why don't you examine some conclusions that you have arrived at in your day-to-day existence, and see if they are based on valid or faulty reasoning?

## EXERCISE A1.2

1. Use deductive reasoning to answer the following:

   (i) Humans are mammals. All mammals are vertebrates. Based on these two statements, what can you conclude about humans?

   (ii) Anthony is a barber. Dinesh had his hair cut. Can you conclude that Antony cut Dinesh's hair?

   (iii) Martians have red tongues. Gulag is a Martian. Based on these two statements, what can you conclude about Gulag?

   (iv) If it rains for more than four hours on a particular day, the gutters will have to be cleaned the next day. It has rained for 6 hours today. What can we conclude about the condition of the gutters tomorrow?

   (v) What is the fallacy in the cow's reasoning in the cartoon below?

All dogs have tails. I have a tail. Therefore I am a dog.

**2.** Once again you are given four cards. Each card has a number printed on one side and a letter on the other side. Which are the only two cards you need to turn over to check whether the following rule holds?

"If a card has a consonant on one side, then it has an odd number on the other side."

| B | 3 | U | 8 |

## A1.4 Theorems, Conjectures and Axioms

So far we have discussed statements and how to check their validity. In this section, you will study how to distinguish between the three different kinds of statements mathematics is built up from, namely, a theorem, a conjecture and an axiom.

You have already come across many theorems before. So, what is a theorem? A mathematical statement whose truth has been established (proved) is called a *theorem*. For example, the following statements are theorems, as you will see in Section A1.5.

**Theorem A1.1 :** *The sum of the interior angles of a triangle is* 180°.

**Theorem A1.2 :** *The product of two even natural numbers is even.*

**Theorem A1.3 :** *The product of any three consecutive even natural numbers is divisible by* 16.

A *conjecture* is a statement which we believe is true, based on our mathematical understanding and experience, that is, our mathematical intuition. The conjecture may turn out to be true or false. If we can prove it, then it becomes a theorem. Mathematicians often come up with conjectures by looking for patterns and making intelligent mathematical guesses. Let us look at some patterns and see what kind of intelligent guesses we can make.

**Example 4 :** Take any three consecutive even numbers and add them, say,

$2 + 4 + 6 = 12, 4 + 6 + 8 = 18, 6 + 8 + 10 = 24, 8 + 10 + 12 = 30, 20 + 22 + 24 = 66$.

Is there any pattern you can guess in these sums? What can you conjecture about them?

**Solution :** One conjecture could be :

(i) the sum of three consecutive even numbers is even.

Another could be :

(ii) the sum of three consecutive even numbers is divisible by 6.

**Example 5 :** Consider the following pattern of numbers called the Pascal's Triangle:

| Line | | | | | | | | Sum of numbers |
|------|---|---|----|----|---|---|---|----------------|
| 1 | | | | 1 | | | | 1 |
| 2 | | | 1 | | 1 | | | 2 |
| 3 | | 1 | | 2 | | 1 | | 4 |
| 4 | 1 | | 3 | | 3 | | 1 | 8 |
| 5 | 1 | 4 | | 6 | | 4 | 1 | 16 |
| 6 | 1 | 5 | 10 | | 10 | 5 | 1 | 32 |
| 7 | | : | | | : | | | : |
| 8 | | : | | | : | | | : |

What can you conjecture about the sum of the numbers in Lines 7 and 8? What about the sum of the numbers in Line 21? Do you see a pattern? Make a guess about a formula for the sum of the numbers in line $n$.

**Solution :** Sum of the numbers in Line 7 = $2 \times 32 = 64 = 2^6$

Sum of the numbers in Line 8 = $2 \times 64 = 128 = 2^7$

Sum of the numbers in Line 21 = $2^{20}$

Sum of the numbers in Line $n$ = $2^{n-1}$

**Example 6 :** Consider the so-called triangular numbers $T_n$:

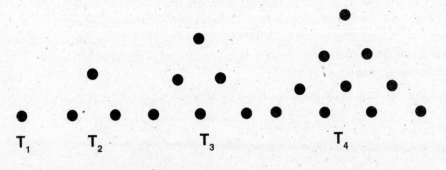

Fig. A1.1

The dots here are arranged in such a way that they form a triangle. Here $T_1 = 1$, $T_2 = 3$, $T_3 = 6$, $T_4 = 10$, and so on. Can you guess what $T_5$ is? What about $T_6$? What about $T_n$?

Make a conjecture about $T_n$.

It might help if you redraw them in the following way.

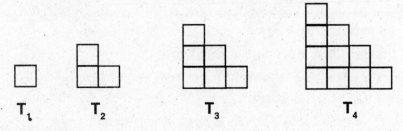

$$T_1 \qquad\qquad T_2 \qquad\qquad\qquad T_3 \qquad\qquad\qquad\qquad T_4$$

**Fig. A1.2**

**Solution :** $T_5 = 1 + 2 + 3 + 4 + 5 = 15 = \dfrac{5 \times 6}{2}$

$$T_6 = 1 + 2 + 3 + 4 + 5 + 6 = 21 = \dfrac{6 \times 7}{2}$$

$$T_n = \dfrac{n \times (n + 1)}{2}$$

A favourite example of a conjecture that has been open (that is, it has not been proved to be true or false) is the Goldbach conjecture named after the mathematician Christian Goldbach (1690 – 1764). This conjecture states that "*every even integer greater than 4 can be expressed as the sum of two odd primes*." Perhaps you will prove that this result is either true or false, and will become famous!

You might have wondered – do we need to prove everything we encounter in mathematics, and if not, why not?

Why do I have to prove everything I say!

The fact is that every area in mathematics is based on some statements which are assumed to be true and are not proved. These are 'self-evident truths' which we take to be true without proof. These statements are called *axioms*. In Chapter 5, you would have studied the axioms and postulates of Euclid. (We do not distinguish between axioms and postulates these days.)

For example, the first postulate of Euclid states:

*A straight line may be drawn from any point to any other point.*

And the third postulate states:

*A circle may be drawn with any centre and any radius.*

These statements appear to be perfectly true and Euclid assumed them to be true. Why? This is because we cannot prove everything and we need to start somewhere. We need some statements which we accept as true and then we can build up our knowledge using the rules of logic based on these axioms.

You might then wonder why we don't just accept all statements to be true when they appear self-evident. There are many reasons for this. Very often our intuition can be wrong, pictures or patterns can deceive and the only way to be sure that something is true is to prove it. For example, many of us believe that if a number is multiplied by another, the result will be larger than both the numbers. But we know that this is not always true: for example, $5 \times 0.2 = 1$, which is less than 5.

Also, look at the Fig. A1.3. Which line segment is longer, AB or CD?

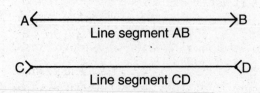

Fig. A1.3

It turns out that both are of exactly the same length, even though AB appears shorter!

You might wonder then, about the validity of axioms. Axioms have been chosen based on our intuition and what appears to be self-evident. Therefore, we expect them to be true. However, it is possible that later on we discover that a particular axiom is not true. What is a safeguard against this possibility? We take the following steps:

(i)  Keep the axioms to the bare minimum. For instance, based on only axioms and five postulates of Euclid, we can derive hundreds of theorems.

(ii) Make sure the axioms are consistent.

We say a collection of axioms is *inconsistent,* if we can use one axiom to show that another axiom is not true. For example, consider the following two statements. We will show that they are inconsistent.

Statement1: No whole number is equal to its successor.

Statement 2: A whole number divided by zero is a whole number.

(Remember, **division by zero is not defined**. But just for the moment, we assume that it is possible, and see what happens.)

From Statement 2, we get $\dfrac{1}{0} = a$, where $a$ is some whole number. This implies that, $1 = 0$. But this disproves Statement 1, which states that no whole number is equal to its successor.

(iii) A false axiom will, sooner or later, result in a contradiction. We say that *there is a contradiction, when we find a statement such that, both the statement and its negation are true.* For example, consider Statement 1 and Statement 2 above once again.

From Statement 1, we can derive the result that $2 \neq 1$.

Now look at $x^2 - x^2$. We will factorise it in two different ways as follows:

(i)  $x^2 - x^2 = x(x - x)$ and

(ii) $x^2 - x^2 = (x + x)(x - x)$

So, $x(x - x) = (x + x)(x - x)$.

From Statement 2, we can cancel $(x - x)$ from both sides.

We get $x = 2x$, which in turn implies $2 = 1$.

So we have both the statement $2 \neq 1$ and its negation, $2 = 1$, true. This is a contradiction. The contradiction arose because of the false axiom, that a whole number divided by zero is a whole number.

So, the statements we choose as axioms require a lot of thought and insight. We must make sure they do not lead to inconsistencies or logical contradictions. Moreover, the choice of axioms themselves, sometimes leads us to new discoveries. From Chapter 5, you are familiar with Euclid's fifth postulate and the discoveries of non-Euclidean geometries. You saw that mathematicians believed that the fifth postulate need not be a postulate and is actually a theorem that can be proved using just the first four postulates. Amazingly these attempts led to the discovery of non-Euclidean geometries.

We end the section by recalling the differences between an axiom, a theorem and a conjecture. An **axiom** is a mathematical statement which is assumed to be true without proof; a **conjecture** is a mathematical statement whose truth or falsity is yet to be established; and a **theorem** is a mathematical statement whose truth has been logically established.

## EXERCISE A1.3

1. Take any three consecutive even numbers and find their product; for example, $2 \times 4 \times 6 = 48$, $4 \times 6 \times 8 = 192$, and so on. Make three conjectures about these products.

2. Go back to Pascal's triangle.

   Line 1 : 1 = $11^0$

   Line 2 : 1  1 = $11^1$

   Line 3 : 1  2  1 = $11^2$

   Make a conjecture about Line 4 and Line 5. Does your conjecture hold? Does your conjecture hold for Line 6 too?

3. Let us look at the triangular numbers (see Fig.A1.2) again. Add two consecutive triangular numbers. For example, $T_1 + T_2 = 4$, $T_2 + T_3 = 9$, $T_3 + T_4 = 16$.

   What about $T_4 + T_5$? Make a conjecture about $T_{n-1} + T_n$.

4. Look at the following pattern:

   $$1^2 = 1$$
   $$11^2 = 121$$
   $$111^2 = 12321$$
   $$1111^2 = 1234321$$
   $$11111^2 = 123454321$$

   Make a conjecture about each of the following:

   $$111111^2 =$$
   $$1111111^2 =$$

   Check if your conjecture is true.

5. List five axioms (postulates) used in this book.

## A1.5 What is a Mathematical Proof?

Let us now look at various aspects of proofs. We start with understanding the difference between verification and proof. Before you studied proofs in mathematics, you were mainly asked to verify statements.

For example, you might have been asked to verify with examples that "the product of two even numbers is even". So you might have picked up two random even numbers, say 24 and 2006, and checked that $24 \times 2006 = 48144$ is even. You might have done so for many more examples.

Also, you might have been asked as an activity to draw several triangles in the class and compute the sum of their interior angles. Apart from errors due to measurement, you would have found that the interior angles of a triangle add up to 180°.

What is the flaw in this method? There are several problems with the process of verification. While it may help you to make a statement you believe is true, you cannot be *sure* that it is true in *all* cases. For example, the multiplication of several pairs of even numbers may lead us to guess that the product of two even numbers is even. However, it does not ensure that the product of all pairs of even numbers is even. You cannot physically check the products of all possible pairs of even numbers. If you did, then like the girl in the cartoon, you will be calculating the products of even numbers for the rest of your life. Similarly, there may be some triangles which you have not yet drawn whose interior angles do not add up to 180°. We cannot measure the interior angles of all possible triangles.

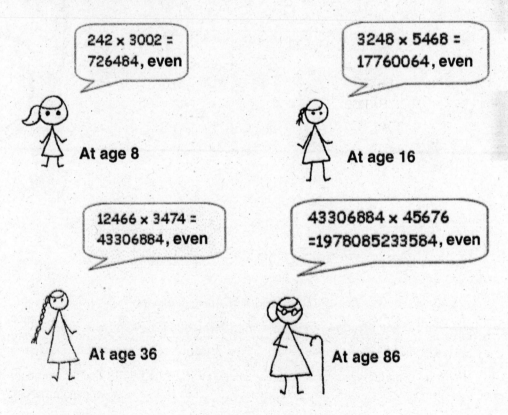

Moreover, verification can often be misleading. For example, we might be tempted to conclude from Pascal's triangle (Q.2 of Exercise A1.3), based on earlier verifications, that $11^5 = 15101051$. But in fact $11^5 = 161051$.

So, you need another approach that does not depend upon verification for some cases only. There is another approach, namely 'proving a statement'. A process which can establish the truth of a mathematical statement based purely on logical arguments is called a *mathematical proof*.

In Example 2 of Section A1.2, you saw that to establish that a mathematical statement is false, it is enough to produce a single counter-example. So while it is not enough to establish the validity of a mathematical statement by checking or verifying it for thousands of cases, it is enough to produce one counter-example to *disprove* a statement (i.e., to show that something is false). This point is worth emphasising.

*To show that a mathematical statement is false, it is enough to find a single counter-example.*

So, $7 + 5 = 12$ is a counter-example to the statement that the sum of two odd numbers is odd.

Let us now look at the list of basic ingredients in a proof:

(i)   To prove a theorem, we should have a rough idea as to how to proceed.

(ii)  The information already given to us in a theorem (i.e., the hypothesis) has to be clearly understood and used.

For example, in Theorem A1.2, which states that the product of two even numbers is even, we are given two even natural numbers. So, we should use their properties. In the Factor Theorem (in Chapter 2), you are given a polynomial $p(x)$ and are told that $p(a) = 0$. You have to use this to show that $(x - a)$ is a factor of $p(x)$. Similarly, for the converse of the Factor Theorem, you are given that $(x - a)$ is a factor of $p(x)$, and you have to use this hypothesis to prove that $p(a) = 0$.

You can also use constructions during the process of proving a theorem. For example, to prove that the sum of the angles of a triangle is 180°, we draw a line parallel to one of the sides through the vertex opposite to the side, and use properties of parallel lines.

(iii) A proof is made up of a successive sequence of mathematical statements. Each statement in a proof is logically deduced from a previous statement in the proof, or from a theorem proved earlier, or an axiom, or our hypothesis.

(iv) The conclusion of a sequence of mathematically true statements laid out in a logically correct order should be what we wanted to prove, that is, what the theorem claims.

To understand these ingredients, we will analyse Theorem A1.1 and its proof. You have already studied this theorem in Chapter 6. But first, a few comments on proofs in geometry. We often resort to diagrams to help us prove theorems, and this is very important. However, each statement in the proof has to be established **using only logic**. Very often, we hear students make statements like "Those two angles are equal because in the drawing they look equal" or "that angle must be 90°, because the two lines look as if they are perpendicular to each other". Beware of being deceived by what you see (remember Fig A1.3)! .

So now let us go to Theorem A1.1.

**Theorem A1.1** : *The sum of the interior angles of a triangle is* 180°.

**Proof** : Consider a triangle ABC (see Fig. A1.4).

We have to prove that $\angle ABC + \angle BCA + \angle CAB = 180°$                     (1)

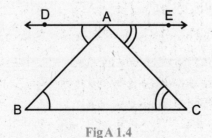

Fig A 1.4

Construct a line DE parallel to BC passing through A. (2)

DE is parallel to BC and AB is a transversal.

So, $\angle$ DAB and $\angle$ ABC are alternate angles. Therefore, by Theorem 6.2, Chapter 6, they are equal, i.e. $\angle$ DAB = $\angle$ ABC (3)

Similarly, $\angle$ CAE = $\angle$ ACB (4)

Therefore, $\angle$ ABC + $\angle$ BAC+ $\angle$ ACB = $\angle$ DAB +$\angle$ BAC + $\angle$ CAE (5)

But $\angle$ DAB +$\angle$ BAC + $\angle$ CAE = 180°, since they form a straight angle. (6)

Hence, $\angle$ ABC + $\angle$ BAC+ $\angle$ ACB = 180°. ■ (7)

Now, we comment on each step of the proof.

**Step 1 :** Our theorem is concerned with a property of triangles, so we begin with a triangle.

**Step 2 :** This is the key idea – the intuitive leap or understanding of how to proceed so as to be able to prove the theorem. Very often geometric proofs require a construction.

**Steps 3 and 4 :** Here we conclude that $\angle$ DAE = $\angle$ ABC and $\angle$ CAE = $\angle$ ACB, by using the fact that DE is parallel to BC (our construction), and the previously proved Theorem 6.2, which states that if two parallel lines are intersected by a transversal, then the alternate angles are equal.

**Step 5 :** Here we use Euclid's axiom (see Chapter 5) which states that: "If equals are added to equals, the wholes are equal" to deduce

$\angle$ ABC + $\angle$ BAC+ $\angle$ ACB = $\angle$ DAB +$\angle$ BAC + $\angle$ CAE.

That is, the sum of the interior angles of the triangle are equal to the sum of the angles on a straight line.

**Step 6 :** Here we use the Linear pair axiom of Chapter 6, which states that the angles on a straight line add up to 180°, to show that $\angle$ DAB +$\angle$ BAC + $\angle$ CAE = 180°.

**Step 7 :** We use Euclid's axiom which states that "things which are equal to the same thing are equal to each other" to conclude that $\angle$ ABC + $\angle$ BAC + $\angle$ ACB = $\angle$ DAB +$\angle$ BAC + $\angle$ CAE = 180°. Notice that Step 7 is the claim made in the theorem we set out to prove.

We now prove Theorems A1.2 and A1.3 without analysing them.

**Theorem A1.2 :** *The product of two even natural numbers is even.*

**Proof :** Let $x$ and $y$ be any two even natural numbers.

We want to prove that $xy$ is even.

Since $x$ and $y$ are even, they are divisible by 2 and can be expressed in the form $x = 2m$, for some natural number $m$ and $y = 2n$, for some natural number $n$.

Then $xy = 4\ mn$. Since $4\ mn$ is divisible by 2, so is $xy$.

Therefore, $xy$ is even. ■

**Theorem A1.3** : *The product of any three consecutive even natural numbers is divisible by* 16.

**Proof** : Any three consecutive even numbers will be of the form $2n$, $2n + 2$ and $2n + 4$, for some natural number $n$. We need to prove that their product $2n(2n + 2)(2n + 4)$ is divisible by 16.

Now, $2n(2n + 2)(2n + 4) = 2n \times 2(n + 1) \times 2(n + 2)$

$= 2 \times 2 \times 2n(n + 1)(n + 2) = 8n(n + 1)(n + 2)$.

Now we have two cases. Either $n$ is even or odd. Let us examine each case.

Suppose $n$ is even : Then we can write $n = 2m$, for some natural number $m$.

And, then $2n(2n + 2)(2n + 4) = 8n(n + 1)(n + 2) = 16m(2m + 1)(2m + 2)$.

Therefore, $2n(2n + 2)(2n + 4)$ is divisible by 16.

Next, suppose $n$ is odd. Then $n + 1$ is even and we can write $n + 1 = 2r$, for some natural number $r$.

We then have :     $2n(2n + 2)(2n + 4) = 8n(n + 1)(n + 2)$

$$= 8(2r - 1) \times 2r \times (2r + 1)$$

$$= 16r(2r - 1)(2r + 1)$$

Therefore, $2n(2n + 2)(2n + 4)$ is divisible by 16.

So, in both cases we have shown that the product of any three consecutive even numbers is divisible by 16. ■

We conclude this chapter with a few remarks on the difference between how mathematicians discover results and how formal rigorous proofs are written down. As mentioned above, each proof has a key intuitive idea (sometimes more than one). Intuition is central to a mathematician's way of thinking and discovering results. Very often the proof of a theorem comes to a mathematician all jumbled up. A mathematician will often experiment with several routes of thought, and logic, and examples, before she/he can hit upon the correct solution or proof. It is only after the creative phase subsides that all the arguments are gathered together to form a proper proof.

It is worth mentioning here that the great Indian mathematician Srinivasa Ramanujan used very high levels of intuition to arrive at many of his statements, which he claimed were true. Many of these have turned out be true and are well known theorems. However, even to this day mathematicians all over the world are struggling to prove (or disprove) some of his claims (conjectures).

**Srinivasa Ramanujan (1887–1920)**
Fig. A1.5

## EXERCISE A1.4

1. Find counter-examples to disprove the following statements:

   (i) If the corresponding angles in two triangles are equal, then the triangles are congruent.

   (ii) A quadrilateral with all sides equal is a square.

   (iii) A quadrilateral with all angles equal is a square.

   (iv) For integers $a$ and $b$, $\sqrt{a^2 + b^2} = a + b$

   (v) $2n^2 + 11$ is a prime for all whole numbers $n$.

   (vi) $n^2 - n + 41$ is a prime for all positive integers $n$.

2. Take your favourite proof and analyse it step-by-step along the lines discussed in Section A1.5 (what is given, what has been proved, what theorems and axioms have been used, and so on).

3. Prove that the sum of two odd numbers is even.

4. Prove that the product of two odd numbers is odd.

5. Prove that the sum of three consecutive even numbers is divisible by 6.

6. Prove that infinitely many points lie on the line whose equation is $y = 2x$.

   (*Hint* : Consider the point $(n, 2n)$ for any integer $n$.)

7. You must have had a friend who must have told you to think of a number and do various things to it, and then without knowing your original number, telling you what number you ended up with. Here are two examples. Examine why they work.

   (i) Choose a number. Double it. Add nine. Add your original number. Divide by three. Add four. Subtract your original number. Your result is seven.

   (ii) Write down any three-digit number (for example, 425). Make a six-digit number by repeating these digits in the same order (425425). Your new number is divisible by 7, 11 and 13.

## A1.6 Summary

In this Appendix, you have studied the following points:

1. In mathematics, a statement is only acceptable if it is either always true or always false.

2. To show that a mathematical statement is false, it is enough to find a single counter-example.

3. Axioms are statements which are assumed to be true without proof.

4. A conjecture is a statement we believe is true based on our mathematical intuition, but which we are yet to prove.

5. A mathematical statement whose truth has been established (or proved) is called a theorem.

6. The main logical tool in proving mathematical statements is deductive reasoning.

7. A proof is made up of a successive sequence of mathematical statements. Each statement in a proof is logically deduced from a previouly known statement, or from a theorem proved earlier, or an axiom, or the hypothesis.

# INTRODUCTION TO MATHEMATICAL MODELLING

## A2.1 Introduction

Right from your earlier classes, you have been solving problems related to the real-world around you. For example, you have solved problems in simple interest using the formula for finding it. The formula (or equation) is a relation between the interest and the other three quantities that are related to it, the principal, the rate of interest and the period. This formula is an example of a **mathematical model**. A **mathematical model** is a mathematical relation that describes some real-life situation.

Mathematical models are used to solve many real-life situations like:

- launching a satellite.
- predicting the arrival of the monsoon.
- controlling pollution due to vehicles.
- reducing traffic jams in big cities.

In this chapter, we will introduce you to the process of constructing mathematical models, which is called **mathematical modelling**. In mathematical modelling, we take a real-world problem and write it as an equivalent mathematical problem. We then solve the mathematical problem, and interpret its solution in terms of the real-world problem. After this we see to what extent the solution is valid in the context of the real-world problem. So, the *stages* involved in mathematical modelling are formulation, solution, interpretation and validation.

We will start by looking at the process you undertake when solving word problems, in Section A2.2. Here, we will discuss some word problems that are similar to the ones you have solved in your earlier classes. We will see later that the steps that are used for solving word problems are some of those used in mathematical modelling also.

In the next section, that is Section A2.3, we will discuss some simple models.

In Section A2.4, we will discuss the overall process of modelling, its advantages and some of its limitations.

## A2.2 Review of Word Problems

In this section, we will discuss some word problems that are similar to the ones that you have solved in your earlier classes. Let us start with a problem on direct variation.

**Example 1 :** I travelled 432 kilometres on 48 litres of petrol in my car. I have to go by my car to a place which is 180 km away. How much petrol do I need?

**Solution :** We will list the steps involved in solving the problem.

**Step 1 : Formulation :** You know that farther we travel, the more petrol we require, that is, the amount of petrol we need varies directly with the distance we travel.

Petrol needed for travelling 432 km = 48 litres

Petrol needed for travelling 180 km = ?

**Mathematical Description :** Let

$$x = \text{distance I travel}$$

$$y = \text{petrol I need}$$

$y$ varies directly with $x$.

So,                            $y = kx$, where $k$ is a constant.

I can travel 432 kilometres with 48 litres of petrol.

So,                            $y = 48, x = 432.$

Therefore,                     $k = \dfrac{y}{x} = \dfrac{48}{432} = \dfrac{1}{9}.$

Since                          $y = kx,$

therefore,                     $y = \dfrac{1}{9}x$                                    (1)

Equation or Formula (1) describes the relationship between the petrol needed and distance travelled.

**Step 2 : Solution :** We want to find the petrol we need to travel 180 kilometres; so, we have to find the value of $y$ when $x = 180$. Putting $x = 180$ in (1), we have

$$y = \frac{180}{9} = 20.$$

**Step 3 : Interpretation :** Since $y = 20$, we need 20 litres of petrol to travel 180 kilometres.

Did it occur to you that you may not be able to use the formula (1) in all situations? For example, suppose the 432 kilometres route is through mountains and the 180 kilometres route is through flat plains. The car will use up petrol at a faster rate in the first route, so we cannot use the same rate for the 180 kilometres route, where the petrol will be used up at a slower rate. So the formula works if all such conditions that affect the rate at which petrol is used are the same in both the trips. Or, if there is a difference in conditions, the effect of the difference on the amount of petrol needed for the car should be very small. The petrol used will vary directly with the distance travelled only in such a situation. We assumed this while solving the problem.

**Example 2 :** Suppose Sudhir has invested ₹ 15,000 at 8% simple interest per year. With the return from the investment, he wants to buy a washing machine that costs ₹ 19,000. For what period should he invest ₹ 15,000 so that he has enough money to buy a washing machine?

**Solution : Step 1 : Formulation of the problem :** Here, we know the principal and the rate of interest. The interest is the amount Sudhir needs in addition to 15,000 to buy the washing machine. We have to find the number of years.

**Mathematical Description :** The formula for simple interest is $I = \dfrac{Pnr}{100}$,

where                                            P = Principal,

                                                    $n$ = Number of years,

                                            $r$ % = Rate of interest

                                                    I = Interest earned

Here,                              the principal = ₹ 15,000

The money required by Sudhir for buying a washing machine = ₹ 19,000

So, the interest to be earned  = ₹ (19,000 – 15,000)

                                            = ₹ 4,000

The number of years for which ₹ 15,000 is deposited = $n$

The interest on ₹ 15,000 for $n$ years at the rate of 8% = I

Then,                                            $I = \dfrac{15000 \times n \times 8}{100}$

So,                                    $I = 1200n$                                    (1)

gives the relationship between the number of years and interest, if ₹ 15000 is invested at an annual interest rate of 8%.

We have to find the period in which the interest earned is ₹ 4000. Putting I = 4000 in (1), we have

$$4000 = 1200n \qquad (2)$$

**Step 2 : Solution of the problem :** Solving Equation (2), we get

$$n = \frac{4000}{1200} = 3\frac{1}{3}.$$

**Step 3 : Interpretation :** Since $n = 3\frac{1}{3}$ and one third of a year is 4 months, Sudhir can buy a washing machine after 3 years and 4 months.

Can you guess the assumptions that you have to make in the example above? We have to assume that the interest rate remains the same for the period for which we calculate the interest. Otherwise, the formula $I = \frac{Pnr}{100}$ will not be valid. We have also assumed that the price of the washing machine does not increase by the time Sudhir has gathered the money.

**Example 3 :** A motorboat goes upstream on a river and covers the distance between two towns on the riverbank in six hours. It covers this distance downstream in five hours. If the speed of the stream is 2 km/h, find the speed of the boat in still water.

**Solution : Step 1 : Formulation :** We know the speed of the river and the time taken to cover the distance between two places. We have to find the speed of the boat in still water.

**Mathematical Description :** Let us write $x$ for the speed of the boat, $t$ for the time taken and $y$ for the distance travelled. Then

$$y = tx \qquad (1)$$

Let $d$ be the distance between the two places.

While going upstream, the actual speed of the boat

= speed of the boat – speed of the river,

because the boat is travelling against the flow of the river.

So, the speed of the boat upstream = $(x - 2)$ km/h

It takes 6 hours to cover the distance between the towns upstream. So, from (1), we get                                    $d = 6(x - 2)$                                    (2)

When going downstream, the speed of the river has to be *added* to the speed of the boat.

So, the speed of the boat downstream = $(x + 2)$ km/h

The boat takes 5 hours to cover the same distance downstream. So,

$$d = 5(x + 2) \tag{3}$$

From (2) and (3), we have

$$5(x + 2) = 6(x - 2) \tag{4}$$

**Step 2 : Finding the Solution**

Solving for $x$ in Equation (4), we get $x = 22$.

**Step 3 : Interpretation**

Since $x = 22$, therefore the speed of the motorboat in still water is 22 km/h.

In the example above, we know that the speed of the river is not the same everywhere. It flows slowly near the shore and faster at the middle. The boat starts at the shore and moves to the middle of the river. When it is close to the destination, it will slow down and move closer to the shore. So, there is a small difference between the speed of the boat at the middle and the speed at the shore. Since it will be close to the shore for a small amount of time, this difference in speed of the river will affect the speed only for a small period. So, we can ignore this difference in the speed of the river. We can also ignore the small variations in speed of the boat. Also, apart from the speed of the river, the friction between the water and surface of the boat will also affect the actual speed of the boat. We also assume that this effect is very small.

So, we have assumed that

1.  The speed of the river and the boat remains constant all the time.

2.  The effect of friction between the boat and water and the friction due to air is negligible.

We have found the speed of the boat in still water with the *assumptions* (*hypotheses*) above.

*As we have seen in the word problems above, there are* 3 *steps in solving a word problem. These are*

1.  **Formulation :** We analyse the problem and see which factors have a major influence on the solution to the problem. These are the **relevant factors**. In our first example, the relevant factors are the distance travelled and petrol consumed. We ignored the other factors like the nature of the route, driving speed, etc. Otherwise, the problem would have been more difficult to solve. The factors that we ignore are the **irrelevant factors**.

> We then describe the problem mathematically, in the form of one or more mathematical equations.

2. **Solution :** We find the solution of the problem by solving the mathematical equations obtained in Step 1 using some suitable method.

3. **Interpretation :** We see what the solution obtained in Step 2 means in the context of the original word problem.

Here are some exercises for you. You may like to check your understanding of the steps involved in solving word problems by carrying out the three steps above for the following problems.

### EXERCISE A 2.1

In each of the following problems, clearly state what the relevant and irrelevant factors are while going through Steps 1, 2 and 3 given above.

1. Suppose a company needs a computer for some period of time. The company can either hire a computer for ₹ 2,000 per month or buy one for ₹ 25,000. If the company has to use the computer for a long period, the company will pay such a high rent, that buying a computer will be cheaper. On the other hand, if the company has to use the computer for say, just one month, then hiring a computer will be cheaper. Find the number of months beyond which it will be cheaper to buy a computer.

2. Suppose a car starts from a place A and travels at a speed of 40 km/h towards another place B. At the same instance, another car starts from B and travels towards A at a speed of 30 km/h. If the distance between A and B is 100 km, after how much time will the cars meet?

3. The moon is about 3,84,000 km from the earth, and its path around the earth is nearly circular. Find the speed at which it orbits the earth, assuming that it orbits the earth in 24 hours. (Use $\pi = 3.14$)

4. A family pays ₹ 1000 for electricity on an average in those months in which it does not use a water heater. In the months in which it uses a water heater, the average electricity bill is ₹ 1240. The cost of using the water heater is ₹ 8.00 per hour. Find the average number of hours the water heater is used in a day.

## A2.3 Some Mathematical Models

So far, nothing was new in our discussion. In this section, we are going to add another step to the three steps that we have discussed earlier. This step is called *validation*. What does validation mean? Let us see. In a real-life situation, we cannot accept a model that gives us an answer that does not match the reality. This process of checking the answer against reality, and modifying the mathematical description if necessary, is called *validation*. This is a very important step in modelling. We will introduce you to this step in this section.

First, let us look at an example, where we do not have to modify our model after validation.

**Example 4 :** Suppose you have a room of length 6 m and breadth 5 m. You want to cover the floor of the room with square mosaic tiles of side 30 cm. How many tiles will you need? Solve this by constructing a mathematical model.

**Solution : Formulation :** We have to consider the area of the room and the area of a tile for solving the problem. The side of the tile is 0.3 m. Since the length is 6 m, we

can fit in $\dfrac{6}{0.3}$ = 20 tiles along the length of the room in one row (see Fig. A2.1.).

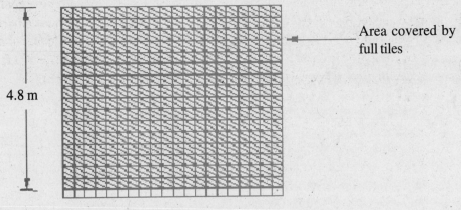

Fig. A2.1

Since the breadth of the room is 5 metres, we have $\dfrac{5}{0.3}$ = 16.67. So, we can fit in 16 tiles in a column. Since $16 \times 0.3 = 4.8$, $5 - 4.8 = 0.2$ metres along the breadth will not be covered by tiles. This part will have to be covered by cutting the other tiles. The breadth of the floor left uncovered, 0.2 metres, is more than half the length of a tile, which is 0.3 m. So we cannot break a tile into two equal halves and use both the halves to cover the remaining portion.

**Mathematical Description :** We have:

Total number of tiles required = (Number of tiles along the length

× Number of tiles along the breadth) + Number of tiles along the uncovered area

(1)

**Solution :** As we said above, the number of tiles along the length is 20 and the number of tiles along the breadth is 16. We need 20 more tiles for the last row. Substituting these values in (1), we get $(20 \times 16) + 20 = 320 + 20 = 340$.

**Interpretation :** We need 340 tiles to cover the floor.

**Validation :** In real-life, your mason may ask you to buy some extra tiles to replace those that get damaged while cutting them to size. This number will of course depend upon the skill of your mason! But, we need not modify Equation (1) for this. This gives you a rough idea of the number of tiles required. So, we can stop here.

Let us now look at another situation now.

**Example 5 :** In the year 2000, 191 member countries of the U.N. signed a declaration. In this declaration, the countries agreed to achieve certain development goals by the year 2015. These are called the *millennium development goals*. One of these goals is to promote gender equality. One indicator for deciding whether this goal has been achieved is the ratio of girls to boys in primary, secondary and tertiary education. India, as a signatory to the declaration, is committed to improve this ratio. The data for the percentage of girls who are enrolled in primary schools is given in Table A2.1.

**Table A2.1**

| Year | Enrolment (in %) |
|---|---|
| 1991-92 | 41.9 |
| 1992-93 | 42.6 |
| 1993-94 | 42.7 |
| 1994-95 | 42.9 |
| 1995-96 | 43.1 |
| 1996-97 | 43.2 |
| 1997-98 | 43.5 |
| 1998-99 | 43.5 |
| 1999-2000 | 43.6[*] |
| 2000-01 | 43.7[*] |
| 2001-02 | 44.1[*] |

**Source :** *Educational statistics, webpage of Department of Education, GOI.*

[*] *indicates that the data is provisional.*

Using this data, mathematically describe the rate at which the proportion of girls enrolled in primary schools grew. Also, estimate the year by which the enrolment of girls will reach 50%.

**Solution :** Let us first convert the problem into a mathematical problem.

**Step 1 : Formulation :** Table A2.1 gives the enrolment for the years 1991-92, 1992-93, etc. Since the students join at the beginning of an academic year, we can take the years as 1991, 1992, etc. Let us assume that the percentage of girls who join primary schools will continue to grow at the same rate as the rate in Table A2.1. So, the number of years is important, not the specific years. (To give a similar situation, when we find the simple interest for, say, ₹ 1500 at the rate of 8% for three years, it does not matter whether the three-year period is from 1999 to 2002 or from 2001 to 2004. What is important is the interest rate in the years being considered). Here also, we will see how the enrolment grows after 1991 by comparing the number of years that has passed after 1991 and the enrolment. Let us take 1991 as the 0th year, and write 1 for 1992 since 1 year has passed in 1992 after 1991. Similarly, we will write 2 for 1993, 3 for 1994, etc. So, Table A2.1 will now look like as Table A2.2.

**Table A2.2**

| Year | Enrolment (in %) |
|:---:|:---:|
| 0 | 41.9 |
| 1 | 42.6 |
| 2 | 42.7 |
| 3 | 42.9 |
| 4 | 43.1 |
| 5 | 43.2 |
| 6 | 43.5 |
| 7 | 43.5 |
| 8 | 43.6 |
| 9 | 43.7 |
| 10 | 44.1 |

The increase in enrolment is given in the following table :

Table A2.3

| Year | Enrolment (in %) | Increase |
|:---:|:---:|:---:|
| 0 | 41.9 | 0 |
| 1 | 42.6 | 0.7 |
| 2 | 42.7 | 0.1 |
| 3 | 42.9 | 0.2 |
| 4 | 43.1 | 0.2 |
| 5 | 43.2 | 0.1 |
| 6 | 43.5 | 0.3 |
| 7 | 43.5 | 0 |
| 8 | 43.6 | 0.1 |
| 9 | 43.7 | 0.1 |
| 10 | 44.1 | 0.4 |

At the end of the one-year period from 1991 to 1992, the enrolment has increased by 0.7% from 41.9% to 42.6%. At the end of the second year, this has increased by 0.1%, from 42.6% to 42.7%. From the table above, we cannot find a definite relationship between the number of years and percentage. But the increase is fairly steady. Only in the first year and in the 10th year there is a jump. The mean of the values is

$$\frac{0.7 + 0.1 + 0.2 + 0.2 + 0.1 + 0.3 + 0 + 0.1 + 0.1 + 0.4}{10} = 0.22$$

Let us assume that the enrolment steadily increases at the rate of 0.22 per cent.

**Mathematical Description :** We have assumed that the enrolment increases steadily at the rate of 0.22% per year.

So, the Enrolment Percentage (EP) in the first year = 41.9 + 0.22

EP in the second year = 41.9 + 0.22 + 0.22 = 41.9 + 2 × 0.22

EP in the third year = 41.9 + 0.22 + 0.22 + 0.22 = 41.9 + 3 × 0.22

So, the enrolment percentage in the $n$th year = 41.9 + 0.22$n$, for $n \geq 1$.          (1)

Now, we also have to find the number of years by which the enrolment will reach 50%. So, we have to find the value of $n$ in the equation or formula

$$50 = 41.9 + 0.22n \qquad (2)$$

Step 2 : **Solution :** Solving (2) for $n$, we get

$$n = \frac{50 - 41.9}{0.22} = \frac{8.1}{0.22} = 36.8$$

Step 3 : **Interpretation :** Since the number of years is an integral value, we will take the next higher integer, 37. So, the enrolment percentage will reach 50% in $1991 + 37 = 2028$.

In a word problem, we generally stop here. But, since we are dealing with a real-life situation, we have to see to what extent this value matches the real situation.

Step 4 : **Validation:** Let us check if Formula (2) is in agreement with the reality. Let us find the values for the years we already know, using Formula (2), and compare it with the known values by finding the difference. The values are given in Table A2.4.

Table A2.4

| Year | Enrolment (in %) | Values given by (2) (in %) | Difference (in %) |
|---|---|---|---|
| 0 | 41.9 | 41.90 | 0 |
| 1 | 42.6 | 42.12 | 0.48 |
| 2 | 42.7 | 42.34 | 0.36 |
| 3 | 42.9 | 42.56 | 0.34 |
| 4 | 43.1 | 42.78 | 0.32 |
| 5 | 43.2 | 43.00 | 0.20 |
| 6 | 43.5 | 43.22 | 0.28 |
| 7 | 43.5 | 43.44 | 0.06 |
| 8 | 43.6 | 43.66 | –0.06 |
| 9 | 43.7 | 43.88 | –0.18 |
| 10 | 44.1 | 44.10 | 0.00 |

As you can see, some of the values given by Formula (2) are less than the actual values by about 0.3% or even by 0.5%. This can give rise to a difference of about 3 to 5 years since the increase per year is actually 1% to 2%. We may decide that this much of a difference is acceptable and stop here. In this case, (2) is our mathematical model.

Suppose we decide that this error is quite large, and we have to improve this model. Then we have to go back to Step 1, the formulation, and change Equation (2). Let us do so.

**Step 1 : Reformulation :** We still assume that the values increase steadily by 0.22%, but we will now introduce a correction factor to reduce the error. For this, we find the mean of all the errors. This is

$$\frac{0 + 0.48 + 0.36 + 0.34 + 0.32 + 0.2 + 0.28 + 0.06 - 0.06 - 0.18 + 0}{10} = 0.18$$

We take the mean of the errors, and correct our formula by this value.

**Revised Mathematical Description :** Let us now add the mean of the errors to our formula for enrolment percentage given in (2). So, our corrected formula is:

Enrolment percentage in the $n$th year $= 41.9 + 0.22n + 0.18 = 42.08 + 0.22n$, for $n \geq 1$           (3)

We will also modify Equation (2) appropriately. The new equation for $n$ is:

$$50 = 42.08 + 0.22n \qquad (4)$$

**Step 2 : Altered Solution :** Solving Equation (4) for $n$, we get

$$n = \frac{50 - 42.08}{0.22} = \frac{7.92}{0.22} = 36$$

**Step 3 : Interpretation:** Since $n = 36$, the enrolment of girls in primary schools will reach 50% in the year $1991 + 36 = 2027$.

**Step 4 : Validation:** Once again, let us compare the values got by using Formula (4) with the actual values. Table A2.5 gives the comparison.

Table A2.5

| Year | Enrolment (in %) | Values given by (2) | Difference between values | Values given by (4) | Difference between values |
|------|------------------|---------------------|---------------------------|---------------------|---------------------------|
| 0 | 41.9 | 41.90 | 0 | 41.9 | 0 |
| 1 | 42.6 | 42.12 | 0.48 | 42.3 | 0.3 |
| 2 | 42.7 | 42.34 | 0.36 | 42.52 | 0.18 |
| 3. | 42.9 | 42.56 | 0.34 | 42.74 | 0.16 |
| 4 | 43.1 | 42.78 | 0.32 | 42.96 | 0.14 |
| 5 | 43.2 | 43.00 | 0.2 | 43.18 | 0.02 |
| 6 | 43.5 | 43.22 | 0.28 | 43.4 | 0.1 |
| 7 | 43.5 | 43.44 | 0.06 | 43.62 | $-0.12$ |
| 8 | 43.6 | 43.66 | $-0.06$ | 43.84 | $-0.24$ |
| 9 | 43.7 | 43.88 | $-0.18$ | 44.06 | $-0.36$ |
| 10 | 44.1 | 44.10 | 0 | 44.28 | $-0.18$ |

As you can see, many of the values that (4) gives are closer to the actual value than the values that (2) gives. The mean of the errors is 0 in this case.

We will stop our process here. So, Equation (4) is our mathematical description that gives a mathematical relationship between years and the percentage of enrolment of girls of the total enrolment. We have constructed a mathematical model that describes the growth.

**The process that we have followed in the situation above is called mathematical modelling**.

We have tried to construct a mathematical model with the mathematical tools that we already have. There are better mathematical tools for making predictions from the data we have. But, they are beyond the scope of this course. Our aim in constructing this model is to explain the process of modelling to you, not to make accurate predictions at this stage.

You may now like to model some real-life situations to check your understanding of our discussion so far. Here is an Exercise for you to try.

## EXERCISE A2.2

1. We have given the timings of the gold medalists in the 400-metre race from the time the event was included in the Olympics, in the table below. Construct a mathematical model relating the years and timings. Use it to estimate the timing in the next Olympics.

Table A2.6

| Year | Timing (in seconds) |
|------|---------------------|
| 1964 | 52.01 |
| 1968 | 52.03 |
| 1972 | 51.08 |
| 1976 | 49.28 |
| 1980 | 48.88 |
| 1984 | 48.83 |
| 1988 | 48.65 |
| 1992 | 48.83 |
| 1996 | 48.25 |
| 2000 | 49.11 |
| 2004 | 49.41 |

## A2.4 The Process of Modelling, its Advantages and Limitations

Let us now conclude our discussion by drawing out aspects of mathematical modelling that show up in the examples we have discussed. With the background of the earlier sections, we are now in a position to give a brief overview of the steps involved in modelling.

Step 1 : Formulation : You would have noticed the difference between the formulation part of Example 1 in Section A2.2 and the formulation part of the model we discussed in A2.3. In Example 1, all the information is in a readily usable form. But, in the model given in A2.3 this is not so. Further, it took us some time to find a mathematical description. We tested our first formula, but found that it was not as good as the second one we got. This is usually true in general, i.e. when trying to model real-life situations; the first model usually needs to be revised. When we are solving a real-life problem, formulation can require a lot of time. For example, Newton's three laws of motion, which are mathematical descriptions of motion, are simple enough to state. But, Newton arrived at these laws after studying a large amount of data and the work the scientists before him had done.

Formulation involves the following three steps :

    **(i) Stating the problem :** Often, the problem is stated vaguely. For example, the broad goal is to ensure that the enrolment of boys and girls are equal. This may mean that 50% of the total number of boys of the school-going age and 50% of the girls of the school-going age should be enrolled. The other way is to ensure that 50% of the school-going children are girls. In our problem, we have used the second approach.

    **(ii) Identifying relevant factors :** Decide which quantities and relationships are important for our problem and which are unimportant and can be neglected. For example, in our problem regarding primary schools enrolment, the percentage of girls enrolled in the previous year can influence the number of girls enrolled this year. This is because, as more and more girls enrol in schools, many more parents will feel they also have to put their daughters in schools. But, we have ignored this factor because this may become important only after the enrolment crosses a certain percentage. Also, adding this factor may make our model more complicated.

    **(iii) Mathematical Description :** Now suppose we are clear about what the problem is and what aspects of it are more relevant than the others. Then we have to find a relationship between the aspects involved in the form of an equation, a graph or any other suitable mathematical description. If it is an equation, then every important aspect should be represented by a variable in our mathematical equation.

    **Step 2 : Finding the solution :** The mathematical formulation does not give the solution. We have to solve this mathematical equivalent of the problem. This is where your mathematical knowledge comes in useful.

    **Step 3 : Interpretating the solution :** The mathematical solution is some value or values of the variables in the model. We have to go back to the real-life problem and see what these values mean in the problem.

    **Step 4 : Validating the solution :** As we saw in A2.3, after finding the solution we will have to check whether the solution matches the reality. If it matches, then the mathematical model is acceptable. If the mathematical solution does not match, *we go back to the formulation step* again and try to improve our model.

    This step in the process is one major difference between solving word problems and mathematical modelling. This is one of the most important step in modelling that is missing in word problems. Of course, it is possible that in some real-life situations, we do not need to validate our answer because the problem is simple and we get the correct solution right away. This was so in the first model we considered in A2.3.

We have given a summary of the order in which the steps in mathematical modelling are carried out in Fig. A2.2 below. Movement from the validation step to the formulation step is shown using a **dotted arrow**. This is because it may not be necessary to carry out this step again.

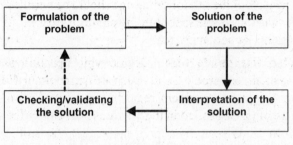

Fig.A2.2

Now that you have studied the stages involved in mathematical modelling, let us discuss some of its aspects.

The *aim* of mathematical modelling is to get some useful information about a real-world problem by converting it into a mathematical problem. This is especially useful when it is not possible or very expensive to get information by other means such as direct observation or by conducting experiments.

You may also wonder why we should undertake mathematical modelling? Let us look at some **advantages of modelling**. Suppose we want to study the corrosive effect of the discharge of the Mathura refinery on the Taj Mahal. We would not like to carry out experiments on the Taj Mahal directly since it may not be safe to do so. Of course, we can use a scaled down physical model, but we may need special facilities for this, which may be expensive. Here is where mathematical modelling can be of great use.

Again, suppose we want to know how many primary schools we will need after 5 years. Then, we can only solve this problem by using a mathematical model. Similarly, it is only through modelling that scientists have been able to explain the existence of so many phenomena.

You saw in Section A2.3, that we could have tried to improve the answer in the second example with better methods. But we stopped because we do not have the mathematical tools. This can happen in real-life also. Often, we have to be satisfied with very approximate answers, because mathematical tools are not available. For example, the model equations used in modelling weather are so complex that mathematical tools to find exact solutions are not available.

You may wonder to what extent we should try to improve our model. Usually, to improve it, we need to take into account more factors. When we do this, we add more variables to our mathematical equations. We may then have a very complicated model that is difficult to use. A model must be simple enough to use. A good model balances two factors:

1.   Accuracy, i.e., how close it is to reality.

2.   Ease of use.

For example, Newton's laws of motion are very simple, but powerful enough to model many physical situations.

So, is mathematical modelling the answer to all our problems? Not quite! It has its limitations.

Thus, we should keep in mind that a model is *only a simplification* of a real-world problem, and the two are not the same. It is something like the difference between a map that gives the physical features of a country, and the country itself. We can find the height of a place above the sea level from this map, but we cannot find the characteristics of the people from it. So, we should use a model only for the purpose it is supposed to serve, remembering all the factors we have neglected while constructing it. We should apply the model only within the limits where it is applicable. In the later classes, we shall discuss this aspect a little more.

### EXERCISE A2.3

1.   How are the solving of word problems that you come across in textbooks different from the process of mathematical modelling?
2.   Suppose you want to minimise the waiting time of vehicles at a traffic junction of four roads. Which of these factors are important and which are not?

     (i)   Price of petrol.

     (ii)   The rate at which the vehicles arrive in the four different roads.

     (iii)   The proportion of slow-moving vehicles like cycles and rickshaws and fast moving vehicles like cars and motorcycles.

## A2.5 Summary

In this Appendix, you have studied the following points :

1.   The steps involved in solving word problems.
2.   Construction of some mathematical models.

3. The steps involved in mathematical modelling given in the box below.

> 1. **Formulation :**
>    (i) Stating the question
>    (ii) Identifying the relevant factors
>    (iii) Mathematical description
> 2. **Finding the solution.**
> 3. **Interpretation of the solution in the context of the real-world problem.**
> 4. **Checking/validating to what extent the model is a good representation of the problem being studied.**

4. The aims, advantages and limitations of mathematical modelling.

# ANSWERS/HINTS

## EXERCISE 1.1

1. Yes. $0 = \dfrac{0}{1} = \dfrac{0}{2} = \dfrac{0}{3}$ etc., denominator $q$ can also be taken as negative integer.

2. There can be infinitely many rationals betwen numbers 3 and 4, one way is to take them

   $3 = \dfrac{21}{6+1}$, $4 = \dfrac{28}{6+1}$. Then the six numbers are $\dfrac{22}{7}, \dfrac{23}{7}, \dfrac{24}{7}, \dfrac{25}{7}, \dfrac{26}{7}, \dfrac{27}{7}$.

3. $\dfrac{3}{5} = \dfrac{30}{50}, \dfrac{4}{5} = \dfrac{40}{50}$. Therefore, five rationals are : $\dfrac{31}{50}, \dfrac{32}{50}, \dfrac{33}{50}, \dfrac{34}{50}, \dfrac{35}{50}$.

4. (i) True, since the collection of whole numbers contains all the natural numbers.

   (ii) False, for example $-2$ is not a whole number.

   (iii) False, for example $\dfrac{1}{2}$ is a rational number but not a whole number.

## EXERCISE 1.2

1. (i) True, since collection of real numbers is made up of rational and irrational numbers.

   (ii) False, no negative number can be the square root of any natural number.

   (iii) False, for example 2 is real but not irrational.

2. No. For example, $\sqrt{4} = 2$ is a rational number.

3. Repeat the procedure as in Fig. 1.8 several times. First obtain $\sqrt{4}$ and then $\sqrt{5}$.

## EXERCISE 1.3

**1.** (i)   0.36, terminating.                                (ii)  $0.\overline{09}$ , non-terminating repeating.

   (iii)  4.125, terminating.                             (iv)  $0.\overline{230769}$ , non-terminating repeating.

   (v)  $0.\overline{18}$  non-terminating repeating.        (vi)  0.8225 terminating.

**2.**  $\dfrac{2}{7} = 2 \times \dfrac{1}{7} = 0.\overline{285714}$,        $\dfrac{3}{7} = 3 \times \dfrac{1}{7} = 0.\overline{428571}$,        $\dfrac{4}{7} = 4 \times \dfrac{1}{7} = 0.\overline{571428}$,

   $\dfrac{5}{7} = 5 \times \dfrac{1}{7} = 0.\overline{714285}$,        $\dfrac{6}{7} = 6 \times \dfrac{1}{7} = 0.\overline{857142}$

**3.** (i)   $\dfrac{2}{3}$  [Let $x = 0.666\ldots$ So $10x = 6.666\ldots$ or, $10x = 6 + x$   or ,   $x = \dfrac{6}{9} = \dfrac{2}{3}$ ]

   (ii)   $\dfrac{43}{90}$                                   (iii)   $\dfrac{1}{999}$

**4.** 1 [Let $x = 0.9999\ldots$ So $10\,x = 9.999\ldots$   or,   $10\,x = 9 + x$   or,   $x = 1$]

**5.**  $0.\overline{0588235294117647}$

**6.** The prime factorisation of $q$ has only powers of 2 or powers of 5 or both.

**7.** $0.01001000100001\ldots, 0.202002000200002\ldots, 0.003000300003\ldots$

**8.** $0.75075007500075000075\ldots, 0.767076700767000767\ldots, 0.808008000800008\ldots$

**9.** (i) and (v) irrational; (ii), (iii) and (iv) rational.

## EXERCISE 1.4

**1.** Proceed as in Section 1.4 for 2.665.

**2.** Proceed as in Example 11.

## EXERCISE 1.5

**1.** (i)   Irrational        (ii) Rational        (iii) Rational        (iv) Irrational
   (v)  Irrational

**2.** (i)   $6 + 3\sqrt{2} + 2\sqrt{3} + \sqrt{6}$        (ii) 6        (iii) $7 + 2\sqrt{10}$        (iv) 3

**3.** There is no contradiction. Remember that when you measure a length with a scale or any other device, you only get an approximate rational value. So, you may not realise that either $c$ or $d$ is irrational.

4. Refer Fig. 1.17.

5. (i) $\dfrac{\sqrt{7}}{7}$    (ii) $\sqrt{7} + \sqrt{6}$    (iii) $\dfrac{\sqrt{5} - \sqrt{2}}{3}$    (iv) $\dfrac{\sqrt{7} + 2}{3}$

## EXERCISE 1.6

1. (i) 8 (ii) 2 (iii) 5    2. (i) 27 (ii) 4 (iii) 8 (iv) $\dfrac{1}{5}\left[ (125)^{-\frac{1}{3}} = \left(5^3\right)^{-\frac{1}{3}} = 5^{-1} \right]$

3. (i) $2^{\frac{13}{15}}$      (ii) $3^{-21}$      (iii) $11^{\frac{1}{4}}$      (iv) $56^{\frac{1}{2}}$

## EXERCISE 2.1

1. (i) and (ii) are polynomials in one variable, (v) is a polynomial in three variables,
   (iii), (iv) are not polynomials, because in each of these exponent of the variable is not a whole number.

2. (i) 1      (ii) –1      (iii) $\dfrac{\pi}{2}$      (iv) 0

3. $3x^{35} - 4$; $\sqrt{2}\, y^{100}$ (You can write some more polynomials with different coefficients.)

4. (i) 3      (ii) 2      (iii) 1      (iv) 0

5. (i) quadratic      (ii) cubic      (iii) quadratic      (iv) linear
   (v) linear      (vi) quadratic      (vii) cubic

## EXERCISE 2.2

1. (i) 3      (ii) –6      (iii) –3
2. (i) 1, 1, 3      (ii) 2, 4, 4      (iii) 0, 1, 8      (iv) –1, 0, 3
3. (i) Yes      (ii) No      (iii) Yes      (iv) Yes
   (v) Yes      (vi) Yes

   (vii) $-\dfrac{1}{\sqrt{3}}$ is a zero, but $\dfrac{2}{\sqrt{3}}$ is not a zero of the polynomial      (viii) No

4. (i) –5      (ii) 5      (iii) $\dfrac{-5}{2}$      (iv) $\dfrac{2}{3}$

   (v) 0      (vi) 0      (vii) $-\dfrac{d}{c}$

## EXERCISE 2.3

1. (i) 0  (ii) $\dfrac{27}{8}$  (iii) 1  (iv) $-\pi^3 + 3\pi^2 - 3\pi + 1$  (v) $-\dfrac{27}{8}$

2. $5a$  3. No, since remainder is not zero.

## EXERCISE 2.4

1. $(x + 1)$ is a factor of (i), but not the factor of (ii), (iii) and (iv).
2. (i) Yes  (ii) No  (iii) Yes

3. (i) $-2$  (ii) $-\left(2 + \sqrt{2}\right)$  (iii) $\sqrt{2} - 1$  (iv) $\dfrac{3}{2}$

4. (i) $(3x - 1)(4x - 1)$  (ii) $(x + 3)(2x + 1)$  (iii) $(2x + 3)(3x - 2)$  (iv) $(x + 1)(3x - 4)$

5. (i) $(x - 2)(x - 1)(x + 1)$  (ii) $(x + 1)(x + 1)(x - 5)$

   (iii) $(x + 1)(x + 2)(x + 10)$  (iv) $(y - 1)(y + 1)(2y + 1)$

## EXERCISE 2.5

1. (i) $x^2 + 14x + 40$  (ii) $x^2 - 2x - 80$  (iii) $9x^2 - 3x - 20$

   (iv) $y^4 - \dfrac{9}{4}$  (v) $9 - 4x^2$

2. (i) 11021  (ii) 9120  (iii) 9984

3. (i) $(3x + y)(3x + y)$  (ii) $(2y - 1)(2y - 1)$  (iii) $\left(x + \dfrac{y}{10}\right)\left(x - \dfrac{y}{10}\right)$

4. (i) $x^2 + 4y^2 + 16z^2 + 4xy + 16yz + 8xz$

   (ii) $4x^2 + y^2 + z^2 - 4xy - 2yz + 4xz$

   (iii) $4x^2 + 9y^2 + 4z^2 - 12xy + 12yz - 8xz$

   (iv) $9a^2 + 49b^2 + c^2 - 42ab + 14bc - 6ac$

   (v) $4x^2 + 25y^2 + 9z^2 - 20xy - 30yz + 12xz$

   (vi) $\dfrac{a^2}{16} + \dfrac{b^2}{4} + 1 - \dfrac{ab}{4} - b + \dfrac{a}{2}$

5. (i) $(2x + 3y - 4z)(2x + 3y - 4z)$  (ii) $\left(-\sqrt{2}\,x + y + 2\sqrt{2}\,z\right)\left(-\sqrt{2}\,x + y + 2\sqrt{2}\,z\right)$

6. (i) $8x^3 + 12x^2 + 6x + 1$  (ii) $8a^3 - 27b^3 - 36a^2b + 54ab^2$

(iii) $\dfrac{27}{8}x^3 + \dfrac{27}{4}x^2 + \dfrac{9}{2}x + 1$                (iv) $x^3 - \dfrac{8}{27}y^3 - 2x^2y + \dfrac{4xy^2}{3}$

7. (i)  970299                (ii) 1061208                (iii) 994011992

8. (i)  $(2a+b)(2a+b)(2a+b)$                (ii) $(2a-b)(2a-b)(2a-b)$

   (iii) $(3-5a)(3-5a)(3-5a)$                (iv) $(4a-3b)(4a-3b)(4a-3b)$

   (v) $\left(3p - \dfrac{1}{6}\right)\left(3p - \dfrac{1}{6}\right)\left(3p - \dfrac{1}{6}\right)$

10. (i) $(3y+5z)(9y^2+25z^2-15yz)$                (ii) $(4m-7n)(16m^2+49n^2+28mn)$

11. $(3x+y+z)(9x^2+y^2+z^2-3xy-yz-3xz)$

12. Simiplify RHS.

13. Put $x+y+z=0$ in Identity VIII.

14. (i)  $-1260$. Let $a=-12, b=7, c=5$. Here $a+b+c=0$. Use the result given in Q13.

    (ii) 16380

15. (i)  One possible answer is : Length = $5a-3$, Breadth = $5a-4$

    (ii) One possible answer is : Length = $7y-3$, Breadth = $5y+4$

16. (i)  One possible answer is : 3, $x$ and $x-4$.

    (ii) One possible answer is : $4k$, $3y+5$ and $y-1$.

## EXERCISE 3.1

1. Consider the lamp as a point and table as a plane. Choose any two perpendicular edges of the table. Measure the distance of the lamp from the longer edge, suppose it is 25 cm. Again, measure the distance of the lamp from the shorter edge, and suppose it is 30 cm. You can write the position of the lamp as (30, 25) or (25, 30), depending on the order you fix.

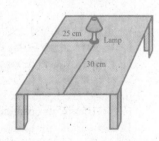

**2.** The Street plan is shown in figure given below.

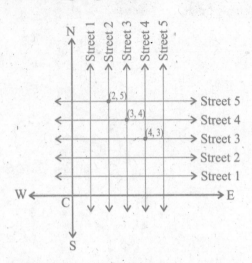

Both the cross-streets are marked in the figure above. They are *uniquely* found because of the two reference lines we have used for locating them.

## EXERCISE 3.2

**1.** (i) The *x* - axis and the *y* - axis   (ii) Quadrants   (iii) The origin

**2.** (i) $(-5, 2)$   (ii) $(5, -5)$   (iii) E   (iv) G   (v) 6   (vi) $-3$   (vii) $(0, 5)$   (viii) $(-3, 0)$

## EXERCISE 3.3

**1.** The point $(-2, 4)$ lies in quadrant II, the point $(3, -1)$ lies in the quadrant IV, the point $(-1, 0)$ lies on the negative *x* - axis, the point $(1, 2)$ lies in the quadrant I and the point $(-3, -5)$ lies in the quadrant III. Locations of the points are shown in the adjoining figure.

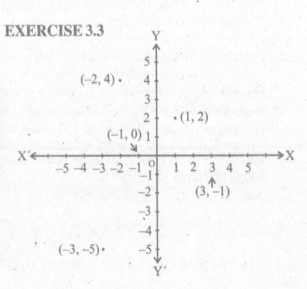

2. Positions of the points are shown by dots in the adjoining figure.

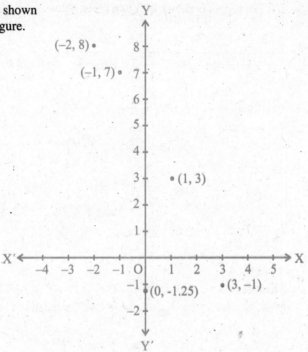

## EXERCISE 4.1

1. $x - 2y = 0$

2. (i) $2x + 3y - 9.3\overline{5} = 0; a = 2, b = 3, c = -9.3\overline{5}$

(ii) $x - \dfrac{y}{5} - 10 = 0; a = 1, b = \dfrac{-1}{5}, c = -10$

(iii) $-2x + 3y - 6 = 0; a = -2, b = 3, c = -6$

(iv) $1.x - 3y + 0 = 0; a = 1, b = -3, c = 0$

(v) $2x + 5y + 0 = 0; a = 2, b = 5, c = 0$

(vi) $3x + 0.y + 2 = 0; a = 3, b = 0, c = 2$

(vii) $0.x + 1.y - 2 = 0; a = 0, b = 1, c = -2$

(viii) $-2x + 0.y + 5 = 0; a = -2, b = 0, c = 5$

## EXERCISE 4.2

1. (iii), because for every value of $x$, there is a corresponding value of $y$ and vice-versa.

**2.** (i)   $(0, 7), (1, 5), (2, 3), (4, -1)$

  (ii)   $(1, 9 - \pi), (0, 9), (-1, 9 + \pi), \left(\dfrac{9}{\pi}, 0\right)$

  (iii)   $(0, 0), (4, 1), (-4, 1), \left(2, \dfrac{1}{2}\right)$

**3.** (i)   No          (ii)  No          (iii)  Yes          (iv)  No          (v)  No

**4.** 7

## EXERCISE 4.3

**1.** (i)

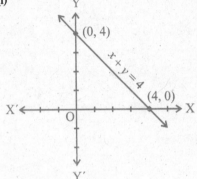

(ii)

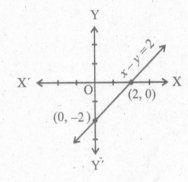

(iii)

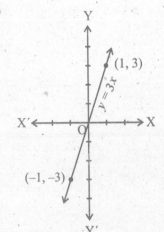

(iv)

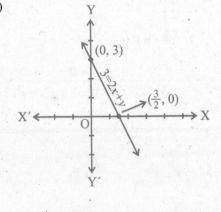

**2.** $7x - y = 0$ and $x + y = 16$; infintely many [Through a point infinitely many lines can be drawn]

**3.** $\dfrac{5}{3}$                                     **4.** $5x - y + 3 = 0$

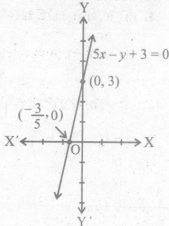

**5.** For Fig. 4.6, $x + y = 0$ and for Fig. 4.7, $y = -x + 2$.

**6.** Supposing $x$ is the distance and $y$ is the work done. Therefore according to the problem the equation will be $y = 5x$.

(i) 10 units                          (ii) 0 unit

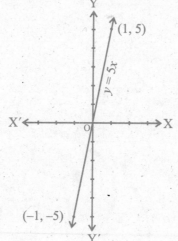

**7.** $x + y = 100$

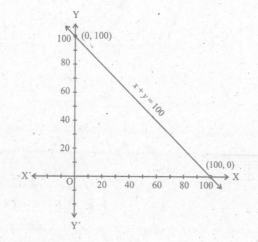

**8.** (i) See adjacent figure.

(ii) 86° F

(iii) 35° C

(iv) 32° F, –17.8° C (approximately)

(v) Yes, – 40° (both in F and C)

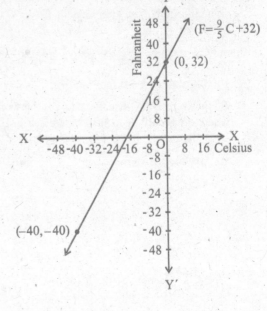

## EXERCISE 4.4

**1.** (i)

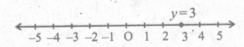

(ii)

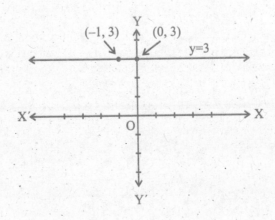

**2.** (i)

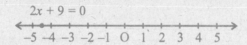

$$2x + 9 = 0$$

(ii)

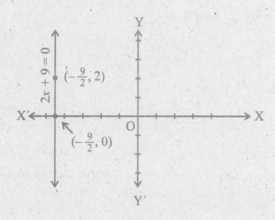

## EXERCISE 5.1

**1.** (i) False. This can be seen visually by the student.

(ii) False. This contradicts Axiom 5.1.

(iii) True. (Postulate 2)

(iv) True. If you superimpose the region bounded by one circle on the other, then they coincide. So, their centres and boundaries coincide. Therefore, their radii will coincide.

(v) True. The first axiom of Euclid.

**3.** There are several undefined terms which the student should list. They are consistent, because they deal with two different situations — (i) says that given two points A and B, there is a point C lying on the line in between them; (ii) says that given A and B, you can take C not lying on the line through A and B.

These 'postulates' do not follow from Euclid's postulates. However, they follow from Axiom 5.1.

**4.** $\qquad\qquad\qquad\qquad$ AC = BC

So, $\qquad\qquad$ AC + AC = BC + AC $\qquad\qquad$ (Equals are added to equals)

i.e., $\qquad\qquad\qquad$ 2AC = AB $\qquad\qquad\qquad$ (BC + AC coincides with AB)

Therefore, $\qquad\qquad\qquad$ $AC = \dfrac{1}{2} AB$

5. Make a temporary assumption that different points C and D are two mid-points of AB. Now, you show that points C and D are not two different points.

6.                           AC = BD                           (Given)    (1)

                            AC = AB + BC    (Point B lies between A and C)    (2)

                            BD = BC + CD    (Point C lies between B and D)    (3)

   Substituting (2) and (3) in (1), you get

                     AB + BC = BC + CD

   So,                      AB = CD                (Subtracting equals from equals)

7. Since this is true for any thing in any part of the world, this is a universal truth.


## EXERCISE 5.2

1. Any formulation the student gives should be discussed in the class for its validity.

2. If a straight line $l$ falls on two straight lines $m$ and $n$ such that sum of the interior angles on one side of $l$ is two right angles, then by Euclid's fifth postulate the line will not meet on this side of $l$. Next, you know that the sum of the interior angles on the other side of line $l$ will also be two right angles. Therefore, they will not meet on the other side also. So, the lines $m$ and $n$ never meet and are, therefore, parallel.


## EXERCISE 6.1

1. $30°, 250°$          2. $126°$          4. Sum of all the angles at a point $= 360°$

5. $\angle QOS = \angle SOR + \angle ROQ$ and $\angle POS = \angle POR - \angle SOR$.          6. $122°, 302°$


## EXERCISE 6.2

1. $130°, 130°$     2. $126°$          3. $126°, 36°, 54°$     4. $60°$          5. $50°, 77°$

6. Angle of incidence = Angle of reflection. At point B, draw $BE \perp PQ$ and at point C, draw $CF \perp RS$.


## EXERCISE 6.3

1. $65°$          2. $32°, 121°$          3. $92°$          4. $60°$          5. $37°, 53°$

6. Sum of the angles of $\triangle PQR$ = Sum of the angles of $\triangle QTR$ and $\angle PRS = \angle QPR + \angle PQR$.


## EXERCISE 7.1

1. They are equal.          6. $\angle BAC = \angle DAE$

## EXERCISE 7.2

**6.** $\angle BCD = \angle BCA + \angle DCA = \angle B + \angle D$     **7.** each is of $45°$

## EXERCISE 7.3

**3.** **(ii)** From (i), $\angle ABM = \angle PQN$

## EXERCISE 7.4

**4.** Join BD and show $\angle B > \angle D$. Join AC and show $\angle A > \angle C$.

**5.** $\angle Q + \angle QPS > \angle R + \angle RPS$, etc.

## EXERCISE 8.1

**1.** $36°, 60°, 108°$ and $156°$.

**6.** (i) From $\triangle DAC$ and $\triangle BCA$, show $\angle DAC = \angle BCA$ and $\angle ACD = \angle CAB$, etc.

(ii) Show $\angle BAC = \angle BCA$, using Theorem 8.4.

## EXERCISE 8.2

**2.** Show PQRS is a parallelogram. Also show PQ $\parallel$ AC and PS $\parallel$ BD. So, $\angle P = 90°$.

**5.** AECF is a parallelogram. So, AF $\parallel$ CE, etc.

## EXERCISE 9.1

**1.** (i)  Base DC, parallels DC and AB;          (iii)  Base QR, parallels QR and PS;

(v)  Base AD, parallels AD and BQ

## EXERCISE 9.2

**1.** 12.8 cm.                    **2.** Join EG; Use result of Example 2.

**6.** Wheat in $\triangle APQ$ and pulses in other two triangles or pulses in $\triangle APQ$ and wheat in other two triangles.

## EXERCISE 9.3

**4.** Draw CM $\perp$ AB and DN $\perp$ AB. Show CM = DN.               **12.** See Example 4.

## EXERCISE 9.4   (Optional)

**7.** Use result of Example 3 repeatedly.

## EXERCISE 10.1

**1.** (i)  Interior                (ii) Exterior                (iii) Diameter

    (iv) Semicircle           (v) The chord           (vi) Three

**2.** (i)  True                    (ii) False                 (iii) False

    (iv) True                   (v) False                  (vi) True

## EXERCISE 10.2

**1.** Prove exactly as Theorem 10.1 by considering chords of congruent circles.

**2.** Use SAS axiom of congruence to show the congruence of the two triangles.

## EXERCISE 10.3

**1.** 0, 1, 2. Two           **2.** Proceed as in Example 1.

**3.** Join the centres O, O′ of the circles to the mid-point M of the common chord AB. Then, show $\angle$ OMA = 90° and $\angle$ O′MA = 90°.

## EXERCISE 10.4

**1.** 6 cm. First show that the line joining centres is perpendicular to the radius of the smaller circle and then that common chord is the diameter of the smaller circle.

**2.** If AB, CD are equal chords of a circle with centre O intersecting at E, draw perpendiculars OM on AB and ON on CD and join OE. Show that right triangles OME and ONE are congruent.

**3.** Proceed as in Example 2.           **4.** Draw perpendicular OM on AD.

**5.** Represent Reshma, Salma and Mandip by R, S and M respectively. Let KR = $x$ m (see figure).

Area of $\triangle$ ORS = $\dfrac{1}{2}x \times 5$. Also, area of $\triangle$ ORS =

$\dfrac{1}{2}$ RS × OL = $\dfrac{1}{2} \times 6 \times 4$.

Find $x$ and hence RM.

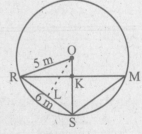

**6.** Use the properties of an equilateral triangle and also Pythagoras Theorem.

## EXERCISE 10.5

1. $45°$       **2.** $150°, 30°$       **3.** $10°$

4. $80°$       **5.** $110°$       **6.** $\angle BCD = 80°$ and $\angle ECD = 50°$

8. Draw perpendiculars AM and BN on CD (AB ‖ CD and AB < CD). Show $\triangle AMD \cong \triangle BNC$. This gives $\angle C = \angle D$ and, therefore, $\angle A + \angle C = 180°$.

## EXERCISE 10.6    (Optional)

2. Let O be the centre of the circle. Then perpendicular bisector of both the chords will be same and passes through O. Let $r$ be the radius, then $r^2 = \left(\dfrac{11}{2}\right)^2 + x^2$

$= \left(\dfrac{5}{2}\right)^2 + (6 - x)^2$, where $x$ is length of the perpendicular from O on the chord of

length 11 cm. This gives $x = 1$. So, $r = \dfrac{5\sqrt{5}}{2}$ cm.       **3.** 3 cm.

4. Let $\angle AOC = x$ and $\angle DOE = y$. Let $\angle AOD = z$. Then $\angle EOC = z$ and $x + y + 2z = 360°$.

$$\angle ODB = \angle OAD + \angle DOA = 90° - \frac{1}{2} z + z = 90° + \frac{1}{2} z. \text{ Also } \angle OEB = 90° + \frac{1}{2} z$$

8. $\angle ABE = \angle ADE$, $\angle ADF = \angle ACF = \dfrac{1}{2} \angle C$.

Therefore, $\angle EDF = \angle ABE + \angle ADF = \dfrac{1}{2} (\angle B + \angle C) = \dfrac{1}{2} (180° - \angle A) = 90° - \dfrac{1}{2} \angle A$.

9. Use Q. 1, Ex. 10.2 and Theorem 10.8.

10. Let angle-bisector of $\angle A$ intersect circumcircle of $\triangle ABC$ at D. Join DC and DB. Then

$\angle BCD = \angle BAD = \dfrac{1}{2} \angle A$ and $\angle DBC = \angle DAC = \dfrac{1}{2} \angle A$. Therefore, $\angle BCD = \angle DBC$ or, DB = DC. So, D lies on the perpendicular bisector of BC.

## EXERCISE 12.1

1. $\dfrac{\sqrt{3}}{4} a^2, 900, 3\,cm^2$       **2.** ₹ 1650000       **3.** $20\sqrt{2}\,m^2$

4. $21\sqrt{11}\,cm^2$       **5.** $9000\,cm^2$       **6.** $9\sqrt{15}\,cm^2$

## EXERCISE 12.2

1.   65.5 m² (approx.)           2.  15.2 cm² (approx.)        3.  19.4 cm² (approx.)

4.   12 cm                        5.  48 m²                      6.  $1000\sqrt{6}$ cm², $1000\sqrt{6}$ cm²

7.   Area of shade I = Area of shade II = 256 cm² and area of shade III = 17.92 cm²

8.   ₹ 705.60                     9.  196 m²

[See the figure. Find area of $\triangle$ BEC = 84 m², then find the height BM. ]

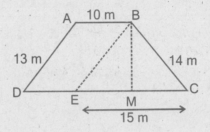

## EXERCISE 13.1

1.   (i) 5.45 m²       (ii) ₹ 109      2. ₹ 555        3. 6 m          4. 100 bricks.

5.   (i) Lateral surface area of cubical box is greater by 40 cm².

      (ii) Total surface area of cuboidal box is greater by 10 cm².

6.   (i) 4250 cm² of glass                    (ii)  320 cm of tape. [Calculate the sum of all the
      edges (The 12 edges consist of 4 lengths, 4 breadths and 4 heights)].

7.   ₹ 2184            8.  47 m²

## EXERCISE 13.2

1.   2 cm              2. 7.48 m²     3. (i) 968 cm²     (ii) 1064.8 cm²   (iii)  2038.08 cm²

[Total surface area of a pipe is (inner curved surface area + outer curved surface
area + areas of the two bases). Each base is a ring of area given by π (R² – r²),
where R = outer radius and r = inner radius].

4.   1584 m²                       5. ₹ 68.75                       6. 1 m

7.   (i) 110 m²           (ii) ₹ 4400                                8. 4.4 m²

9.   (i) 59.4 m²          (ii) 95.04 m²

[Let the actual area of steel used be $x$ m². Since $\dfrac{1}{12}$ of the actual steel used was wasted, the area of steel which has gone into the tank $= \dfrac{11}{12}$ of $x$. This means that the

actual area of steel used $= \dfrac{12}{11} \times 87.12\, \text{m}^2$ ]

**10.** 2200 cm²; Height of the cylinder should be treated as (30 + 2.5 + 2.5) cm

**11.** 7920 cm²

## EXERCISE 13.3

**1.** 165 cm²  **2.** 1244.57 m²  **3.** (i) 7 cm  (ii) 462 cm²

**4.** (i) 26 m  (ii) ₹ 137280  **5.** 63 m  **6.** ₹ 1155

**7.** 5500 cm²  **8.** ₹ 384.34 (approx.)

## EXERCISE 13.4

**1.** (i) 1386 cm²  (ii) 394.24 cm²  (iii) 2464 cm²

**2.** (i) 616 cm²  (ii) 1386 cm²  (iii) 38.5 m²

**3.** 942 cm²  **4.** 1 : 4  **5.** ₹ 27.72

**6.** 3.5 cm  **7.** 1 : 16  **8.** 173.25 cm²

**9.** (i) $4\pi r^2$  (ii) $4\pi r^2$  (iii) 1 : 1

## EXERCISE 13.5

**1.** 180 cm³  **2.** 135000 litres  **3.** 4.75 m  **4.** ₹ 4320  **5.** 2 m

**6.** 3 days  **7.** 16000  **8.** 6 cm, 4 : 1  **9.** 4000 m³

## EXERCISE 13.6

**1.** 34.65 litres

**2.** 3.432 kg [Volume of a pipe $= \pi h \times (R^2 - r^2)$, where R is the outer radius and $r$ is the inner radius].

**3.** The cylinder has the greater capacity by 85 cm³.

**4.** (i) 3 cm  (ii) 141.3 cm³

**5.** (i) 110 m²  (ii) 1.75 m  (iii) 96.25 $kl$  **6.** 0.4708 m²

**7.** Volume of wood = 5.28 cm³, Volume of graphite = 0.11 cm³.

**8.** 38500 cm³ or 38.5$l$ of soup

## EXERCISE 13.7

**1.** (i) $264\,cm^3$     (ii) $154\,cm^3$          **2.** (i) $1.232\,l$          (ii) $\dfrac{11}{35}\,l$

**3.** $10\,cm$          **4.** $8\,cm$          **5.** $38.5\,kl$

**6.** (i) $48\,cm$ (ii) $50\,cm$ (iii) $2200\,cm^2$          **7.** $100\pi\,cm^3$          **8.** $240\pi\,cm^3$; $5:12$

**9.** $86.625x\,m^3$, $99.825\,m^2$

## EXERCISE 13.8

**1.** (i) $1437\,\dfrac{1}{3}\,cm^3$     (ii) $1.05\,m^3$ (approx.)

**2.** (i) $11498\,\dfrac{2}{3}\,cm^3$     (ii) $0.004851\,m^3$     **3.** $345.39\,g$ (approx.)     **4.** $\dfrac{1}{64}$

**5.** $0.303\,l$ (approx.)                    **6.** $0.06348\,m^3$ (approx.)

**7.** $179\,\dfrac{2}{3}\,cm^3$     **8.** (i) $249.48\,m^2$     (ii) $523.9\,m^3$ (approx.)     **9.** (i) $3r$  (ii) $1:9$

**10.** $22.46\,mm^3$ (approx.)

## EXERCISE 13.9  (Optional)

**1.** ₹6275

**2.** ₹2784.32 (approx.) [Rememeber to subtract the part of the sphere that is resting on the support while calculating the cost of silver paint].          **3.** $43.75\%$

## EXERCISE 14.1

**1.** Five examples of data that we can gather from our day-to-day life are :

(i)   Number of students in our class.

(ii)  Number of fans in our school.

(iii) Electricity bills of our house for last two years.

(iv) Election results obtained from television or newspapers.

(v)  Literacy rate figures obtained from Educational Survey.

Of course, remember that there can be many more different answers.

2. Primary data; (i), (ii) and (iii)

   Secondary data; (iv) and (v)

## EXERCISE 14.2

1.

| Blood group | Number of students |
|:---:|:---:|
| A | 9 |
| B | 6 |
| O | 12 |
| AB | 3 |
| **Total** | 30 |

Most common – O  ,  Rarest – AB

2.

| Distances (in km) | Tally Marks | Frequency |
|:---:|:---:|:---:|
| 0 - 5 | ℕ | 5 |
| 5 - 10 | ℕ ℕ I | 11 |
| 10 - 15 | ℕ ℕ I | 11 |
| 15 - 20 | ℕ IIII | 9 |
| 20 - 25 | I | 1 |
| 25 - 30 | I | 1 |
| 30 - 35 | II | 2 |
| **Total** | | 40 |

3. (i)

| Relative humidity (in %) | Frequency |
|:---:|:---:|
| 84 - 86 | 1 |
| 86 - 88 | 1 |
| 88 - 90 | 2 |
| 90 - 92 | 2 |
| 92 - 94 | 7 |
| 94 - 96 | 6 |
| 96 - 98 | 7 |
| 98 - 100 | 4 |
| **Total** | 30 |

(ii)    The data appears to be taken in the rainy season as the relative humidity is high.

(iii)   Range = 99.2 – 84.9 = 14.3

4.   (i)

| Heights (in cm) | Frequency |
|---|---|
| 150 - 155 | 12 |
| 155 - 160 | 9 |
| 160 - 165 | 14 |
| 165 - 170 | 10 |
| 170 - 175 | 5 |
| **Total** | 50 |

(ii)   One conclusion that we can draw from the above table is that more than 50% of students are shorter than 165 cm.

5.   (i)

| Concentration of Sulphur dioxide (in ppm) | Frequency |
|---|---|
| 0.00 - 0.04 | 4 |
| 0.04 - 0.08 | 9 |
| 0.08 - 0.12 | 9 |
| 0.12 - 0.16 | 2 |
| 0.16 - 0.20 | 4 |
| 0.20 - 0.24 | 2 |
| **Total** | 30 |

(ii)   The concentration of sulphur dioxide was more than 0.11 ppm for 8 days.

6.

| Number of heads | Frequency |
|---|---|
| 0 | 6 |
| 1 | 10 |
| 2 | 9 |
| 3 | 5 |
| **Total** | 30 |

7. (i)

| Digits | Frequency |
|:---:|:---:|
| 0 | 2 |
| 1 | 5 |
| 2 | 5 |
| 3 | 8 |
| 4 | 4 |
| 5 | 5 |
| 6 | 4 |
| 7 | 4 |
| 8 | 5 |
| 9 | 8 |
| **Total** | 50 |

(ii) The most frequently occurring digits are 3 and 9. The least occurring is 0.

8. (i)

| Number of hours | Frequency |
|:---:|:---:|
| 0 - 5 | 10 |
| 5 - 10 | 13 |
| 10 - 15 | 5 |
| 15 - 20 | 2 |
| **Total** | 30 |

(ii) 2 children.

9.

| Life of batteries (in years) | Frequency |
|:---:|:---:|
| 2.0 - 2.5 | 2 |
| 2.5 - 3.0 | 6 |
| 3.0 - 3.5 | 14 |
| 3.5 - 4.0 | 11 |
| 4.0 - 4.5 | 4 |
| 4.5 - 5.0 | 3 |
| **Total** | 40 |

## EXERCISE 14.3

**1.** (ii) Reproductive health conditions.

**3.** (ii) Party A  **4.** (ii) Frequency polygon  (iii) No  **5.** (ii) 184

**8.**

| Age (in years) | Frequency | Width | Length of the rectangle |
|:---:|:---:|:---:|:---:|
| 1 - 2 | 5 | 1 | $\dfrac{5}{1} \times 1 = 5$ |
| 2 - 3 | 3 | 1 | $\dfrac{3}{1} \times 1 = 3$ |
| 3 - 5 | 6 | 2 | $\dfrac{6}{2} \times 1 = 3$ |
| 5 - 7 | 12 | 2 | $\dfrac{12}{2} \times 1 = 6$ |
| 7 - 10 | 9 | 3 | $\dfrac{9}{3} \times 1 = 3$ |
| 10 - 15 | 10 | 5 | $\dfrac{10}{5} \times 1 = 2$ |
| 15 - 17 | 4 | 2 | $\dfrac{4}{2} \times 1 = 2$ |

Now, you can draw the histogram, using these lengths.

**9.** (i)

| Number of letters | Frequency | Width of interval | Length of rectangle |
|:---:|:---:|:---:|:---:|
| 1 - 4 | 6 | 3 | $\dfrac{6}{3} \times 2 = 4$ |
| 4 - 6 | 30 | 2 | $\dfrac{30}{2} \times 2 = 30$ |
| 6 - 8 | 44 | 2 | $\dfrac{44}{2} \times 2 = 44$ |
| 8 - 12 | 16 | 4 | $\dfrac{16}{4} \times 2 = 8$ |
| 12 - 20 | 4 | 8 | $\dfrac{4}{8} \times 2 = 1$ |

Now, draw the histogram.

(ii)  6 - 8

## EXERCISE 14.4

1.  Mean = 2.8;  Median = 3;  Mode = 3
2.  Mean = 54.8;  Median = 52;  Mode = 52
3.  $x = 62$         **4.** 14
5.  Mean salary of 60 workers is Rs 5083.33.

## EXERCISE 15.1

1.  $\dfrac{24}{30}$, i.e., $\dfrac{4}{5}$   **2.** (i) $\dfrac{19}{60}$   (ii) $\dfrac{407}{750}$   (iii) $\dfrac{21 \cdot 1}{1500}$   **3.** $\dfrac{3}{20}$   **4.** $\dfrac{9}{25}$

5.  (i) $\dfrac{29}{2400}$   (ii) $\dfrac{579}{2400}$   (iii) $\dfrac{1}{240}$   (iv) $\dfrac{1}{96}$   (v) $\dfrac{1031}{1200}$   **6.** (i) $\dfrac{7}{90}$   (ii) $\dfrac{23}{90}$

7.  (i) $\dfrac{27}{40}$   (ii) $\dfrac{13}{40}$   **8.** (i) $\dfrac{9}{40}$   (ii) $\dfrac{31}{40}$   (iii) 0   **11.** $\dfrac{7}{11}$   **12.** $\dfrac{1}{15}$   **13.** $\dfrac{1}{10}$

## EXERCISE A1.1

1.  (i)   Always false. There are 12 months in a year.
    (ii)   Ambiguous. In a given year, Diwali may or may not fall on a Friday.
    (iii)   Ambiguous. At some time in the year, the temperature in Magadi, may be 26° C.
    (iv)   Always true.
    (v)   Always false. Dogs cannot fly.
    (vi)   Ambiguous. In a leap year, February has 29 days.
2.  (i)   False. The sum of the interior angles of a quadrilateral is 360°.
    (ii)   True                              (iii) True                              (iv) True
    (v)   False, for example, $7 + 5 = 12$, which is not an odd number.
3.  (i) All prime numbers greater than 2 are odd.   (ii) Two times a natural number is always even.   (iii) For any $x > 1$, $3x + 1 > 4$.   (iv) For any $x \geq 0$, $x^3 \geq 0$.
    (v) In an equilateral triangle, a median is also an angle bisector.

## EXERCISE A1.2

1.  (i) Humans are vertebrates.   (ii) No. Dinesh could have got his hair cut by anybody else.   (iii) Gulag has a red tongue.   (iv) We conclude that the gutters will have to be cleaned tomorrow.   (v) All animals having tails need not be dogs. For example, animals such as buffaloes, monkeys, cats, etc. have tails but are not dogs.
2.  You need to turn over B and 8. If B has an even number on the other side, then the rule

has been broken. Similarly, if 8 has a consonant on the other side, then the rule has been broken.

EXERCISE A1.3

1.   Three possible conjectures are:

    (i) The product of any three consecutive even numbers is even.   (ii) The product of any three consecutive even numbers is divisible by 4.   (iii) The product of any three consecutive even numbers is divisible by 6.

2.   Line 4: 1 3 3 1 $=11^3$;   Line 5: 1 4 6 4 1$=11^4$; the conjecture holds for Line 4 and Line 5; No, because $11^5 \neq 15101051$.

3.   $T_4 + T_5 = 25 = 5^2$;   $T_{n-1} + T_n = n^2$.

4.   $111111^2 = 12345654321$ ;   $1111111^2 = 1234567654321$

5.   Student's own answer. For example, Euclid's postulates.

EXERCISE A1.4

1.   (i)   You can give any two  triangles with the same angles but of different sides.

    (ii)   A rhombus has equal sides but may not be a square.

    (iii)   A rectangle has equal angles but may not be a square.

    (iv)   For $a = 3$ and $b = 4$, the statement is not true.

    (v)   For $n = 11$, $2n^2 + 11 = 253$ which is not a prime.

    (vi)   For $n = 41$, $n^2 - n + 41$ is not a prime.

2.   Student's own answer.

3.   Let $x$ and $y$ be two odd numbers. Then $x = 2m + 1$ for some natural number $m$ and $y = 2n + 1$ for some natural number $n$.

    $x + y = 2(m + n + 1)$. Therefore, $x + y$ is divisible by 2 and is even.

4.   See Q.3. $xy = (2m + 1)(2n + 1) = 2(2mn + m + n) + 1$.

    Therefore, $x y$ is not divisible by 2, and so it is odd.

5.   Let $2n$, $2n + 2$ and $2n + 4$ be three consecutive even numbers. Then their sum is $6(n + 1)$, which is divisible by 6.

7.   (i)   Let your original number be $n$. Then we are doing the following operations:

$$n \to 2n \to 2n + 9 \to 2n + 9 + n = 3n + 9 \to \frac{3n + 9}{3} = n + 3 \to n + 3 + 4 = n + 7 \to$$

    $n + 7 - n = 7$.

    (ii)   Note that $7 \times 11 \times 13 = 1001$. Take any three digit number say, $abc$. Then $abc \times 1001 = abcabc$. Therefore, the six digit number $abcabc$ is divisible by 7, 11 and 13.